Texas
PROMULGATED FORMS

Supplement

Peggy Santmyer, Contributing Author

This publication is designed to provide accurate and authoritative information in regard to the subject matter covered. It is sold with the understanding that the publisher is not engaged in rendering legal, accounting, or other professional advice. If legal advice or other expert assistance is required, the services of a competent professional should be sought.

President: Dr. Andrew Temte
Chief Learning Officer: Dr. Tim Smaby
Executive Director, Real Estate Education: Melissa Kleeman-Moy
Development Editor: Julia Mart

TEXAS PROMULGATED FORMS SUPPLEMENT
©2015 Kaplan, Inc.
Published by DF Institute, Inc., d/b/a Dearborn Real Estate Education
332 Front St. S., Suite 501
La Crosse, WI 54601

Printed in the United States of America

ISBN: 978-1-4754-2751-6 / 1-4754-2751-4
PPN: 3200-5493

Contents

Approved Optional/Voluntary Use Forms   87

Case Studies   97

About This Supplement

This supplement contains the Texas Real Estate Commission (TREC) forms discussed in the textbook *Texas Promulgated Forms*. These forms are available on the Texas Real Estate Commission's website at http://trec.state.tx.us/formslawscontracts/forms/forms-contracts.asp (or go to http://trec.state.tx.us/, click the Forms, Laws & Contracts tab, and then click the Contract Forms and Addenda link).

As you read through the textbook, look up the form in this supplement and carefully read the language in it. Thoughtful study of these forms will ensure success on the exam and in your real estate practice. For ease of use, all forms are listed in the table of contents. Refer to the contents page for the location of the form. The forms are provided in this supplement according to the form's type (etc. promulgated contract, promulgated addenda, approved form, etc.) and in the same order they are listed in *Texas Promulgated Forms* under the Use of Promulgated Forms section in Chapter 2.

There are case studies in the textbook in Chapters 5, 6, and 9. The forms needed for those activities are in this supplement in the Case Studies section. You will fill out the forms according to the scenario transaction in the textbook. When you have filled them out entirely, you can check them against the filled-out forms that appear immediately after the blank forms for that case study.

Promulgated Contracts

FIGURE 1

One to Four Family Residential Contract (Resale)

4-28-2014

PROMULGATED BY THE TEXAS REAL ESTATE COMMISSION (TREC)
ONE TO FOUR FAMILY RESIDENTIAL CONTRACT (RESALE)
NOTICE: Not For Use For Condominium Transactions

1. PARTIES: The parties to this contract are _____
(Seller) and _____(Buyer).
Seller agrees to sell and convey to Buyer and Buyer agrees to buy from Seller the Property defined below.

2. PROPERTY: The land, improvements and accessories are collectively referred to as the "Property".
    A. LAND: Lot _____ Block_____, _____
       Addition, City of _____ , County of _____,
       Texas, known as _____
       (address/zip code), or as described on attached exhibit.
    B. IMPROVEMENTS: The house, garage and all other fixtures and improvements attached to the above-described real property, including without limitation, the following **permanently installed and built-in items,** if any: all equipment and appliances, valances, screens, shutters, awnings, wall-to-wall carpeting, mirrors, ceiling fans, attic fans, mail boxes, television antennas, mounts and brackets for televisions and speakers, heating and air-conditioning units, security and fire detection equipment, wiring, plumbing and lighting fixtures, chandeliers, water softener system, kitchen equipment, garage door openers, cleaning equipment, shrubbery, landscaping, outdoor cooking equipment, and all other property owned by Seller and attached to the above described real property.
    C. ACCESSORIES: The following described related accessories, if any: window air conditioning units, stove, fireplace screens, curtains and rods, blinds, window shades, draperies and rods, door keys, mailbox keys, above ground pool, swimming pool equipment and maintenance accessories, artificial fireplace logs, and controls for: (i) garage doors, (ii) entry gates, and (iii) other improvements and accessories.
    D. EXCLUSIONS: The following improvements and accessories will be retained by Seller and must be removed prior to delivery of possession:_____
       _____.

3. SALES PRICE:
    A. Cash portion of Sales Price payable by Buyer at closing .... $_____
    B. Sum of all financing described below (excluding any loan funding
       fee or mortgage insurance premium) .... $_____
    C. Sales Price (Sum of A and B).. $_____

4. FINANCING (Not for use with reverse mortgage financing): The portion of Sales Price not payable in cash will be paid as follows: (Check applicable boxes below)
❑ A. THIRD PARTY FINANCING: One or more third party mortgage loans in the total amount of $_____ (excluding any loan funding fee or mortgage insurance premium).
    (1) Property Approval: If the Property does not satisfy the lenders' underwriting requirements for the loan(s) (including, but not limited to appraisal, insurability and lender required repairs), Buyer may terminate this contract by giving notice to Seller prior to closing and the earnest money will be refunded to Buyer.
    (2) Credit Approval: (Check one box only)
      ❑ (a) This contract is subject to Buyer being approved for the financing described in the attached Third Party Financing Addendum for Credit Approval.
      ❑ (b) This contract is not subject to Buyer being approved for financing and does not involve FHA or VA financing.
❑ B. ASSUMPTION: The assumption of the unpaid principal balance of one or more promissory notes described in the attached TREC Loan Assumption Addendum.
❑ C. SELLER FINANCING: A promissory note from Buyer to Seller of $_____, secured by vendor's and deed of trust liens, and containing the terms and conditions described in the attached TREC Seller Financing Addendum. If an owner policy of title insurance is furnished, Buyer shall furnish Seller with a mortgagee policy of title insurance.

Initialed for identification by Buyer_____ _____ and Seller _____ _____   TREC NO. 20-12

FIGURE 1

One to Four Family Residential Contract (Resale) (continued)

Contract Concerning _____Page 2 of 9   4-28-2014
(Address of Property)

5. EARNEST MONEY: Upon execution of this contract by all parties, Buyer shall deposit $_____ as earnest money with _____, as escrow agent, at _____ (address). Buyer shall deposit additional earnest money of $_____ with escrow agent within ____days after the effective date of this contract. If Buyer fails to deposit the earnest money as required by this contract, Buyer will be in default.

6. TITLE POLICY AND SURVEY:

A. TITLE POLICY: Seller shall furnish to Buyer at ❑ Seller's ❑ Buyer's expense an owner policy of title insurance (Title Policy) issued by _____ (Title Company) in the amount of the Sales Price, dated at or after closing, insuring Buyer against loss under the provisions of the Title Policy, subject to the promulgated exclusions (including existing building and zoning ordinances) and the following exceptions:

(1) Restrictive covenants common to the platted subdivision in which the Property is located.

(2) The standard printed exception for standby fees, taxes and assessments.

(3) Liens created as part of the financing described in Paragraph 4.

(4) Utility easements created by the dedication deed or plat of the subdivision in which the Property is located.

(5) Reservations or exceptions otherwise permitted by this contract or as may be approved by Buyer in writing.

(6) The standard printed exception as to marital rights.

(7) The standard printed exception as to waters, tidelands, beaches, streams, and related matters.

(8) The standard printed exception as to discrepancies, conflicts, shortages in area or boundary lines, encroachments or protrusions, or overlapping improvements: ❑(i) will not be amended or deleted from the title policy; ❑(ii) will be amended to read, "shortages in area" at the expense of ❑Buyer ❑Seller.

B. COMMITMENT: Within 20 days after the Title Company receives a copy of this contract, Seller shall furnish to Buyer a commitment for title insurance (Commitment) and, at Buyer's expense, legible copies of restrictive covenants and documents evidencing exceptions in the Commitment (Exception Documents) other than the standard printed exceptions. Seller authorizes the Title Company to deliver the Commitment and Exception Documents to Buyer at Buyer's address shown in Paragraph 21. If the Commitment and Exception Documents are not delivered to Buyer within the specified time, the time for delivery will be automatically extended up to 15 days or 3 days before the Closing Date, whichever is earlier. If, due to factors beyond Seller's control, the Commitment and Exception Documents are not delivered within the time required, Buyer may terminate this contract and the earnest money will be refunded to Buyer.

C. SURVEY: The survey must be made by a registered professional land surveyor acceptable to the Title Company and Buyer's lender(s). (Check one box only)

❑(1)Within _____ days after the effective date of this contract, Seller shall furnish to Buyer and Title Company Seller's existing survey of the Property and a Residential Real Property Affidavit promulgated by the Texas Department of Insurance (T-47 Affidavit). **If Seller fails to furnish the existing survey or affidavit within the time prescribed, Buyer shall obtain a new survey at Seller's expense no later than 3 days prior to Closing Date.** If the existing survey or affidavit is not acceptable to Title Company or Buyer's lender(s), Buyer shall obtain a new survey at ❑Seller's ❑Buyer's expense no later than 3 days prior to Closing Date.

❑(2)Within _____ days after the effective date of this contract, Buyer shall obtain a new survey at Buyer's expense. Buyer is deemed to receive the survey on the date of actual receipt or the date specified in this paragraph, whichever is earlier.

❑(3)Within _____ days after the effective date of this contract, Seller, at Seller's expense shall furnish a new survey to Buyer.

D. OBJECTIONS: Buyer may object in writing to defects, exceptions, or encumbrances to title: disclosed on the survey other than items 6A(1) through (7) above; disclosed in the Commitment other than items 6A(1) through (8) above; or which prohibit the following use or activity: _____
_____.
Buyer must object the earlier of (i) the Closing Date or (ii) _____ days after Buyer receives the Commitment, Exception Documents, and the survey. Buyer's failure to object within the time allowed will constitute a waiver of Buyer's right to object; except that the requirements in Schedule C of the Commitment are not waived by Buyer. Provided Seller is not obligated to incur any expense, Seller shall cure the timely objections of Buyer or any third party lender

Initialed for identification by Buyer_____ _____ and Seller _____ _____   TREC NO. 20-12

FIGURE 1

One to Four Family Residential Contract (Resale) (continued)

---

within 15 days after Seller receives the objections and the Closing Date will be extended as necessary. If objections are not cured within such 15 day period, this contract will terminate and the earnest money will be refunded to Buyer unless Buyer waives the objections.

E. TITLE NOTICES:

(1) ABSTRACT OR TITLE POLICY: Broker advises Buyer to have an abstract of title covering the Property examined by an attorney of Buyer's selection, or Buyer should be furnished with or obtain a Title Policy. If a Title Policy is furnished, the Commitment should be promptly reviewed by an attorney of Buyer's choice due to the time limitations on Buyer's right to object.

(2) MEMBERSHIP IN PROPERTY OWNERS ASSOCIATION(S): The Property ❑is ❑is not subject to mandatory membership in a property owners association(s). If the Property is subject to mandatory membership in a property owners association(s), Seller notifies Buyer under §5.012, Texas Property Code, that, as a purchaser of property in the residential community identified in Paragraph 2A in which the Property is located, you are obligated to be a member of the property owners association(s). Restrictive covenants governing the use and occupancy of the Property and all dedicatory instruments governing the establishment, maintenance, or operation of this residential community have been or will be recorded in the Real Property Records of the county in which the Property is located. Copies of the restrictive covenants and dedicatory instruments may be obtained from the county clerk. **You are obligated to pay assessments to the property owners association(s). The amount of the assessments is subject to change. Your failure to pay the assessments could result in enforcement of the association's lien on and the foreclosure of the Property.**
Section 207.003, Property Code, entitles an owner to receive copies of any document that governs the establishment, maintenance, or operation of a subdivision, including, but not limited to, restrictions, bylaws, rules and regulations, and a resale certificate from a property owners' association. A resale certificate contains information including, but not limited to, statements specifying the amount and frequency of regular assessments and the style and cause number of lawsuits to which the property owners' association is a party, other than lawsuits relating to unpaid ad valorem taxes of an individual member of the association. These documents must be made available to you by the property owners' association or the association's agent on your request.
If Buyer is concerned about these matters, the TREC promulgated Addendum for Property Subject to Mandatory Membership in a Property Owners Association(s) should be used.

(3) STATUTORY TAX DISTRICTS: If the Property is situated in a utility or other statutorily created district providing water, sewer, drainage, or flood control facilities and services, Chapter 49, Texas Water Code, requires Seller to deliver and Buyer to sign the statutory notice relating to the tax rate, bonded indebtedness, or standby fee of the district prior to final execution of this contract.

(4) TIDE WATERS: If the Property abuts the tidally influenced waters of the state, §33.135, Texas Natural Resources Code, requires a notice regarding coastal area property to be included in the contract. An addendum containing the notice promulgated by TREC or required by the parties must be used.

(5) ANNEXATION: If the Property is located outside the limits of a municipality, Seller notifies Buyer under §5.011, Texas Property Code, that the Property may now or later be included in the extraterritorial jurisdiction of a municipality and may now or later be subject to annexation by the municipality. Each municipality maintains a map that depicts its boundaries and extraterritorial jurisdiction. To determine if the Property is located within a municipality's extraterritorial jurisdiction or is likely to be located within a municipality's extraterritorial jurisdiction, contact all municipalities located in the general proximity of the Property for further information.

(6) PROPERTY LOCATED IN A CERTIFICATED SERVICE AREA OF A UTILITY SERVICE PROVIDER: Notice required by §13.257, Water Code: The real property, described in Paragraph 2, that you are about to purchase may be located in a certificated water or sewer service area, which is authorized by law to provide water or sewer service to the properties in the certificated area. If your property is located in a certificated area there may be special costs or charges that you will be required to pay before you can receive water or sewer service. There may be a period required to construct lines or other facilities necessary to provide water or sewer service to your property. You are advised to determine if the property is in a certificated area and contact the utility service provider to determine the cost that you will be required to pay and the period, if any, that is required to provide water or sewer service to your property. The undersigned Buyer hereby acknowledges receipt of the foregoing notice at or before the execution of a binding contract for the purchase of the real property described in Paragraph 2 or at closing of purchase of the real property.

FIGURE 1

One to Four Family Residential Contract (Resale) (continued)

    (7) PUBLIC IMPROVEMENT DISTRICTS: If the Property is in a public improvement district, §5.014, Property Code, requires Seller to notify Buyer as follows: As a purchaser of this parcel of real property you are obligated to pay an assessment to a municipality or county for an improvement project undertaken by a public improvement district under Chapter 372, Local Government Code. The assessment may be due annually or in periodic installments. More information concerning the amount of the assessment and the due dates of that assessment may be obtained from the municipality or county levying the assessment. The amount of the assessments is subject to change. Your failure to pay the assessments could result in a lien on and the foreclosure of your property.

    (8) TRANSFER FEES: If the Property is subject to a private transfer fee obligation, §5.205, Property Code, requires Seller to notify Buyer as follows: The private transfer fee obligation may be governed by Chapter 5, Subchapter G of the Texas Property Code.

    (9) PROPANE GAS SYSTEM SERVICE AREA: If the Property is located in a propane gas system service area owned by a distribution system retailer, Seller must give Buyer written notice as required by §141.010, Texas Utilities Code. An addendum containing the notice approved by TREC or required by the parties should be used.

7. PROPERTY CONDITION:

    A. ACCESS, INSPECTIONS AND UTILITIES: Seller shall permit Buyer and Buyer's agents access to the Property at reasonable times. Buyer may have the Property inspected by inspectors selected by Buyer and licensed by TREC or otherwise permitted by law to make inspections. Seller at Seller's expense shall immediately cause existing utilities to be turned on and shall keep the utilities on during the time this contract is in effect.

    B. SELLER'S DISCLOSURE NOTICE PURSUANT TO §5.008, TEXAS PROPERTY CODE (Notice): (Check one box only)

    ❑ (1) Buyer has received the Notice.

    ❑ (2) Buyer has not received the Notice. Within _____ days after the effective date of this contract, Seller shall deliver the Notice to Buyer. If Buyer does not receive the Notice, Buyer may terminate this contract at any time prior to the closing and the earnest money will be refunded to Buyer. If Seller delivers the Notice, Buyer may terminate this contract for any reason within 7 days after Buyer receives the Notice or prior to the closing, whichever first occurs, and the earnest money will be refunded to Buyer.

    ❑ (3) The Seller is not required to furnish the notice under the Texas Property Code.

    C. SELLER'S DISCLOSURE OF LEAD-BASED PAINT AND LEAD-BASED PAINT HAZARDS is required by Federal law for a residential dwelling constructed prior to 1978.

    D. ACCEPTANCE OF PROPERTY CONDITION: "As Is" means the present condition of the Property with any and all defects and without warranty except for the warranties of title and the warranties in this contract. Buyer's agreement to accept the Property As Is under Paragraph 7D(1) or (2) does not preclude Buyer from inspecting the Property under Paragraph 7A, from negotiating repairs or treatments in a subsequent amendment, or from terminating this contract during the Option Period, if any.
(Check one box only)

    ❑ (1) Buyer accepts the Property As Is.

    ❑ (2) Buyer accepts the Property As Is provided Seller, at Seller's expense, shall complete the following specific repairs and treatments: _____.
_____
(Do not insert general phrases, such as "subject to inspections" that do not identify specific repairs and treatments.)

    E. LENDER REQUIRED REPAIRS AND TREATMENTS: Unless otherwise agreed in writing, neither party is obligated to pay for lender required repairs, which includes treatment for wood destroying insects. If the parties do not agree to pay for the lender required repairs or treatments, this contract will terminate and the earnest money will be refunded to Buyer. If the cost of lender required repairs and treatments exceeds 5% of the Sales Price, Buyer may terminate this contract and the earnest money will be refunded to Buyer.

    F. COMPLETION OF REPAIRS AND TREATMENTS: Unless otherwise agreed in writing: (i) Seller shall complete all agreed repairs and treatments prior to the Closing Date; and (ii) all required permits must be obtained, and repairs and treatments must be performed by persons who are licensed to provide such repairs or treatments or, if no license is required by law, are commercially engaged in the trade of providing such repairs or treatments. At Buyer's election, any transferable warranties received by Seller with respect to the repairs and treatments will be transferred to Buyer at Buyer's expense. If Seller fails to complete any agreed repairs and treatments prior to the Closing Date, Buyer may exercise remedies under Paragraph 15 or extend the Closing Date up to 5 days if necessary for Seller to complete the repairs and treatments.

    G. ENVIRONMENTAL MATTERS: Buyer is advised that the presence of wetlands, toxic substances, including asbestos and wastes or other environmental hazards, or the presence of a threatened or endangered species or its habitat may affect Buyer's intended use of the

6 Texas Promulgated Forms Supplement

FIGURE 1

One to Four Family Residential Contract (Resale) (continued)

Contract Concerning _____ Page 5 of 9   4-28-2014
(Address of Property)

Property. If Buyer is concerned about these matters, an addendum promulgated by TREC or required by the parties should be used.

H. RESIDENTIAL SERVICE CONTRACTS: Buyer may purchase a residential service contract from a residential service company licensed by TREC. If Buyer purchases a residential service contract, Seller shall reimburse Buyer at closing for the cost of the residential service contract in an amount not exceeding $_____. Buyer should review any residential service contract for the scope of coverage, exclusions and limitations. **The purchase of a residential service contract is optional. Similar coverage may be purchased from various companies authorized to do business in Texas.**

8. **BROKERS' FEES:** All obligations of the parties for payment of brokers' fees are contained in separate written agreements.

9. **CLOSING:**
   A. The closing of the sale will be on or before _____, 20____, or within 7 days after objections made under Paragraph 6D have been cured or waived, whichever date is later (Closing Date). If either party fails to close the sale by the Closing Date, the non-defaulting party may exercise the remedies contained in Paragraph 15.
   B. At closing:
      (1) Seller shall execute and deliver a general warranty deed conveying title to the Property to Buyer and showing no additional exceptions to those permitted in Paragraph 6 and furnish tax statements or certificates showing no delinquent taxes on the Property.
      (2) Buyer shall pay the Sales Price in good funds acceptable to the escrow agent.
      (3) Seller and Buyer shall execute and deliver any notices, statements, certificates, affidavits, releases, loan documents and other documents reasonably required for the closing of the sale and the issuance of the Title Policy.
      (4) There will be no liens, assessments, or security interests against the Property which will not be satisfied out of the sales proceeds unless securing the payment of any loans assumed by Buyer and assumed loans will not be in default.
      (5)If the Property is subject to a residential lease, Seller shall transfer security deposits (as defined under §92.102, Property Code), if any, to Buyer. In such an event, Buyer shall deliver to the tenant a signed statement acknowledging that the Buyer has received the security deposit and is responsible for the return of the security deposit, and specifying the exact dollar amount of the security deposit.

10. **POSSESSION:**
   A Buyer's Possession: Seller shall deliver to Buyer possession of the Property in its present or required condition, ordinary wear and tear excepted: ❑upon closing and funding ❑according to a temporary residential lease form promulgated by TREC or other written lease required by the parties. Any possession by Buyer prior to closing or by Seller after closing which is not authorized by a written lease will establish a tenancy at sufferance relationship between the parties. **Consult your insurance agent prior to change of ownership and possession because insurance coverage may be limited or terminated. The absence of a written lease or appropriate insurance coverage may expose the parties to economic loss.**
   B. Leases:
      (1)After the Effective Date, Seller may not execute any lease (including but not limited to mineral leases) or convey any interest in the Property without Buyer's written consent.
      (2) If the Property is subject to any lease to which Seller is a party, Seller shall deliver to Buyer copies of the lease(s) and any move-in condition form signed by the tenant within 7 days after the Effective Date of the contract.

11. **SPECIAL PROVISIONS:**   (Insert only factual statements and business details applicable to the sale. TREC rules prohibit licensees from adding factual statements or business details for which a contract addendum, lease or other form has been promulgated by TREC for mandatory use.)

12. **SETTLEMENT AND OTHER EXPENSES:**
   A. The following expenses must be paid at or prior to closing:
      (1) Expenses payable by Seller (Seller's Expenses):
         (a) Releases of existing liens, including prepayment penalties and recording fees; release of Seller's loan liability; tax statements or certificates; preparation of deed; one-half of escrow fee; and other expenses payable by Seller under this contract.
         (b) Seller shall also pay an amount not to exceed $_____ to be applied in the

Initialed for identification by Buyer_____ _____ and Seller _____ _____   TREC NO. 20-12

F I G U R E   1

One to Four Family Residential Contract (Resale) (continued)

Contract Concerning _____ Page 6 of 9   4-28-2014
(Address of Property)

following order: Buyer's Expenses which Buyer is prohibited from paying by FHA, VA, Texas Veterans Land Board or other governmental loan programs, and then to other Buyer's Expenses as allowed by the lender.

(2) Expenses payable by Buyer (Buyer's Expenses): Appraisal fees; loan application fees; adjusted origination charges; credit reports; preparation of loan documents; interest on the notes from date of disbursement to one month prior to dates of first monthly payments; recording fees; copies of easements and restrictions; loan title policy with endorsements required by lender; loan-related inspection fees; photos; amortization schedules; one-half of escrow fee; all prepaid items, including required premiums for flood and hazard insurance, reserve deposits for insurance, ad valorem taxes and special governmental assessments; final compliance inspection; courier fee; repair inspection; underwriting fee; wire transfer fee; expenses incident to any loan; Private Mortgage Insurance Premium (PMI), VA Loan Funding Fee, or FHA Mortgage Insurance Premium (MIP) as required by the lender; and other expenses payable by Buyer under this contract.

B. If any expense exceeds an amount expressly stated in this contract for such expense to be paid by a party, that party may terminate this contract unless the other party agrees to pay such excess. Buyer may not pay charges and fees expressly prohibited by FHA, VA, Texas Veterans Land Board or other governmental loan program regulations.

13. **PRORATIONS:** Taxes for the current year, interest, maintenance fees, assessments, dues and rents will be prorated through the Closing Date. The tax proration may be calculated taking into consideration any change in exemptions that will affect the current year's taxes. If taxes for the current year vary from the amount prorated at closing, the parties shall adjust the prorations when tax statements for the current year are available. If taxes are not paid at or prior to closing, Buyer shall pay taxes for the current year.

14. **CASUALTY LOSS:** If any part of the Property is damaged or destroyed by fire or other casualty after the effective date of this contract, Seller shall restore the Property to its previous condition as soon as reasonably possible, but in any event by the Closing Date. If Seller fails to do so due to factors beyond Seller's control, Buyer may (a) terminate this contract and the earnest money will be refunded to Buyer (b) extend the time for performance up to 15 days and the Closing Date will be extended as necessary or (c) accept the Property in its damaged condition with an assignment of insurance proceeds and receive credit from Seller at closing in the amount of the deductible under the insurance policy. Seller's obligations under this paragraph are independent of any other obligations of Seller under this contract.

15. **DEFAULT:** If Buyer fails to comply with this contract, Buyer will be in default, and Seller may (a) enforce specific performance, seek such other relief as may be provided by law, or both, or (b) terminate this contract and receive the earnest money as liquidated damages, thereby releasing both parties from this contract. If Seller fails to comply with this contract, Seller will be in default and Buyer may (a) enforce specific performance, seek such other relief as may be provided by law, or both, or (b) terminate this contract and receive the earnest money, thereby releasing both parties from this contract.

16. **MEDIATION:** It is the policy of the State of Texas to encourage resolution of disputes through alternative dispute resolution procedures such as mediation. Any dispute between Seller and Buyer related to this contract which is not resolved through informal discussion will be submitted to a mutually acceptable mediation service or provider. The parties to the mediation shall bear the mediation costs equally. This paragraph does not preclude a party from seeking equitable relief from a court of competent jurisdiction.

17. **ATTORNEY'S FEES:** A Buyer, Seller, Listing Broker, Other Broker, or escrow agent who prevails in any legal proceeding related to this contract is entitled to recover reasonable attorney's fees and all costs of such proceeding.

18. **ESCROW:**
A. ESCROW: The escrow agent is not (i) a party to this contract and does not have liability for the performance or nonperformance of any party to this contract, (ii) liable for interest on the earnest money and (iii) liable for the loss of any earnest money caused by the failure of any financial institution in which the earnest money has been deposited unless the financial institution is acting as escrow agent.

B. EXPENSES: At closing, the earnest money must be applied first to any cash down payment, then to Buyer's Expenses and any excess refunded to Buyer. If no closing occurs, escrow agent may: (i) require a written release of liability of the escrow agent from all parties, (ii) require payment of unpaid expenses incurred on behalf of a party, and (iii) only deduct from the earnest money the amount of unpaid expenses incurred on behalf of the party receiving the earnest money.

C. DEMAND: Upon termination of this contract, either party or the escrow agent may send a release of earnest money to each party and the parties shall execute counterparts of

Initialed for identification by Buyer_____ _____ and Seller _____ _____   TREC NO. 20-12

F I G U R E   1

One to Four Family Residential Contract (Resale) (continued)

Contract Concerning _____ Page 7 of 9   4-28-2014
(Address of Property)

the release and deliver same to the escrow agent. If either party fails to execute the release, either party may make a written demand to the escrow agent for the earnest money. If only one party makes written demand for the earnest money, escrow agent shall promptly provide a copy of the demand to the other party. If escrow agent does not receive written objection to the demand from the other party within 15 days, escrow agent may disburse the earnest money to the party making demand reduced by the amount of unpaid expenses incurred on behalf of the party receiving the earnest money and escrow agent may pay the same to the creditors. If escrow agent complies with the provisions of this paragraph, each party hereby releases escrow agent from all adverse claims related to the disbursal of the earnest money.

   D. DAMAGES: Any party who wrongfully fails or refuses to sign a release acceptable to the escrow agent within 7 days of receipt of the request will be liable to the other party for liquidated damages in an amount equal to the sum of: (i) three times the amount of the earnest money; (ii) the earnest money; (iii) reasonable attorney's fees; and (iv) all costs of suit.

   E. NOTICES: Escrow agent's notices will be effective when sent in compliance with Paragraph 21. Notice of objection to the demand will be deemed effective upon receipt by escrow agent.

19. REPRESENTATIONS: All covenants, representations and warranties in this contract survive closing. If any representation of Seller in this contract is untrue on the Closing Date, Seller will be in default. Unless expressly prohibited by written agreement, Seller may continue to show the Property and receive, negotiate and accept back up offers.

20. FEDERAL TAX REQUIREMENTS: If Seller is a "foreign person," as defined by applicable law, or if Seller fails to deliver an affidavit to Buyer that Seller is not a "foreign person," then Buyer shall withhold from the sales proceeds an amount sufficient to comply with applicable tax law and deliver the same to the Internal Revenue Service together with appropriate tax forms. Internal Revenue Service regulations require filing written reports if currency in excess of specified amounts is received in the transaction.

21. NOTICES: All notices from one party to the other must be in writing and are effective when mailed to, hand-delivered at, or transmitted by facsimile or electronic transmission as follows:

To Buyer at: _____   **To Seller at:** _____

_____   _____

Telephone:	( )		Telephone:	( )
Facsimile:	( )		Facsimile:	( )
E-mail:			E-mail:	

22. AGREEMENT OF PARTIES: This contract contains the entire agreement of the parties and cannot be changed except by their written agreement. Addenda which are a part of this contract are (Check all applicable boxes):

❑ Third Party Financing Addendum for Credit Approval

❑ Seller Financing Addendum

❑ Addendum for Property Subject to Mandatory Membership in a Property Owners Association

❑ Buyer's Temporary Residential Lease

❑ Loan Assumption Addendum

❑ Addendum for Sale of Other Property by Buyer

❑ Addendum for Reservation of Oil, Gas and Other Minerals

❑ Addendum for "Back-Up" Contract

❑ Addendum for Coastal Area Property

❑ Environmental Assessment, Threatened or Endangered Species and Wetlands Addendum

❑ Seller's Temporary Residential Lease

❑ Short Sale Addendum

❑ Addendum for Property Located Seaward of the Gulf Intracoastal Waterway

❑ Addendum for Seller's Disclosure of Information on Lead-based Paint and Lead-based Paint Hazards as Required by Federal Law

❑ Addendum for Property in a Propane Gas System Service Area

❑ Other (list): _____

_____

_____

Initialed for identification by Buyer_____ _____ and Seller _____ _____   TREC NO. 20-12

FIGURE 1

One to Four Family Residential Contract (Resale) (continued)

Contract Concerning _____ Page 8 of 9   4-28-2014
(Address of Property)

23. **TERMINATION OPTION:** For nominal consideration, the receipt of which is hereby acknowledged by Seller, and Buyer's agreement to pay Seller $_____ (Option Fee) within 3 days after the effective date of this contract, Seller grants Buyer the unrestricted right to terminate this contract by giving notice of termination to Seller within _____ days after the effective date of this contract (Option Period). If no dollar amount is stated as the Option Fee or if Buyer fails to pay the Option Fee to Seller within the time prescribed, this paragraph will not be a part of this contract and Buyer shall not have the unrestricted right to terminate this contract. If Buyer gives notice of termination within the time prescribed, the Option Fee will not be refunded; however, any earnest money will be refunded to Buyer. The Option Fee ☐ will ☐ will not be credited to the Sales Price at closing. **Time is of the essence for this paragraph and strict compliance with the time for performance is required.**

24. **CONSULT AN ATTORNEY BEFORE SIGNING:** TREC rules prohibit real estate licensees from giving legal advice. READ THIS CONTRACT CAREFULLY.

Buyer's
Attorney is: _____

Seller's
Attorney is: _____

_____

_____

Telephone: (_____)_____

Telephone: (_____)_____

Facsimile: (_____)_____

Facsimile: (_____)_____

E-mail: _____

E-mail: _____

**EXECUTED the _____day of _____, 20_____ (EFFECTIVE DATE).
(BROKER: FILL IN THE DATE OF FINAL ACCEPTANCE.)**

_____
Buyer

_____
Seller

_____
Buyer

_____
Seller

TREC NO. 20-12

F I G U R E   1

One to Four Family Residential Contract (Resale) (continued)

Contract Concerning _____   Page 9 of 9   4-28-2014
                              (Address of Property)

BROKER   INFORMATION
(Print name(s) only. Do not sign)

_____	_____
Other Broker Firm License No.	Listing Broker Firm License No.
represents ☐ Buyer only as Buyer's agent	represents ☐ Seller and Buyer as an intermediary
☐ Seller as Listing Broker's subagent	☐ Seller only as Seller's agent
_____	_____
Name of Associate's Licensed Supervisor Telephone	Name of Associate's Licensed Supervisor Telephone
_____	_____
Associate's Name Telephone	Listing Associate's Name Telephone
_____	_____
Other Broker's Address Facsimile	Listing Broker's Office Address Facsimile
_____	_____
City State Zip	City State Zip
_____	_____
Associate's Email Address	Listing Associate's Email Address
	_____
	Selling Associate's Name Telephone
	_____
	Name of Selling Associate's Licensed Supervisor Telephone
	_____
	Selling Associate's Office Address Facsimile
	_____
	City State Zip
	_____
	Selling Associate's Email Address

Listing Broker has agreed to pay Other Broker_____of the total sales price when the Listing Broker's fee is received. Escrow agent is authorized and directed to pay other Broker from Listing Broker's fee at closing.

OPTION FEE RECEIPT

Receipt of $_____ (Option Fee) in the form of _____ is acknowledged.

_____   _____
Seller or Listing Broker   Date

CONTRACT AND EARNEST MONEY RECEIPT

Receipt of ☐ Contract and ☐ $_____Earnest Money in the form of _____
is acknowledged.

Escrow Agent: _____   Date: _____

By: _____   _____
_____   Email Address
Address   Telephone (____)_____

_____   Facsimile: (____) _____
City   State   Zip

TREC NO. 20-12

FIGURE 2

New Home Contract (Incomplete Construction)

PROMULGATED BY THE TEXAS REAL ESTATE COMMISSION (TREC)   4-28-2014
NEW HOME CONTRACT
(Incomplete Construction)
NOTICE: Not For Use For Condominium Transactions or Closings Prior to Completion of Construction

1. PARTIES: The parties to this contract are _____
(Seller) and _____(Buyer). Seller agrees to sell and convey to Buyer and Buyer agrees to buy from Seller the Property defined below.

2. PROPERTY: Lot _____, Block_____, _____
Addition, City of_____, County of _____ Texas, known as _____(address/zip code), or as described on attached exhibit, together with: (i) improvements, fixtures and all other property described in the Construction Documents; and (ii) all rights, privileges and appurtenances thereto, including but not limited to: permits, easements, and cooperative and association memberships. All property sold by this contract is called the "Property".

3. SALES PRICE:
A. Cash portion of Sales Price payable by Buyer at closing...................... $_____
B. Sum of all financing described below (excluding any loan funding fee or mortgage insurance premium) .... $_____
C. Sales Price (Sum of A and B) .... $_____

4. FINANCING (Not for use with reverse mortgage financing): The portion of Sales Price not payable in cash will be paid as follows: (Check applicable boxes below)
❑A. THIRD PARTY FINANCING: One or more third party mortgage loans in the total amount of $_____ (excluding any loan funding fee or mortgage insurance premium).
(1) Property Approval: If the Property does not satisfy the lenders' underwriting requirements for the loan(s), (including, but not limited to appraisal, insurability and lender required repairs), Buyer may terminate this contract by giving notice to Seller prior to closing and the earnest money will be refunded to Buyer.
(2) Credit Approval: (Check one box only)
❑ (a) This contract is subject to Buyer being approved for the financing described in the attached Third Party Financing Addendum for Credit Approval.
❑ (b) This contract is not subject to Buyer being approved for financing and does not involve FHA or VA financing.
❑B. ASSUMPTION: The assumption of the unpaid principal balance of one or more promissory notes described in the attached TREC Loan Assumption Addendum.
❑C. SELLER FINANCING: A promissory note from Buyer to Seller of $_____, secured by vendor's and deed of trust liens, and containing the terms and conditions described in the attached TREC Seller Financing Addendum. If an owner policy of title insurance is furnished, Buyer shall furnish Seller with a mortgagee policy of title insurance.

5. EARNEST MONEY: Upon execution of this contract by all parties, Buyer shall deposit $_____ as earnest money with _____, as escrow agent, at _____(address). Buyer shall deposit additional earnest money of $_____ with escrow agent within _____ days after the effective date of this contract. If Buyer fails to deposit the earnest money as required by this contract, Buyer will be in default.

6. TITLE POLICY AND SURVEY:
A. TITLE POLICY: Seller shall furnish to Buyer at ❑Seller's ❑Buyer's expense an owner policy of title insurance (Title Policy) issued by _____ (Title Company) in the amount of the Sales Price, dated at or after closing, insuring Buyer against loss under the provisions of the Title Policy, subject to the promulgated exclusions (including existing building and zoning ordinances) and the following exceptions:
(1) Restrictive covenants common to the platted subdivision in which the Property is located.
(2) The standard printed exception for standby fees, taxes and assessments.
(3) Liens created as part of the financing described in Paragraph 4.
(4) Utility easements created by the dedication deed or plat of the subdivision in which the Property is located.
(5) Reservations or exceptions otherwise permitted by this contract or as may be approved by Buyer in writing.
(6) The standard printed exception as to marital rights.
(7) The standard printed exception as to waters, tidelands, beaches, streams, and related matters.
(8) The standard printed exception as to discrepancies, conflicts, shortages in area or boundary lines, encroachments or protrusions, or overlapping improvements: ❑ (i) will not be amended or deleted from the title policy; ❑(ii) will be amended to read, "shortages in area" at the expense of ❑Buyer ❑Seller.
B. COMMITMENT: Within 20 days after the Title Company receives a copy of this contract, Seller shall furnish to Buyer a commitment for title insurance (Commitment) and, at Buyer's expense, legible copies of restrictive covenants and documents evidencing exceptions in the

Initialed for identification by Buyer_____ _____ and Seller _____ _____   TREC NO. 23-13

FIGURE 2

New Home Contract (Incomplete Construction) (continued)

Contract Concerning _____Page 2 of 9 4-28-2014
                            (Address of Property)

Commitment (Exception Documents) other than the standard printed exceptions.   Seller authorizes the Title Company to deliver the Commitment and Exception Documents to Buyer at Buyer's address shown in Paragraph 21.   If the Commitment and Exception Documents are not delivered to Buyer within the specified time, the time for delivery will be automatically extended up to 15 days or 3 days before the Closing Date, whichever is earlier. If, due to factors beyond Seller's control, the Commitment and Exception Documents are not delivered within the time required, Buyer may terminate this contract and the earnest money will be refunded to Buyer.

C. SURVEY: The survey must be made after the Substantial Completion Date by a registered professional land surveyor acceptable to the Title Company and Buyer's lender(s). (Check one box only)

❑ (1) At least _____ days prior to the Closing Date, Seller, at Seller's expense, shall provide a new survey to Buyer.

❑ (2) At least _____ days prior to the Closing Date, Buyer, at Buyer's expense, shall obtain a new survey. Buyer is deemed to receive the survey on the date of actual receipt or the date specified in this paragraph, whichever is earlier.

D. OBJECTIONS: Buyer may object in writing to defects, exceptions, or encumbrances to title: disclosed on the survey other than items 6A(1) through (7) above; disclosed in the Commitment other than items 6A(1) through (8) above; or which prohibit the following use or activity: _____.
_____
Buyer must object the earlier of (i) the Closing Date or (ii) _____ days after Buyer receives the Commitment, Exception Documents, and the survey. Buyer's failure to object within the time allowed will constitute a waiver of Buyer's right to object; except that the requirements in Schedule C of the Commitment are not waived by Buyer.   Provided Seller is not obligated to incur any expense, Seller shall cure the timely objections of Buyer or any third party lender within 15 days after Seller receives the objections and the Closing Date will be extended as necessary.   If objections are not cured within such 15 day period, this contract will terminate and the earnest money will be refunded to Buyer unless Buyer waives the objections.

E. TITLE NOTICES:

(1) ABSTRACT OR TITLE POLICY: Broker advises Buyer to have an abstract of title covering the Property examined by an attorney of Buyer's selection, or Buyer should be furnished with or obtain a Title Policy.   If a Title Policy is furnished, the Commitment should be promptly reviewed by an attorney of Buyer's choice due to the time limitations on Buyer's right to object.

(2) MEMBERSHIP IN PROPERTY OWNERS ASSOCIATION(S): The Property ❑ is ❑ is not subject to mandatory membership in a property owners association(s). If the Property is subject to mandatory membership in a property owners association(s), Seller notifies Buyer under §5.012, Texas Property Code, that, as a purchaser of property in the residential community identified in Paragraph 2A in which the Property is located, you are obligated to be a member of the property owners association(s). Restrictive covenants governing the use and occupancy of the Property and all dedicatory instruments governing the establishment, maintenance, and operation of this residential community have been or will be recorded in the Real Property Records of the county in which the Property is located. Copies of the restrictive covenants and dedicatory instruments may be obtained from the county clerk. **You are obligated to pay assessments to the property owners association(s). The amount of the assessments is subject to change. Your failure to pay the assessments could result in enforcement of the association's lien on and the foreclosure of the Property.**
Section 207.003, Property Code, entitles an owner to receive copies of any document that governs the establishment, maintenance, or operation of a subdivision, including, but not limited to, restrictions, bylaws, rules and regulations, and a resale certificate from a property owners' association. A resale certificate contains information including, but not limited to, statements specifying the amount and frequency of regular assessments and the style and cause number of lawsuits to which the property owners' association is a party, other than lawsuits relating to unpaid ad valorem taxes of an individual member of the association.   These documents must be made available to you by the property owners' association or the association's agent on your request.
If Buyer is concerned about these matters, the TREC promulgated Addendum for Property Subject to Mandatory Membership in a Property Owners Association should be used.

(3) STATUTORY TAX DISTRICTS: If the Property is situated in a utility or other statutorily created district providing water, sewer, drainage, or flood control facilities and services, Chapter 49, Texas Water Code, requires Seller to deliver and Buyer to sign the statutory notice relating to the tax rate, bonded indebtedness, or standby fee of the district prior to final execution of this contract.

(4) TIDE WATERS: If the Property abuts the tidally influenced waters of the state, §33.135, Texas Natural Resources Code, requires a notice regarding coastal area property to be included in the contract. An addendum containing the notice promulgated by TREC or

---

Initialed for identification by Buyer_____ _____ and Seller _____ _____   TREC NO. 23-13

FIGURE 2

New Home Contract (Incomplete Construction) (continued)

Contract Concerning _____ Page 3 of 9 4-28-2014
(Address of Property)

required by the parties must be used.

(5) ANNEXATION: If the Property is located outside the limits of a municipality, Seller notifies Buyer under §5.011, Texas Property Code, that the Property may now or later be included in the extraterritorial jurisdiction of a municipality and may now or later be subject to annexation by the municipality. Each municipality maintains a map that depicts its boundaries and extraterritorial jurisdiction. To determine if the Property is located within a municipality's extraterritorial jurisdiction or is likely to be located within a municipality's extraterritorial jurisdiction, contact all municipalities located in the general proximity of the Property for further information.

(6) PROPERTY LOCATED IN A CERTIFICATED SERVICE AREA OF A UTILITY SERVICE PROVIDER: Notice required by §13.257, Water Code: The real property, described in Paragraph 2, that you are about to purchase may be located in a certificated water or sewer service area, which is authorized by law to provide water or sewer service to the properties in the certificated area. If your property is located in a certificated area there may be special costs or charges that you will be required to pay before you can receive water or sewer service. There may be a period required to construct lines or other facilities necessary to provide water or sewer service to your property. You are advised to determine if the property is in a certificated area and contact the utility service provider to determine the cost that you will be required to pay and the period, if any, that is required to provide water or sewer service to your property. The undersigned Buyer hereby acknowledges receipt of the foregoing notice at or before the execution of a binding contract for the purchase of the real property described in Paragraph 2 or at closing of purchase of the real property.

(7) PUBLIC IMPROVEMENT DISTRICTS: If the Property is in a public improvement district, §5.014, Property Code, requires Seller to notify Buyer as follows: As a purchaser of this parcel of real property you are obligated to pay an assessment to a municipality or county for an improvement project undertaken by a public improvement district under Chapter 372, Local Government Code. The assessment may be due annually or in periodic installments. More information concerning the amount of the assessment and the due dates of that assessment may be obtained from the municipality or county levying the assessment. The amount of the assessments is subject to change. Your failure to pay the assessments could result in a lien on and the foreclosure of your property.

(8) TRANSFER FEES: If the Property is subject to a private transfer fee obligation, §5.205, Property Code, requires Seller to notify Buyer as follows: The private transfer fee obligation may be governed by Chapter 5, Subchapter G of the Texas Property Code.

(9) PROPANE GAS SYSTEM SERVICE AREA: If the Property is located in a propane gas system service area owned by a distribution system retailer, Seller must give Buyer written notice as required by §141.010, Texas Utilities Code. An addendum containing the notice approved by TREC or required by the parties should be used.

7. PROPERTY CONDITION:
A. ACCESS AND INSPECTIONS: Seller shall permit Buyer and Buyer's agents access to the Property at reasonable times. Buyer may have the Property inspected by inspectors selected by Buyer and licensed by TREC or otherwise permitted by law to make inspections.
B. CONSTRUCTION DOCUMENTS: Seller shall complete all improvements to the Property with due diligence in accordance with the Construction Documents. "Construction Documents" means the plans and specifications, the finish out schedules, any change orders, and any allowances related to the plans and specifications, finish out schedules, and change orders. The Construction Documents have been signed by the parties and are incorporated into this contract by reference.
C. COST ADJUSTMENTS: All change orders must be in writing. Increase in costs resulting from change orders or items selected by Buyer which exceed the allowances specified in the Construction Documents will be paid by Buyer as follows:_____
_____.
A decrease in costs resulting from change orders and unused allowances will reduce the Sales Price, with proportionate adjustments to the amounts in Paragraphs 3A and 3B as required by lender.
D. BUYER'S SELECTIONS: If the Construction Documents permit selections by Buyer, Buyer's selections will conform to Seller's normal standards as set out in the Construction Documents or will not, in Seller's judgment, adversely affect the marketability of the Property. Buyer will make required selections within _____ days after notice from Seller.
E. COMPLETION: Seller must commence construction no later than _____ days after the effective date of this contract. The improvements will be substantially completed in accordance with the Construction Documents and ready for occupancy not later than _____, 20____ . The improvements will be deemed to be substantially completed in accordance with the Construction Documents upon the final inspection and approval by all applicable governmental authorities and any lender (Substantial Completion Date). Construction delays caused by acts of God, fire or other casualty, strikes, boycotts or nonavailability of materials for which no substitute of comparable quality and price is available will be added to the time allowed for substantial completion of the construction. However, in no event may the time for substantial completion extend beyond the Closing Date. Seller may substitute materials,

Initialed for identification by Buyer_____ _____ and Seller _____ _____   TREC NO. 23-13

FIGURE 2

New Home Contract (Incomplete Construction) (continued)

Contract Concerning _____ Page 4 of 9 4-28-2014
(Address of Property)

equipment and appliances of comparable quality for those specified in the Construction Documents.

F. WARRANTIES: Except as expressly set forth in this contract, a separate writing, or provided by law, Seller makes no other express warranties. Seller shall assign to Buyer at closing all assignable manufacturer warranties.

G. INSULATION: As required by Federal Trade Commission Regulations, the information relating to the insulation installed or to be installed in the Improvements at the Property is: (check only one box below)

☐ (1) as shown in the attached specifications.

☐ (2) as follows:

    (a) Exterior walls of improved living areas: insulated with _____ insulation to a thickness of _____ inches which yields an R-Value of _____.

    (b) Walls in other areas of the home: insulated with_____ insulation to a thickness of _____ inches which yields an R-Value of _____.

    (c) Ceilings in improved living areas: insulated with_____ insulation to a thickness of _____ inches which yields an R-Value of _____.

    (d) Floors of improved living areas not applied to a slab foundation: insulated with_____ _____insulation to a thickness of_____ inches which yields an R-Value of _____.

    (e) Other insulated areas: insulated with _____insulation to a thickness of _____ inches which yields an R-Value of _____.

    All stated R-Values are based on information provided by the manufacturer of the insulation.

H. ENVIRONMENTAL MATTERS: Buyer is advised that the presence of wetlands, toxic substances, including asbestos and wastes or other environmental hazards, or the presence of a threatened or endangered species or its habitat may affect Buyer's intended use of the Property. If Buyer is concerned about these matters, an addendum promulgated by TREC or required by the parties should be used.

I. SELLER'S DISCLOSURE: Except as otherwise disclosed in this contract, Seller has no knowledge of the following:

    (1) any flooding of the Property which has had a material adverse effect on the use of the Property;

    (2) any pending or threatened litigation, condemnation, or special assessment affecting the Property;

    (3) any environmental hazards that materially and adversely affect the Property;

    (4) any dumpsite, landfill, or underground tanks or containers now or previously located on the Property;

    (5) any wetlands, as defined by federal or state law or regulation, affecting the Property; or any threatened or endangered species or their habitat affecting the Property.

8. BROKERS' FEES: All obligations of the parties for payment of brokers' fees are contained in separate written agreements.

9. CLOSING:

A. The closing of the sale will be on or before _____, 20_____, or within 7 days after objections made under Paragraph 6D have been cured or waived, whichever date is later (Closing Date). If either party fails to close the sale by the Closing Date, the non-defaulting party may exercise the remedies contained in Paragraph 15.

B. At closing:

    (1) Seller shall execute and deliver a general warranty deed conveying title to the Property to Buyer and showing no additional exceptions to those permitted in Paragraph 6 and furnish tax statements or certificates showing no delinquent taxes on the Property.

    (2) Buyer shall pay the Sales Price in good funds acceptable to the escrow agent.

    (3) Seller and Buyer shall execute and deliver any notices, statements, certificates, affidavits, releases, loan documents and other documents reasonably required for the closing of the sale and the issuance of the Title Policy.

    (4) There will be no liens, assessments, or security interests against the Property which will not be satisfied out of the sales proceeds unless securing payment of any loans assumed by Buyer and assumed loans will not be in default.

10. POSSESSION:

A. Buyer's Possession: Seller shall deliver to Buyer possession of the Property: ☐ upon closing and funding ☐ according to a temporary residential lease form promulgated by TREC or other written lease required by the parties. Any possession by Buyer prior to closing or by Seller after closing which is not authorized by a written lease will establish a tenancy at sufferance relationship between the parties. **Consult your insurance agent prior to change of ownership and possession because insurance coverage may be limited or terminated. The absence of a written lease or appropriate insurance coverage may expose the parties to economic loss.**

B. Leases: After the Effective Date, Seller may not execute any lease (including but not limited to mineral leases) or convey any interest in the Property without Buyer's written consent.

Initialed for identification by Buyer_____ _____ and Seller _____ _____   TREC NO. 23-13

FIGURE 2
_____

New Home Contract (Incomplete Construction) (continued)

Contract Concerning _____ Page 5 of 9 4-28-2014
(Address of Property)

11. SPECIAL PROVISIONS: (Insert only factual statements and business details applicable to the sale. TREC rules prohibit licensees from adding factual statements or business details for which a contract addendum, lease or other form has been promulgated by TREC for mandatory use.)

12. SETTLEMENT AND OTHER EXPENSES:
    A. The following expenses must be paid at or prior to closing:
        (1)Expenses payable by Seller (Seller's Expenses):
           (a)Releases of existing liens, including prepayment penalties and recording fees; release of Seller's loan liability; tax statements or certificates; preparation of deed; one-half of escrow fee; and other expenses payable by Seller under this contract.
           (b)Seller shall also pay an amount not to exceed $ _____ to be applied in the following order: Buyer's Expenses which Buyer is prohibited from paying by FHA, VA, Texas Veterans Land Board or other governmental loan programs, and then to other Buyer's Expenses as allowed by the lender.
      (2) Expenses payable by Buyer (Buyer's Expenses): Appraisal fees; loan application fees; adjusted origination charges; credit reports; preparation of loan documents; interest on the notes from date of disbursement to one month prior to dates of first monthly payments; recording fees; copies of easements and restrictions; loan title policy with endorsements required by lender; loan-related inspection fees; photos; amortization schedules; one-half of escrow fee; all prepaid items, including required premiums for flood and hazard insurance, reserve deposits for insurance, ad valorem taxes and special governmental assessments; final compliance inspection; courier fee; repair inspection; underwriting fee; wire transfer fee; expenses incident to any loan; Private Mortgage Insurance Premium (PMI), VA Loan Funding Fee, or FHA Mortgage Insurance Premium (MIP) as required by the lender; and other expenses payable by Buyer under this contract.
    B. If any expense exceeds an amount expressly stated in this contract for such expense to be paid by a party, that party may terminate this contract unless the other party agrees to pay such excess. Buyer may not pay charges and fees expressly prohibited by FHA, VA, Texas Veterans Land Board or other governmental loan program regulations.

13. PRORATIONS AND ROLLBACK TAXES:
    A. PRORATIONS: Taxes for the current year, maintenance fees, assessments, dues and rents will be prorated through the Closing Date. The tax proration may be calculated taking into consideration any change in exemptions that will affect the current year's taxes. If taxes for the current year vary from the amount prorated at closing, the parties shall adjust the prorations when tax statements for the current year are available. If taxes are not paid at or prior to closing, Buyer will be obligated to pay taxes for the current year.
    B. ROLLBACK TAXES: If Seller's change in use of the Property prior to closing or denial of a special use valuation on the Property results in additional taxes, penalties or interest (Assessments) for periods prior to closing, the Assessments will be the obligation of Seller. Obligations imposed by this paragraph will survive closing.

14. CASUALTY LOSS: If any part of the Property is damaged or destroyed by fire or other casualty after the effective date of this contract, Seller shall restore the Property to its previous condition as soon as reasonably possible, but in any event by the Closing Date. If Seller fails to do so due to factors beyond Seller's control, Buyer may (a) terminate this contract and the earnest money will be refunded to Buyer (b) extend the time for performance up to 45 days and the Closing Date will be extended as necessary or (c) accept the Property in its damaged condition with an assignment of insurance proceeds and receive credit from Seller at closing in the amount of the deductible under the insurance policy. Seller's obligations under this paragraph are independent of any other obligations of Seller under this contract.

15. DEFAULT: If Buyer fails to comply with this contract, Buyer will be in default, and Seller may (a) enforce specific performance, seek such other relief as may be provided by law, or both, or (b) terminate this contract and receive the earnest money as liquidated damages, thereby releasing both parties from this contract. If Seller fails to comply with this contract Seller will be in default and Buyer may (a) enforce specific performance, seek such other relief as may be provided by law, or both, or (b) terminate this contract and receive the earnest money, thereby releasing both parties from this contract.

16. MEDIATION: It is the policy of the State of Texas to encourage resolution of disputes through alternative dispute resolution procedures such as mediation. Subject to applicable law, any dispute between Seller and Buyer related to this contract which is not resolved through informal discussion will be submitted to a mutually acceptable mediation service or provider. The parties to the mediation shall bear the mediation costs equally. This paragraph does not preclude a party from

Initialed for identification by Buyer_____ _____ and Seller _____ _____   TREC NO. 23-13

FIGURE 2

New Home Contract (Incomplete Construction) (continued)

Contract Concerning _____ Page 6 of 9 4-28-2014
(Address of Property)

seeking equitable relief from a court of competent jurisdiction.

17. ATTORNEY'S FEES: A Buyer, Seller, Listing Broker, Other Broker, or escrow agent who prevails in any legal proceeding related to this contract is entitled to recover reasonable attorney's fees and all costs of such proceeding.

18. ESCROW:
   A. ESCROW: The escrow agent is not (i) a party to this contract and does not have liability for the performance or nonperformance of any party to this contract, (ii) liable for interest on the earnest money and (iii) liable for the loss of any earnest money caused by the failure of any financial institution in which the earnest money has been deposited unless the financial institution is acting as escrow agent.
   B. EXPENSES: At closing, the earnest money must be applied first to any cash down payment, then to Buyer's Expenses and any excess refunded to Buyer. If no closing occurs, escrow agent may: (i) require a written release of liability of the escrow agent from all parties, (ii) require payment of unpaid expenses incurred on behalf of a party, and (iii) only deduct from the earnest money the amount of unpaid expenses incurred on behalf of the party receiving the earnest money.
   C. DEMAND: Upon termination of this contract, either party or the escrow agent may send a release of earnest money to each party and the parties shall execute counterparts of the release and deliver same to the escrow agent. If either party fails to execute the release, either party may make a written demand to the escrow agent for the earnest money. If only one party makes written demand for the earnest money, escrow agent shall promptly provide a copy of the demand to the other party. If escrow agent does not receive written objection to the demand from the other party within 15 days, escrow agent may disburse the earnest money to the party making demand reduced by the amount of unpaid expenses incurred on behalf of the party receiving the earnest money and escrow agent may pay the same to the creditors. If escrow agent complies with the provisions of this paragraph, each party hereby releases escrow agent from all adverse claims related to the disbursal of the earnest money.
   D. DAMAGES: Any party who wrongfully fails or refuses to sign a release acceptable to the escrow agent within 7 days of receipt of the request will be liable to the other party for liquidated damages in an amount equal to the sum of: (i) three times the amount of the earnest money; (ii) the earnest money; (iii) reasonable attorney's fees; and (iv) all costs of suit.
   E. NOTICES: Escrow agent's notices will be effective when sent in compliance with Paragraph 21. Notice of objection to the demand will be deemed effective upon receipt by escrow agent.

19. REPRESENTATIONS: All covenants, representations and warranties in this contract survive closing. If any representation of Seller in this contract is untrue on the Closing Date, Seller will be in default. Unless expressly prohibited by written agreement, Seller may continue to show the Property and receive, negotiate and accept back up offers.

20. FEDERAL TAX REQUIREMENTS: If Seller is a "foreign person," as defined by applicable law, or if Seller fails to deliver an affidavit to Buyer that Seller is not a "foreign person," then Buyer shall withhold from the sales proceeds an amount sufficient to comply with applicable tax law and deliver the same to the Internal Revenue Service together with appropriate tax forms. Internal Revenue Service regulations require filing written reports if currency in excess of specified amounts is received in the transaction.

21. NOTICES: All notices from one party to the other must be in writing and are effective when mailed to, hand-delivered at, or transmitted by facsimile or electronic transmission as follows:

**To Buyer
at:** _____

**To Seller
at:** _____

_____

_____

Telephone: (____) _____

Telephone: (____) _____

Facsimile: (____) _____

Facsimile: (____) _____

E-mail: _____

E-mail: _____

Initialed for identification by Buyer_____ _____ and Seller _____ _____   TREC NO. 23-13

FIGURE 2

New Home Contract (Incomplete Construction) (continued)

Contract Concerning _____ Page 7 of 9 4-28-2014
(Address of Property)

22. **AGREEMENT OF PARTIES:** This contract contains the entire agreement of the parties and cannot be changed except by their written agreement. Addenda which are a part of this contract are (check all applicable boxes):

- ❏ Third Party Financing Addendum for Credit Approval
- ❏ Seller Financing Addendum
- ❏ Addendum for Property Subject to Mandatory Membership in a Property Owners Association
- ❏ Buyer's Temporary Residential Lease
- ❏ Loan Assumption Addendum
- ❏ Addendum for Sale of Other Property by Buyer
- ❏ Addendum for Reservation of Oil, Gas and Other Minerals
- ❏ Addendum for "Back-Up" Contract

- ❏ Addendum for Coastal Area Property
- ❏ Environmental Assessment, Threatened or Endangered Species and Wetlands Addendum
- ❏ Seller's Temporary Residential Lease
- ❏ Short Sale Addendum
- ❏ Addendum for Property Located Seaward of the Gulf Intracoastal Waterway
- ❏ Addendum for Property in a Propane Gas System Service Area
- ❏ Other (list): _____
  _____

23. **TERMINATION OPTION:** For nominal consideration, the receipt of which is hereby acknowledged by Seller, and Buyer's agreement to pay Seller $_____ (Option Fee) within 3 days after the effective date of this contract, Seller grants Buyer the unrestricted right to terminate this contract by giving notice of termination to Seller within _____ days after the effective date of this contract (Option Period).   If no dollar amount is stated as the Option Fee or if Buyer fails to pay the Option Fee to Seller within the time prescribed, this paragraph will not be a part of this contract and Buyer shall not have the unrestricted right to terminate this contract. If Buyer gives notice of termination within the time prescribed, the Option Fee will not be refunded; however, any earnest money will be refunded to Buyer. The Option Fee ❏will ❏will not be credited to the Sales Price at closing. **Time is of the essence for this paragraph and strict compliance with the time for performance is required.**

24. **CONSULT AN ATTORNEY BEFORE SIGNING:** TREC rules prohibit real estate licensees from giving legal advice. READ THIS CONTRACT CAREFULLY.

Buyer's
Attorney is: _____

Seller's
Attorney is: _____

_____

_____

Telephone: (____) _____

Telephone: (____) _____

Facsimile: (____) _____

Facsimile: (____) _____

E-mail: _____

E-mail: _____

Initialed for identification by Buyer_____ _____ and Seller _____ _____   TREC NO. 23-13

FIGURE 2

New Home Contract (Incomplete Construction) (continued)

Contract Concerning _____ Page 8 of 9 4-28-2014
(Address of Property)

**EXECUTED the _____day of _____, 20_____ (EFFECTIVE DATE).
(BROKER: FILL IN THE DATE OF FINAL ACCEPTANCE.)**

This contract is subject to Chapter 27 of the Texas Property Code. The provisions of that chapter may affect your right to recover damages arising from a construction defect. If you have a complaint concerning a construction defect and that defect has not been corrected as may be required by law or by contract, you must provide the notice required by Chapter 27 of the Texas Property Code to the contractor by certified mail, return receipt requested, not later than the 60th day before the date you file suit to recover damages in a court of law or initiate arbitration. The notice must refer to Chapter 27 of the Texas Property Code and must describe the construction defect. If requested by the contractor, you must provide the contractor an opportunity to inspect and cure the defect as provided by Section 27.004 of the Texas Property Code.

_____
Buyer

_____
Buyer

_____
Seller

_____
Seller

TREC NO. 23-13

F I G U R E 2

New Home Contract (Incomplete Construction) (continued)

Contract Concerning _____ Page 9 of 9 4-28-2014

(Address of Property)

BROKER INFORMATION
(Print name(s) only. Do not sign)

Other Broker Firm _____ License No.

represents ☐ Buyer only as Buyer's agent

☐ Seller as Listing Broker's subagent

Name of Associate's Licensed Supervisor   Telephone

Associate's Name   Telephone

Other Broker's Address   Facsimile

City   State   Zip

Associate's Email Address

Listing Broker Firm   License No.

represents ☐ Seller and Buyer as an intermediary

☐ Seller only as Seller's agent

Name of Associate's Licensed Supervisor   Telephone

Listing Associate's Name   Telephone

Listing Broker's Office Address   Facsimile

City   State   Zip

Listing Associate's Email Address

Selling Associate's Name   Telephone

Name of Selling Associate's Licensed Supervisor   Telephone

Selling Associate's Office Address   Facsimile

City   State   Zip

Selling Associate's Email Address

Listing Broker has agreed to pay Other Broker_____ of the total sales price when the Listing Broker's fee is received. Escrow agent is authorized and directed to pay other Broker from Listing Broker's fee at closing.

OPTION FEE RECEIPT

Receipt of $_____ (Option Fee) in the form of _____ is acknowledged.

Seller or Listing Broker   Date

CONTRACT AND EARNEST MONEY RECEIPT

Receipt of ☐Contract and ☐$_____ Earnest Money in the form of _____ is acknowledged.

Escrow Agent: _____   Date: _____

By: _____

_____ Email Address

Address   Telephone (____) _____

City   State   Zip   Facsimile: (_____) _____

TREC NO. 23-13

FIGURE 3

New Home Contract (Completed Construction)

PROMULGATED BY THE TEXAS REAL ESTATE COMMISSION (TREC)   4-28-2014
NEW HOME CONTRACT
(Completed Construction)
NOTICE: Not For Use For Condominium Transactions or Closings Prior to Completion of Construction

1. PARTIES: The parties to this contract are _____
(Seller) and _____(Buyer). Seller agrees
to sell and convey to Buyer and Buyer agrees to buy from Seller the Property defined below.

2. PROPERTY: Lot _____,Block_____,
_____Addition, City
of_____,County of_____,
Texas, known as _____
(address/zip code), or as described on attached exhibit, together with: (i) improvements,
fixtures and all other property located thereon; and (ii) all rights, privileges and appurtenances
thereto, including but not limited to: permits, easements, and cooperative and association
memberships. All property sold by this contract is called the "Property".

3. SALES PRICE:
  A. Cash portion of Sales Price payable by Buyer at closing .... $_____
  B. Sum of all financing described below (excluding any loan funding
     fee or mortgage insurance premium).. $_____
  C. Sales Price (Sum of A and B).. $_____

4. FINANCING (Not for use with reverse mortgage financing): The portion of Sales Price not
payable in cash will be paid as follows: (Check applicable boxes below)
❑A. THIRD PARTY FINANCING: One or more third party mortgage loans in the total amount of
    $_____ (excluding any loan funding fee or mortgage insurance premium).
    (1) Property Approval: If the Property does not satisfy the lenders' underwriting requirements
       for the loan(s), (including, but not limited to appraisal, insurability and lender required
       repairs), Buyer may terminate this contract by giving notice to Seller prior to closing and
       the earnest money will be refunded to Buyer.
    (2) Credit Approval: (Check one box only)
      ❑ (a) This contract is subject to Buyer being approved for the financing described in the
          attached Third Party Financing Addendum for Credit Approval.
      ❑ (b) This contract is not subject to Buyer being approved for financing and does not involve
          FHA or VA financing.
❑B. ASSUMPTION: The assumption of the unpaid principal balance of one or more promissory
    notes described in the attached TREC Loan Assumption Addendum.
❑C. SELLER FINANCING: A promissory note from Buyer to Seller of $_____,
    secured by vendor's and deed of trust liens, and containing the terms and conditions
    described in the attached TREC Seller Financing Addendum. If an owner policy of title
    insurance is furnished, Buyer shall furnish Seller with a mortgagee policy of title insurance.

5. EARNEST MONEY: Upon execution of this contract by all parties, Buyer shall
deposit $_____ as earnest money with _____,
as escrow agent, at _____
(address). Buyer shall deposit additional earnest money of $_____ with escrow
agent within _____ days after the effective date of this contract. If Buyer fails to deposit the
earnest money as required by this contract, Buyer will be in default.

6. TITLE POLICY AND SURVEY:
  A. TITLE POLICY: Seller shall furnish to Buyer at ❑Seller's ❑Buyer's expense an owner policy of
    title insurance (Title Policy) issued by _____.
    (Title Company) in the amount of the Sales Price, dated at or after closing, insuring Buyer
    against loss under the provisions of the Title Policy, subject to the promulgated exclusions
    (including existing building and zoning ordinances) and the following exceptions:
    (1) Restrictive covenants common to the platted subdivision in which the Property is located.
    (2) The standard printed exception for standby fees, taxes and assessments.
    (3) Liens created as part of the financing described in Paragraph 4.
    (4) Utility easements created by the dedication deed or plat of the subdivision in which the
       Property is located.
    (5) Reservations or exceptions otherwise permitted by this contract or as may be approved by
       Buyer in writing.
    (6) The standard printed exception as to marital rights.
    (7) The standard printed exception as to waters, tidelands, beaches, streams, and related
       matters.
    (8) The standard printed exception as to discrepancies, conflicts, shortages in area or boundary
       lines, encroachments or protrusions, or overlapping improvement: ❑(i) will not be amended
       or deleted from the title policy; ❑(ii) will be amended to read, "shortages in area" at the
       expense of ❑Buyer ❑Seller.
  B. COMMITMENT: Within 20 days after the Title Company receives a copy of this contract, Seller
    shall furnish to Buyer a commitment for title insurance (Commitment) and, at Buyer's

Initialed for identification by Buyer_____ _____ and Seller _____ _____   TREC NO. 24-13

FIGURE 3

New Home Contract (Completed Construction) (continued)

Contract Concerning _____ Page 2 of 9 4-28-2014
(Address of Property)

expense, legible copies of restrictive covenants and documents evidencing exceptions in the Commitment (Exception Documents) other than the standard printed exceptions. Seller authorizes the Title Company to deliver the Commitment and Exception Documents to Buyer at Buyer's address shown in Paragraph 21. If the Commitment and Exception Documents are not delivered to Buyer within the specified time, the time for delivery will be automatically extended up to 15 days or 3 days before the Closing Date, whichever is earlier. If, due to factors beyond Seller's control, the Commitment and Exception Documents are not delivered within the time required, Buyer may terminate this contract and the earnest money will be refunded to Buyer.

C. SURVEY: The survey must be made by a registered professional land surveyor acceptable to the Title Company and Buyer's lender(s). (Check one box only)

❑ (1) Within _____ days after the effective date of this contract, Seller shall furnish to Buyer and Title Company Seller's existing survey of the Property and a Residential Real Property Affidavit promulgated by the Texas Department of Insurance (T-47 Affidavit). **If Seller fails to furnish the existing survey or affidavit within the time prescribed, Buyer shall obtain a new survey at Seller's expense no later than 3 days prior to Closing Date.** If the existing survey or affidavit is not acceptable to Title Company or Buyer's lender(s), Buyer shall obtain a new survey at ❑ Seller's ❑ Buyer's expense no later than 3 days prior to Closing Date.

❑ (2) Within _____ days after the effective date of this contract, Buyer shall obtain a new survey at Buyer's expense. Buyer is deemed to receive the survey on the date of actual receipt or the date specified in this paragraph, whichever is earlier.

❑ (3) Within _____ days after the effective date of this contract, Seller, at Seller's expense shall furnish a new survey to Buyer.

D. OBJECTIONS: Buyer may object in writing to defects, exceptions, or encumbrances to title: disclosed on the survey other than items 6A(1) through (7) above; disclosed in the Commitment other than items 6A(1) through (8) above; or which prohibit the following use or activity: _____
_____.
Buyer must object the earlier of (i) the Closing Date or (ii) _____ days after Buyer receives the Commitment, Exception Documents, and the survey. Buyer's failure to object within the time allowed will constitute a waiver of Buyer's right to object; except that the requirements in Schedule C of the Commitment are not waived by Buyer. Provided Seller is not obligated to incur any expense, Seller shall cure the timely objections of Buyer or any third party lender within 15 days after Seller receives the objections and the Closing Date will be extended as necessary. If objections are not cured within such 15 day period, this contract will terminate and the earnest money will be refunded to Buyer unless Buyer waives the objections.

E. TITLE NOTICES:

(1) ABSTRACT OR TITLE POLICY: Broker advises Buyer to have an abstract of title covering the Property examined by an attorney of Buyer's selection, or Buyer should be furnished with or obtain a Title Policy. If a Title Policy is furnished, the Commitment should be promptly reviewed by an attorney of Buyer's choice due to the time limitations on Buyer's right to object.

(2) MEMBERSHIP IN PROPERTY OWNERS ASSOCIATION(S): The Property ❑is ❑is not subject to mandatory membership in a property owners association(s). If the Property is subject to mandatory membership in a property owners association(s), Seller notifies Buyer under §5.012, Texas Property Code, that, as a purchaser of property in the residential community identified in Paragraph 2A in which the Property is located, you are obligated to be a member of the property owners association(s). Restrictive covenants governing the use and occupancy of the Property and all dedicatory instruments governing the establishment, maintenance, and operation of this residential community have been or will be recorded in the Real Property Records of the county in which the Property is located. Copies of the restrictive covenants and dedicatory instruments may be obtained from the county clerk. **You are obligated to pay assessments to the property owners association(s). The amount of the assessments is subject to change. Your failure to pay the assessments could result in enforcement of the association's lien on and the foreclosure of the Property.** Section 207.003, Property Code, entitles an owner to receive copies of any document that governs the establishment, maintenance, or operation of a subdivision, including, but not limited to, restrictions, bylaws, rules and regulations, and a resale certificate from a property owners' association. A resale certificate contains information including, but not limited to, statements specifying the amount and frequency of regular assessments and the style and cause number of lawsuits to which the property owners' association is a party, other than lawsuits relating to unpaid ad valorem taxes of an individual member of the association. These documents must be made available to you by the property owners' association or the association's agent on your request. **If Buyer is concerned about these matters, the TREC promulgated Addendum for Property Subject to Mandatory Membership in a Property Owners Association**

FIGURE 3

New Home Contract (Completed Construction) (continued)

Contract Concerning _____ Page 3 of 9 4-28-2014
(Address of Property)

    should be used.

    (3) STATUTORY TAX DISTRICTS: If the Property is situated in a utility or other statutorily created district providing water, sewer, drainage, or flood control facilities and services, Chapter 49, Texas Water Code, requires Seller to deliver and Buyer to sign the statutory notice relating to the tax rate, bonded indebtedness, or standby fee of the district prior to final execution of this contract.

    (4) TIDE WATERS: If the Property abuts the tidally influenced waters of the state, §33.135, Texas Natural Resources Code, requires a notice regarding coastal area property to be included in the contract. An addendum containing the notice promulgated by TREC or required by the parties must be used.

    (5) ANNEXATION: If the Property is located outside the limits of a municipality, Seller notifies Buyer under §5.011, Texas Property Code, that the Property may now or later be included in the extraterritorial jurisdiction of a municipality and may now or later be subject to annexation by the municipality. Each municipality maintains a map that depicts its boundaries and extraterritorial jurisdiction. To determine if the Property is located within a municipality's extraterritorial jurisdiction or is likely to be located within a municipality's extraterritorial jurisdiction, contact all municipalities located in the general proximity of the Property for further information.

    (6) PROPERTY LOCATED IN A CERTIFICATED SERVICE AREA OF A UTILITY SERVICE PROVIDER: Notice required by §13.257, Water Code: The real property, described in Paragraph 2, that you are about to purchase may be located in a certificated water or sewer service area, which is authorized by law to provide water or sewer service to the properties in the certificated area. If your property is located in a certificated area there may be special costs or charges that you will be required to pay before you can receive water or sewer service. There may be a period required to construct lines or other facilities necessary to provide water or sewer service to your property. You are advised to determine if the property is in a certificated area and contact the utility service provider to determine the cost that you will be required to pay and the period, if any, that is required to provide water or sewer service to your property. The undersigned Buyer hereby acknowledges receipt of the foregoing notice at or before the execution of a binding contract for the purchase of the real property described in Paragraph 2 or at closing of purchase of the real property.

    (7) PUBLIC IMPROVEMENT DISTRICTS: If the Property is in a public improvement district, §5.014, Property Code, requires Seller to notify Buyer as follows: As a purchaser of this parcel of real property you are obligated to pay an assessment to a municipality or county for an improvement project undertaken by a public improvement district under Chapter 372, Local Government Code. The assessment may be due annually or in periodic installments. More information concerning the amount of the assessment and the due dates of that assessment may be obtained from the municipality or county levying the assessment. The amount of the assessments is subject to change. Your failure to pay the assessments could result in a lien on and the foreclosure of your property.

    (8) TRANSFER FEES: If the Property is subject to a private transfer fee obligation, §5.205, Property Code, requires Seller to notify Buyer as follows: The private transfer fee obligation may be governed by Chapter 5, Subchapter G of the Texas Property Code.

    (9) PROPANE GAS SYSTEM SERVICE AREA: If the Property is located in a propane gas system service area owned by a distribution system retailer, Seller must give Buyer written notice as required by §141.010, Texas Utilities Code. An addendum containing the notice approved by TREC or required by the parties should be used.

7. PROPERTY CONDITION:

    A. ACCESS, INSPECTIONS AND UTILITIES: Seller shall permit Buyer and Buyer's agents access to the Property at reasonable times. Buyer may have the Property inspected by inspectors selected by Buyer and licensed by TREC or otherwise permitted by law to make inspections. Seller at Seller's expense shall immediately cause existing utilities to be turned on and shall keep the utilities on during the time this contract is in effect.

    B. ACCEPTANCE OF PROPERTY CONDITION: "As Is" means the present condition of the Property with any and all defects and without warranty except for the warranties of title and the warranties in this contract. Buyer's agreement to accept the Property As Is under Paragraph 7B(1) or (2) does not preclude Buyer from inspecting the Property under Paragraph 7A, from negotiating repairs or treatments in a subsequent amendment, or from terminating this contract during the Option Period, if any.

    (Check one box only)

    ❑ (1) Buyer accepts the Property As Is.

    ❑ (2) Buyer accepts the Property As Is provided Seller, at Seller's expense, shall complete the following specific repairs and treatments:_____
_____(Do not insert general phrases, such as "subject to inspections," that do not identify specific repairs and treatments.)

Initialed for identification by Buyer_____ _____ and Seller _____ _____   TREC NO. 24-13

FIGURE 3

New Home Contract (Completed Construction) (continued)

Contract Concerning _____Page 4 of 9 4-28-2014
(Address of Property)

   C. WARRANTIES: Except as expressly set forth in this contract, a separate writing, or provided by law, Seller makes no other express warranties. Seller shall assign to Buyer at closing all assignable manufacturer warranties.

   D. INSULATION: As required by Federal Trade Commission Regulations, the information relating to the insulation installed or to be installed in the Improvements at the Property is: (check only one box below)

   ❑ (1) as shown in the attached specifications.

   ❑ (2) as follows:

      (a) Exterior walls of improved living areas: insulated with_____
          insulation to a thickness of _____ inches which yields an R-Value of _____.

      (b) Walls in other areas of the home: insulated with_____
          insulation to a thickness of _____ inches which yields an R-Value of _____.

      (c) Ceilings in improved living areas: insulated with___
          insulation to a thickness of _____ inches which yields an R-Value of _____.

      (d) Floors of improved living areas not applied to a slab foundation: insulated with_____
         _____ insulation to a thickness of _____ inches which yields an R-Value of _____.

      (e) Other insulated areas: insulated with _____insulation to a thickness of _____ inches which yields an R-Value of _____.

   All stated R-Values are based on information provided by the manufacturer of the insulation.

   E. LENDER REQUIRED REPAIRS AND TREATMENTS: Unless otherwise agreed in writing, neither party is obligated to pay for lender required repairs, which includes treatment for wood destroying insects. If the parties do not agree to pay for the lender required repairs or treatments, this contract will terminate and the earnest money will be refunded to Buyer. If the cost of lender required repairs and treatments exceeds 5% of the Sales Price, Buyer may terminate this contract and the earnest money will be refunded to Buyer.

   F. COMPLETION OF REPAIRS, TREATMENTS, AND IMPROVEMENTS: Unless otherwise agreed in writing: (i) Seller shall complete all agreed repairs, treatments, and improvements (Work) prior to the Closing Date; and (ii) all required permits must be obtained, and Work must be performed by persons who are licensed to provide such Work or, if no license is required by law, are commercially engaged in the trade of providing such Work. At Buyer's election, any transferable warranties received by Seller with respect to the Work will be transferred to Buyer at Buyer's expense. If Seller fails to complete any agreed Work prior to the Closing Date, Buyer may exercise remedies under Paragraph 15 or extend the Closing Date up to 5 days if necessary for Seller to complete Work.

   G. ENVIRONMENTAL MATTERS: Buyer is advised that the presence of wetlands, toxic substances, including asbestos and wastes or other environmental hazards or the presence of a threatened or endangered species or its habitat may affect Buyer's intended use of the Property. If Buyer is concerned about these matters, an addendum promulgated by TREC or required by the parties should be used.

   H. SELLER'S DISCLOSURE: Except as otherwise disclosed in this contract, Seller has no knowledge of the following:

      (1) any flooding of the Property which has had a material adverse effect on the use of the Property;

      (2) any pending or threatened litigation, condemnation, or special assessment affecting the Property;

      (3) any environmental hazards that materially and adversely affect the Property;

      (4) any dumpsite, landfill, or underground tanks or containers now or previously located on the Property;

      (5) any wetlands, as defined by federal or state law or regulation, affecting the Property; or

      (6) any threatened or endangered species or their habitat affecting the Property.

   I. RESIDENTIAL SERVICE CONTRACTS: Buyer may purchase a residential service contract from a residential service company licensed by TREC. If Buyer purchases a residential service contract, Seller shall reimburse Buyer at closing for the cost of the residential service contract in an amount not exceeding $_____ . Buyer should review any residential service contract for the scope of coverage, exclusions and limitations. **The purchase of a residential service contract is optional. Similar coverage may be purchased from various companies authorized to do business in Texas.**

8. BROKERS' FEES: All obligations of the parties for payment of brokers' fees are contained in separate written agreements.

9. CLOSING:

   A. The closing of the sale will be on or before _____, 20_____, or within 7 days after objections made under Paragraph 6D have been cured or waived, whichever date is later (Closing Date). If either party fails to close the sale by the Closing Date, the non-defaulting party may exercise the remedies contained in Paragraph 15.

Initialed for identification by Buyer_____ _____ and Seller _____ _____   TREC NO. 24-13

FIGURE 3

New Home Contract (Completed Construction) (continued)

Contract Concerning _____ Page 5 of 9 4-28-2014
(Address of Property)

B. At closing:
   (1) Seller shall execute and deliver a general warranty deed conveying title to the Property to Buyer and showing no additional exceptions to those permitted in Paragraph 6 and furnish tax statements or certificates showing no delinquent taxes on the Property.
   (2) Buyer shall pay the Sales Price in good funds acceptable to the escrow agent.
   (3) Seller and Buyer shall execute and deliver any notices, statements, certificates, affidavits, releases, loan documents and other documents reasonably required for the closing of the sale and the issuance of the Title Policy.
   (4) There will be no liens, assessments, or security interests against the Property which will not be satisfied out of the sales proceeds unless securing the payment of any loans assumed by Buyer and assumed loans will not be in default.

10. POSSESSION:
   A. Buyer's Possession: Seller shall deliver to Buyer possession of the Property in its present or required condition, ordinary wear and tear excepted: ❑ upon closing and funding ❑ according to a temporary residential lease form promulgated by TREC or other written lease required by the parties. Any possession by Buyer prior to closing or by Seller after closing which is not authorized by a written lease will establish a tenancy at sufferance relationship between the parties. **Consult your insurance agent prior to change of ownership and possession because insurance coverage may be limited or terminated. The absence of a written lease or appropriate insurance coverage may expose the parties to economic loss.**
   B. Leases: After the Effective Date, Seller may not execute any lease (including but not limited to mineral leases) or convey any interest in the Property without Buyer's written consent.

11. SPECIAL PROVISIONS: (Insert only factual statements and business details applicable to the sale. TREC rules prohibit licensees from adding factual statements or business details for which a contract addendum, lease or other form has been promulgated by TREC for mandatory use.)

12. SETTLEMENT AND OTHER EXPENSES:
   A. The following expenses must be paid at or prior to closing:
   (1) Expenses payable by Seller (Seller's Expenses):
      (a) Releases of existing liens, including prepayment penalties and recording fees; release of Seller's loan liability; tax statements or certificates; preparation of deed; one-half of escrow fee; and other expenses payable by Seller under this contract.
      (b) Seller shall also pay an amount not to exceed $ _____ to be applied in the following order: Buyer's Expenses which Buyer is prohibited from paying by FHA, VA, Texas Veterans Land Board or other governmental loan programs, and then to other Buyer's Expenses as allowed by the lender.
   (2) Expenses payable by Buyer (Buyer's Expenses): Appraisal fees; loan application fees; adjusted origination charges; credit reports; preparation of loan documents; interest on the notes from date of disbursement to one month prior to dates of first monthly payments; recording fees; copies of easements and restrictions; loan title policy with endorsements required by lender; loan-related inspection fees; photos; amortization schedules; one-half of escrow fee; all prepaid items, including required premiums for flood and hazard insurance, reserve deposits for insurance, ad valorem taxes and special governmental assessments; final compliance inspection; courier fee; repair inspection; underwriting fee; wire transfer fee; expenses incident to any loan; Private Mortgage Insurance Premium (PMI), VA Loan Funding Fee, or FHA Mortgage Insurance Premium (MIP) as required by the lender; and other expenses payable by Buyer under this contract.
   B. If any expense exceeds an amount expressly stated in this contract for such expense to be paid by a party, that party may terminate this contract unless the other party agrees to pay such excess. Buyer may not pay charges and fees expressly prohibited by FHA, VA, Texas Veterans Land Board or other governmental loan program regulations.

13. PRORATIONS AND ROLLBACK TAXES:
   A. PRORATIONS: Taxes for the current year, maintenance fees, assessments, dues and rents will be prorated through the Closing Date. The tax proration may be calculated taking into consideration any change in exemptions that will affect the current year's taxes. If taxes for the current year vary from the amount prorated at closing, the parties shall adjust the prorations when tax statements for the current year are available. If taxes are not paid at or prior to closing, Buyer will be obligated to pay taxes for the current year.
   B. ROLLBACK TAXES: If Seller's change in use of the Property prior to closing or denial of a special use valuation on the Property results in additional taxes, penalties or interest (Assessments) for periods prior to closing, the Assessments will be the obligation of Seller. Obligations imposed by this paragraph will survive closing.

Initialed for identification by Buyer_____ _____ and Seller _____ _____   TREC NO. 24-13

FIGURE 3

New Home Contract (Completed Construction) (continued)

Contract Concerning _____ Page 6 of 9 4-28-2014
(Address of Property)

14. **CASUALTY LOSS:** If any part of the Property is damaged or destroyed by fire or other casualty after the effective date of this contract, Seller shall restore the Property to its previous condition as soon as reasonably possible, but in any event by the Closing Date. If Seller fails to do so due to factors beyond Seller's control, Buyer may (a) terminate this contract and the earnest money will be refunded to Buyer (b) extend the time for performance up to 15 days and the Closing Date will be extended as necessary or (c) accept the Property in its damaged condition with an assignment of insurance proceeds and receive credit from Seller at closing in the amount of the deductible under the insurance policy. Seller's obligations under this paragraph are independent of any other obligations of Seller under this contract.

15. **DEFAULT:** If Buyer fails to comply with this contract, Buyer will be in default, and Seller may (a) enforce specific performance, seek such other relief as may be provided by law, or both, or (b) terminate this contract and receive the earnest money as liquidated damages, thereby releasing both parties from this contract. If Seller fails to comply with this contract Seller will be in default and Buyer may (a) enforce specific performance, seek such other relief as may be provided by law, or both, or (b) terminate this contract and receive the earnest money, thereby releasing both parties from this contract.

16. **MEDIATION:** It is the policy of the State of Texas to encourage resolution of disputes through alternative dispute resolution procedures such as mediation. Subject to applicable law, any dispute between Seller and Buyer related to this contract which is not resolved through informal discussion will be submitted to a mutually acceptable mediation service or provider. The parties to the mediation shall bear the mediation costs equally. This paragraph does not preclude a party from seeking equitable relief from a court of competent jurisdiction.

17. **ATTORNEY'S FEES:** A Buyer, Seller, Listing Broker, Other Broker, or escrow agent who prevails in any legal proceeding related to this contract is entitled to recover reasonable attorney's fees and all costs of such proceeding.

18. **ESCROW:**
    A. ESCROW: The escrow agent is not (i) a party to this contract and does not have liability for the performance or nonperformance of any party to this contract, (ii) liable for interest on the earnest money and (iii) liable for the loss of any earnest money caused by the failure of any financial institution in which the earnest money has been deposited unless the financial institution is acting as escrow agent.
    B. EXPENSES: At closing, the earnest money must be applied first to any cash down payment, then to Buyer's Expenses and any excess refunded to Buyer. If no closing occurs, escrow agent may: (i) require a written release of liability of the escrow agent from all parties, (ii) require payment of unpaid expenses incurred on behalf of a party, and (iii) only deduct from the earnest money the amount of unpaid expenses incurred on behalf of the party receiving the earnest money.
    C. DEMAND: Upon termination of this contract, either party or the escrow agent may send a release of earnest money to each party and the parties shall execute counterparts of the release and deliver same to the escrow agent. If either party fails to execute the release, either party may make a written demand to the escrow agent for the earnest money. If only one party makes written demand for the earnest money, escrow agent shall promptly provide a copy of the demand to the other party. If escrow agent does not receive written objection to the demand from the other party within 15 days, escrow agent may disburse the earnest money to the party making demand reduced by the amount of unpaid expenses incurred on behalf of the party receiving the earnest money and escrow agent may pay the same to the creditors. If escrow agent complies with the provisions of this paragraph, each party hereby releases escrow agent from all adverse claims related to the disbursal of the earnest money.
    D. DAMAGES: Any party who wrongfully fails or refuses to sign a release acceptable to the escrow agent within 7 days of receipt of the request will be liable to the other party for liquidated damages in an amount equal to the sum of: (i) three times the amount of the earnest money; (ii) the earnest money; (iii) reasonable attorney's fees; and (iv) all costs of suit.
    E. NOTICES: Escrow agent's notices will be effective when sent in compliance with Paragraph 21. Notice of objection to the demand will be deemed effective upon receipt by escrow agent.

19. **REPRESENTATIONS:** All covenants, representations and warranties in this contract survive closing. If any representation of Seller in this contract is untrue on the Closing Date, Seller will be in default. Unless expressly prohibited by written agreement, Seller may continue to show the Property and receive, negotiate and accept back up offers.

20. **FEDERAL TAX REQUIREMENTS:** If Seller is a "foreign person," as defined by applicable law, or if Seller fails to deliver an affidavit to Buyer that Seller is not a "foreign person," then Buyer shall withhold from the sales proceeds an amount sufficient to comply with applicable tax law and deliver the same to the Internal Revenue Service together with appropriate tax forms. Internal Revenue Service regulations require filing written reports if currency in excess of specified amounts is received in the transaction.

Initialed for identification by Buyer_____ _____ and Seller _____ _____   TREC NO. 24-13

FIGURE 3

New Home Contract (Completed Construction) (continued)

Contract Concerning _____ Page 7 of 9 4-28-2014
(Address of Property)

21. NOTICES: All notices from one party to the other must be in writing and are effective when mailed to, hand-delivered at, or transmitted by facsimile or electronic transmission as follows:

To Buyer at:

_____

_____

_____

Telephone: (___)_____

Facsimile: (___)_____

E-mail: _____

To Seller at:

_____

_____

_____

Telephone: (___)_____

Facsimile: (___)_____

E-mail: _____

22. AGREEMENT OF PARTIES: This contract contains the entire agreement of the parties and cannot be changed except by their written agreement. Addenda which are a part of this contract are (check all applicable boxes):

❑ Third Party Financing Addendum for Credit Approval

❑ Seller Financing Addendum

❑ Addendum for Property Subject to Mandatory Membership in a Property Owners Association

❑ Buyer's Temporary Residential Lease

❑ Loan Assumption Addendum

❑ Addendum for Sale of Other Property by Buyer

❑ Addendum for Reservation of Oil, Gas and Other Minerals

❑ Addendum for "Back-Up" Contract

❑ Addendum for Coastal Area Property

❑ Environmental Assessment, Threatened or Endangered Species and Wetlands Addendum

❑ Seller's Temporary Residential Lease

❑ Short Sale Addendum

❑ Addendum for Property Located Seaward of the Gulf Intracoastal Waterway

❑ Addendum for Property in a Propane Gas System Service Area

❑ Other (list): _____

_____

_____

23. TERMINATION OPTION: For nominal consideration, the receipt of which is hereby acknowledged by Seller, and Buyer's agreement to pay Seller $_____ (Option Fee) within 3 days after the effective date of this contract, Seller grants Buyer the unrestricted right to terminate this contract by giving notice of termination to Seller within _____ days after the effective date of this contract (Option Period). If no dollar amount is stated as the Option Fee or if Buyer fails to pay the Option Fee to Seller within the time prescribed, this paragraph will not be a part of this contract and Buyer shall not have the unrestricted right to terminate this contract. If Buyer gives notice of termination within the time prescribed, the Option Fee will not be refunded; however, any earnest money will be refunded to Buyer. The Option Fee ❑will ❑ will not be credited to the Sales Price at closing. **Time is of the essence for this paragraph and strict compliance with the time for performance is required.**

24. CONSULT AN ATTORNEY BEFORE SIGNING: TREC rules prohibit real estate licensees from giving legal advice. READ THIS CONTRACT CAREFULLY.

Buyer's
Attorney is: _____

_____

Telephone: (___)_____

Facsimile: (___)_____

E-mail: _____

Seller's
Attorney is: _____

_____

Telephone: (___)_____

Facsimile: (___)_____

E-mail: _____

Initialed for identification by Buyer_____ _____ and Seller _____ _____   TREC NO. 24-13

FIGURE 3

New Home Contract (Completed Construction) (continued)

Contract Concerning _____ Page 8 of 9 4-28-2014
(Address of Property)

EXECUTED the _____ day of _____, 20____ (EFFECTIVE DATE).
(BROKER: FILL IN THE DATE OF FINAL ACCEPTANCE.)

This contract is subject to Chapter 27 of the Texas Property Code. The provisions of that chapter may affect your right to recover damages arising from a construction defect. If you have a complaint concerning a construction defect and that defect has not been corrected as may be required by law or by contract, you must provide the notice required by Chapter 27 of the Texas Property Code to the contractor by certified mail, return receipt requested, not later than the 60th day before the date you file suit to recover damages in a court of law or initiate arbitration. The notice must refer to Chapter 27 of the Texas Property Code and must describe the construction defect. If requested by the contractor, you must provide the contractor an opportunity to inspect and cure the defect as provided by Section 27.004 of the Texas Property Code.

_____
Buyer

_____
Buyer

_____
Seller

_____
Seller

TREC NO. 24-13

FIGURE 3

New Home Contract (Completed Construction) (continued)

Contract Concerning _____ Page 9 of 9 4-28-2014
(Address of Property)

BROKER INFORMATION
(Print name(s) only. Do not sign)

_____ _____
Other Broker Firm   License No.   Listing Broker Firm   License No.

represents ☐ Buyer only as Buyer's agent   represents ☐ Seller and Buyer as an intermediary
            ☐ Seller as Listing Broker's subagent   ☐ Seller only as Seller's agent

_____ _____
Name of Associate's Licensed Supervisor   Telephone   Name of Associate's Licensed Supervisor   Telephone

_____ _____
Associate's Name   Telephone   Listing Associate's Name   Telephone

_____ _____
Other Broker's Address   Facsimile   Listing Broker's Office Address   Facsimile

_____ _____
City   State   Zip   City   State   Zip

_____ _____
Associate's Email Address   Listing Associate's Email Address

_____
Selling Associate's Name   Telephone

_____
Name of Selling Associate's Licensed Supervisor   Telephone

_____
Selling Associate's Office Address   Facsimile

_____
City   State   Zip

_____
Selling Associate's Email Address

Listing Broker has agreed to pay Other Broker_____ of the total sales price when the Listing Broker's fee is received. Escrow agent is authorized and directed to pay other Broker from Listing Broker's fee at closing.

OPTION FEE RECEIPT

Receipt of $_____ (Option Fee) in the form of _____ is acknowledged.

_____   _____
Seller or Listing Broker   Date

CONTRACT AND EARNEST MONEY RECEIPT

Receipt of ☐Contract and ☐$_____ Earnest Money in the form of _____
is acknowledged.
Escrow Agent: _____   Date: _____

By: _____
                                            _____
                                            Email Address

_____   Telephone (_____) _____
Address

                                            Facsimile: (_____) _____
City   State   Zip

TREC NO. 24-13

FIGURE 4

Farm and Ranch Contract

PROMULGATED BY THE TEXAS REAL ESTATE COMMISSION (TREC)   4-28-2014
FARM AND RANCH CONTRACT

1. PARTIES: The parties to this contract are _____
(Seller) and _____(Buyer). Seller agrees to sell and convey to Buyer and Buyer agrees to buy from Seller the Property defined below.

2. PROPERTY: The land, improvements, accessories and crops except for the exclusions and reservations, are collectively referred to as the "Property".
   A. LAND: The land situated in the County of _____, Texas, described as follows:_____
   _____
   or as described on attached exhibit, also known as _____
   (address/zip code), together with all rights, privileges, and appurtenances pertaining thereto, including but not limited to: water rights, claims, permits, strips and gores, easements, and cooperative or association memberships.
   B. IMPROVEMENTS:
      (1) FARM and RANCH IMPROVEMENTS: The following **permanently installed and built-in items**, if any: windmills, tanks, barns, pens, fences, gates, sheds, outbuildings, and corrals.
      (2) RESIDENTIAL IMPROVEMENTS: The house, garage, and all other fixtures and improvements attached to the above-described real property, including without limitation, the following **permanently installed and built-in items,** if any: all equipment and appliances, valances, screens, shutters, awnings, wall-to-wall carpeting, mirrors, ceiling fans, attic fans, mail boxes, television antennas, mounts and brackets for televisions and speakers, heating and air-conditioning units, security and fire detection equipment, wiring, plumbing and lighting fixtures, chandeliers, water softener system, kitchen equipment, garage door openers, cleaning equipment, shrubbery, landscaping, outdoor cooking equipment, and all other property owned by Seller and attached to the above described real property.
   C. ACCESSORIES:
      (1) FARM AND RANCH ACCESSORIES: The following described related accessories: (check boxes of conveyed accessories) ❑ portable buildings ❑ hunting blinds ❑ game feeders ❑ livestock feeders and troughs ❑ irrigation equipment ❑ fuel tanks ❑ submersible pumps ❑ pressure tanks ❑ corrals ❑ gates ❑ chutes ❑ other:_____
      _____
      (2) RESIDENTIAL ACCESSORIES: The following described related accessories, if any: window air conditioning units, stove, fireplace screens, curtains and rods, blinds, window shades, draperies and rods, door keys, mailbox keys, above ground pool, swimming pool equipment and maintenance accessories, artificial fireplace logs, and controls for:
      (i) garages, (ii) entry gates, and (iii) other improvements and accessories.
   D. CROPS: Unless otherwise agreed in writing, Seller has the right to harvest all growing crops until delivery of possession of the Property.
   E. EXCLUSIONS: The following improvements, accessories, and crops will be retained by Seller and must be removed prior to delivery of possession: _____
   _____.
   F. RESERVATIONS: Any reservation for oil, gas, or other minerals, water, timber, or other interests is made in accordance with an attached addendum or Special Provisions.

3. SALES PRICE:
   A. Cash portion of Sales Price payable by Buyer at closing.................... $_____
   B. Sum of all financing described below (excluding any loan funding
      fee or mortgage insurance premium) .... $_____
   C. Sales Price (Sum of A and B) .... $_____
   D. The Sales Price ❑ will ❑ will not be adjusted based on the survey required by Paragraph 6C. If the Sales Price is adjusted, the Sales Price will be calculated on the basis of $ _____ per acre. If the Sales Price is adjusted by more than 10%, either party may terminate this contract by providing written notice to the other party within ____ days after the terminating party receives the survey. If neither party terminates this contract or if the variance is 10% or less, the adjustment will be made to the amount in ❑ 3A ❑ 3B ❑ proportionately to 3A and 3B.

4. FINANCING (Not for use with reverse mortgage financing): The portion of Sales Price not payable in cash will be paid as follows: (Check applicable boxes below)
❑ A. THIRD PARTY FINANCING: One or more third party mortgage loans in the total amount of $_____ (excluding any loan funding fee or mortgage insurance premium).
   (1) Property Approval: If the Property does not satisfy the lenders' underwriting requirements for the loan(s) (including, but not limited to appraisal, insurability and lender required repairs), Buyer may terminate this contract by giving notice to Seller prior to closing and the earnest money will be refunded to Buyer.

Initialed for identification by Buyer_____ _____ and Seller _____ _____   TREC NO. 25-10

FIGURE 4

Farm and Ranch Contract (continued)

Contract Concerning _____ Page 2 of 9   4-28-2014
(Address of Property)

(2) Credit Approval: (Check one box only)
  ❑ (a) This contract is subject to Buyer being approved for the financing described in the attached Third Party Financing Addendum for Credit Approval.
  ❑ (b) This contract is not subject to Buyer being approved for financing and does not involve FHA or VA financing.
❑ B. ASSUMPTION: The assumption of the unpaid principal balance of one or more promissory notes described in the attached TREC Loan Assumption Addendum.
❑ C. SELLER FINANCING: A promissory note from Buyer to Seller of $_____, secured by vendor's and deed of trust liens, and containing the terms and conditions described in the attached TREC Seller Financing Addendum. If an owner policy of title insurance is furnished, Buyer shall furnish Seller with a mortgagee policy of title insurance.

5. EARNEST MONEY: Upon execution of this contract by all parties, Buyer shall deposit $_____ as earnest money with _____, as escrow agent, at _____ (address). Buyer shall deposit additional earnest money of $_____ with escrow agent within _____ days after the effective date of this contract. If Buyer fails to deposit the earnest money as required by this contract, Buyer will be in default.

6. TITLE POLICY AND SURVEY:
A. TITLE POLICY: Seller shall furnish to Buyer at ❑Seller's ❑Buyer's expense an owner policy of title insurance (Title Policy) issued by: _____ (Title Company) in the amount of the Sales Price, dated at or after closing, insuring Buyer against loss under the provisions of the Title Policy, subject to the promulgated exclusions (including existing building and zoning ordinances) and the following exceptions:
  (1) The standard printed exception for standby fees, taxes and assessments.
  (2) Liens created as part of the financing described in Paragraph 4.
  (3) Reservations or exceptions otherwise permitted by this contract or as may be approved by Buyer in writing.
  (4) The standard printed exception as to marital rights.
  (5) The standard printed exception as to waters, tidelands, beaches, streams, and related matters.
  (6) The standard printed exception as to discrepancies, conflicts, shortages in area or boundary lines, encroachments or protrusions, or overlapping improvements: ❑ (i) will not be amended or deleted from the title policy; ❑(ii) will be amended to read, "shortages in area" at the expense of ❑Buyer ❑Seller.
B. COMMITMENT: Within 20 days after the Title Company receives a copy of this contract, Seller shall furnish to Buyer a commitment for title insurance (Commitment) and, at Buyer's expense, legible copies of restrictive covenants and documents evidencing exceptions in the Commitment (Exception Documents) other than the standard printed exceptions. Seller authorizes the Title Company to deliver the Commitment and Exception Documents to Buyer at Buyer's address shown in Paragraph 21. If the Commitment and Exception Documents are not delivered to Buyer within the specified time, the time for delivery will be automatically extended up to 15 days or 3 days before the Closing Date, whichever is earlier. If, due to factors beyond Seller's control, the Commitment and Exception Documents are not delivered within the time required, Buyer may terminate this contract and the earnest money will be refunded to Buyer.
C. SURVEY: The survey must be made by a registered professional land surveyor acceptable to the Title Company and Buyer's lender(s). (Check one box only):
❑ (1) Within _____ days after the effective date of this contract, Seller shall furnish to Buyer and Title Company Seller's existing survey of the Property and a Residential Real Property Affidavit promulgated by the Texas Department of Insurance (T-47 Affidavit). **If Seller fails to furnish the existing survey or affidavit within the time prescribed, Buyer shall obtain a new survey at Seller's expense no later than 3 days prior to Closing Date.** The existing survey ❑ will ❑ will not be recertified to a date subsequent to the effective date of this contract at the expense of ❑ Buyer ❑ Seller. If the existing survey is not approved by the Title Company or Buyer's lender(s), a new survey will be obtained at the expense of ❑ Buyer ❑ Seller no later than 3 days prior to Closing Date.
❑ (2) Within _____ days after the effective date of this contract, Buyer shall obtain a new survey at Buyer's expense. Buyer is deemed to receive the survey on the date of actual receipt or the date specified in this paragraph, whichever is earlier.
❑ (3) Within _____ days after the effective date of this contract, Seller, at Seller's expense shall furnish a new survey to Buyer.
❑ (4) No survey is required.
D. OBJECTIONS: Buyer may object in writing to (i) defects, exceptions, or encumbrances to title disclosed on the survey other than items 6A(1) through (5) above; or disclosed in the Commitment other than items 6A(1) through (6) above; (ii) any portion of the Property lying in a special flood hazard area (Zone V or A) as shown on the current Federal Emergency

Initialed for identification by Buyer_____ _____ and Seller _____ _____   TREC NO. 25-10

F I G U R E   4

Farm and Ranch Contract (continued)

Contract Concerning _____ Page 3 of 9   4-28-2014
(Address of Property)

Management Agency map; or (iii) any exceptions which prohibit the following use or activity:
_____

Buyer must object the earlier of (i) the Closing Date or (ii) _____ days after Buyer receives the Commitment, Exception Documents, and the survey. Buyer's failure to object within the time allowed will constitute a waiver of Buyer's right to object; except that the requirements in Schedule C of the Commitment are not waived by Buyer. Provided Seller is not obligated to incur any expense, Seller shall cure the timely objections of Buyer or any third party lender within 15 days after Seller receives the objections and the Closing Date will be extended as necessary. If objections are not cured within such 15 day period, this contract will terminate and the earnest money will be refunded to Buyer unless Buyer waives the objections.

E. EXCEPTION DOCUMENTS: Prior to the execution of the contract, Seller has provided Buyer with copies of the Exception Documents listed below or on the attached exhibit. Matters reflected in the Exception Documents listed below or on the attached exhibit will be permitted exceptions in the Title Policy and will not be a basis for objection to title:

Document	Date	Recording Reference
_____	_____	_____
_____	_____	_____
_____	_____	_____

F.   SURFACE LEASES: Prior to the execution of the contract, Seller has provided Buyer with copies of written leases and given notice of oral leases (Leases) listed below or on the attached exhibit. The following Leases will be permitted exceptions in the Title Policy and will not be a basis for objection to title:_____
_____

G. TITLE NOTICES:
(1) ABSTRACT OR TITLE POLICY: Broker advises Buyer to have an abstract of title covering the Property examined by an attorney of Buyer's selection, or Buyer should be furnished with or obtain a Title Policy. If a Title Policy is furnished, the Commitment should be promptly reviewed by an attorney of Buyer's choice due to the time limitations on Buyer's right to object.
(2) STATUTORY TAX DISTRICTS: If the Property is situated in a utility or other statutorily created district providing water, sewer, drainage, or flood control facilities and services, Chapter 49, Texas Water Code, requires Seller to deliver and Buyer to sign the statutory notice relating to the tax rate, bonded indebtedness, or standby fee of the district prior to final execution of this contract.
(3) TIDE WATERS: If the Property abuts the tidally influenced waters of the state, §33.135, Texas Natural Resources Code, requires a notice regarding coastal area property to be included in the contract.   An addendum containing the notice promulgated by TREC or required by the parties must be used.
(4) ANNEXATION: If the Property is located outside the limits of a municipality, Seller notifies Buyer under §5.011, Texas Property Code, that the Property may now or later be included in the extraterritorial jurisdiction of a municipality and may now or later be subject to annexation by the municipality. Each municipality maintains a map that depicts its boundaries and extraterritorial jurisdiction. To determine if the Property is located within a municipality's extraterritorial jurisdiction or is likely to be located within a municipality's extraterritorial jurisdiction, contact all municipalities located in the general proximity of the Property for further information.
(5) PROPERTY LOCATED IN A CERTIFICATED SERVICE AREA OF A UTILITY SERVICE PROVIDER: Notice required by §13.257, Water Code: The real property, described in Paragraph 2, that you are about to purchase may be located in a certificated water or sewer service area, which is authorized by law to provide water or sewer service to the properties in the certificated area. If your property is located in a certificated area there may be special costs or charges that you will be required to pay before you can receive water or sewer service.   There may be a period required to construct lines or other facilities necessary to provide water or sewer service to your property. You are advised to determine if the property is in a certificated area and contact the utility service provider to determine the cost that you will be required to pay and the period, if any, that is required to provide water or sewer service to your property. The undersigned Buyer hereby acknowledges receipt of the foregoing notice at or before the execution of a binding contract for the purchase of the real property described in Paragraph 2 or at closing of purchase of the real property.
(6) PUBLIC IMPROVEMENT DISTRICTS: If the Property is in a public improvement district, §5.014, Property Code, requires Seller to notify Buyer as follows: As a purchaser of this parcel of real property you are obligated to pay an assessment to a municipality or county for an improvement project undertaken by a public improvement district under Chapter 372, Local Government Code. The assessment may be due annually or in periodic

Initialed for identification by Buyer_____ _____ and Seller _____ _____   TREC NO. 25-10

FIGURE 4

Farm and Ranch Contract (continued)

Contract Concerning _____ Page 4 of 9   4-28-2014
(Address of Property)

installments. More information concerning the amount of the assessment and the due dates of that assessment may be obtained from the municipality or county levying the assessment. The amount of the assessments is subject to change. Your failure to pay the assessments could result in a lien on and the foreclosure of your property.
(7) TEXAS AGRICULTURAL DEVELOPMENT DISTRICT: The Property ☐ is ☐ is not located in a Texas Agricultural Development District. For additional information contact the Texas Department of Agriculture
(8) TRANSFER FEES: If the Property is subject to a private transfer fee obligation, §5.205, Property Code, requires Seller to notify Buyer as follows: The private transfer fee obligation may be governed by Chapter 5, Subchapter G of the Texas Property Code.
(9) PROPANE GAS SYSTEM SERVICE AREA: If the Property is located in a propane gas system service area owned by a distribution system retailer, Seller must give Buyer written notice as required by §141.010, Texas Utilities Code. An addendum containing the notice approved by TREC or required by the parties should be used.

7. PROPERTY CONDITION:
A. ACCESS, INSPECTIONS AND UTILITIES: Seller shall permit Buyer and Buyer's agents access to the Property at reasonable times. Buyer may have the Property inspected by inspectors selected by Buyer and licensed by TREC or otherwise permitted by law to make inspections. Seller at Seller's expense shall immediately cause existing utilities to be turned on and shall keep the utilities on during the time this contract is in effect .
NOTICE: Buyer should determine the availability of utilities to the Property suitable to satisfy Buyer's needs.
B. SELLER'S DISCLOSURE NOTICE PURSUANT TO §5.008, TEXAS PROPERTY CODE (Notice): (Check one box only)
☐ (1) Buyer has received the Notice.
☐ (2) Buyer has not received the Notice. Within ___ days after the effective date of this contract, Seller shall deliver the Notice to Buyer. If Buyer does not receive the Notice, Buyer may terminate this contract at any time prior to the closing and the earnest money will be refunded to Buyer. If Seller delivers the Notice, Buyer may terminate this contract for any reason within 7 days after Buyer receives the Notice or prior to the closing, whichever first occurs, and the earnest money will be refunded to Buyer.
☐ (3) The Texas Property Code does not require this Seller to furnish the Notice.
C. SELLER'S DISCLOSURE OF LEAD-BASED PAINT AND LEAD-BASED PAINT HAZARDS is required by Federal law for a residential dwelling constructed prior to 1978.
D. ACCEPTANCE OF PROPERTY CONDITION: "As Is" means the present condition of the Property with any and all defects and without warranty except for the warranties of title and the warranties in this contract. Buyer's agreement to accept the Property As Is under Paragraph 7D(1) or (2) does not preclude Buyer from inspecting the Property under Paragraph 7A, from negotiating repairs or treatments in a subsequent amendment, or from terminating this contract during the Option Period, if any.
(Check one box only)
☐ (1) Buyer accepts the Property As Is.
☐ (2) Buyer accepts the Property As Is provided Seller, at Seller's expense, shall complete the following specific repairs and treatments: _____
_____.
(Do not insert general phrases, such as "subject to inspections," that do not identify specific repairs and treatments.)
E. COMPLETION OF REPAIRS: Unless otherwise agreed in writing: (i) Seller shall complete all agreed repairs and treatments prior to the Closing Date; and (ii) all required permits must be obtained, and repairs and treatments must be performed by persons who are licensed to provide such repairs or treatments or, if no license is required by law, are commercially engaged in the trade of providing such repairs or treatments. At Buyer's election, any transferable warranties received by Seller with respect to the repairs will be transferred to Buyer at Buyer's expense. If Seller fails to complete any agreed repairs prior to the Closing Date, Buyer may exercise remedies under Paragraph 15 or extend the Closing Date up to 5 days if necessary for Seller to complete repairs.
F. LENDER REQUIRED REPAIRS AND TREATMENTS: Unless otherwise agreed in writing, neither party is obligated to pay for lender required repairs, which includes treatment for wood destroying insects. If the parties do not agree to pay for the lender required repairs or treatments, this contract will terminate and the earnest money will be refunded to Buyer. If the cost of lender required repairs and treatments exceeds 5% of the Sales Price, Buyer may terminate this contract and the earnest money will be refunded to Buyer.
G. ENVIRONMENTAL MATTERS: Buyer is advised that the presence of wetlands, toxic substances, including asbestos and wastes or other environmental hazards, or the presence of a threatened or endangered species or its habitat may affect Buyer's intended use of the Property. If Buyer is concerned about these matters, an addendum promulgated by TREC or required by the parties should be used.

Initialed for identification by Buyer_____ _____ and Seller _____ _____   TREC NO. 25-10

FIGURE 4

Farm and Ranch Contract (continued)

Contract Concerning _____ Page 5 of 9   4-28-2014
(Address of Property)

H. SELLER'S DISCLOSURES: Except as otherwise disclosed in this contract, Seller has no knowledge of the following:
  (1) any flooding of the Property which has had a material adverse effect on the use of the Property;
  (2) any pending or threatened litigation, condemnation, or special assessment affecting the Property;
  (3) any environmental hazards that materially and adversely affect the Property;
  (4) any dumpsite, landfill, or underground tanks or containers now or previously located on the Property;
  (5) any wetlands, as defined by federal or state law or regulation, affecting the Property; or
  (6) any threatened or endangered species or their habitat affecting the Property.
I. RESIDENTIAL SERVICE CONTRACTS: Buyer may purchase a residential service contract from a residential service company licensed by TREC. If Buyer purchases a residential service contract, Seller shall reimburse Buyer at closing for the cost of the residential service contract in an amount not exceeding $_____. Buyer should review any residential service contract for the scope of coverage, exclusions and limitations. **The purchase of a residential service contract is optional. Similar coverage may be purchased from various companies authorized to do business in Texas.**
J. GOVERNMENT PROGRAMS: The Property is subject to the government programs listed below or on the attached exhibit:_____
_____.
Seller shall provide Buyer with copies of all governmental program agreements. Any allocation or proration of payment under governmental programs is made by separate agreement between the parties which will survive closing.

8. **BROKERS' FEES:** All obligations of the parties for payment of brokers' fees are contained in separate written agreements.

9. **CLOSING:**
  A. The closing of the sale will be on or before _____, 20_____, or within 7 days after objections made under Paragraph 6D have been cured or waived, whichever date is later (Closing Date). If either party fails to close the sale by the Closing Date, the non-defaulting party may exercise the remedies contained in Paragraph 15.
  B. At closing:
    (1) Seller shall execute and deliver a general warranty deed conveying title to the Property to Buyer and showing no additional exceptions to those permitted in Paragraph 6, an assignment of Leases, and furnish tax statements or certificates showing no delinquent taxes on the Property.
    (2) Buyer shall pay the Sales Price in good funds acceptable to the escrow agent.
    (3) Seller and Buyer shall execute and deliver any notices, statements, certificates, affidavits, releases, loan documents and other documents reasonably required for the closing of the sale and the issuance of the Title Policy.
    (4) There will be no liens, assessments, or security interests against the Property which will not be satisfied out of the sales proceeds unless securing the payment of any loans assumed by Buyer and assumed loans will not be in default.
    (5) If the Property is subject to a residential lease, Seller shall transfer security deposits (as defined under §92.102, Property Code), if any, to Buyer. In such an event, Buyer shall deliver to the tenant a signed statement acknowledging that the Buyer has received the security deposit and is responsible for the return of the security deposit, and specifying the exact dollar amount of the security deposit.

10. **POSSESSION:**
  A. Buyer's Possession: Seller shall deliver to Buyer possession of the Property in its present or required condition, ordinary wear and tear excepted: ❑ upon closing and funding ❑ according to a temporary residential lease form promulgated by TREC or other written lease required by the parties. Any possession by Buyer prior to closing or by Seller after closing which is not authorized by a written lease will establish a tenancy at sufferance relationship between the parties. **Consult your insurance agent prior to change of ownership and possession because insurance coverage may be limited or terminated. The absence of a written lease or appropriate insurance coverage may expose the parties to economic loss.**
  B. Leases:
    (1) After the Effective Date, Seller may not execute any lease (including but not limited to mineral leases) or convey any interest in the Property without Buyer's written consent.
    (2) If the Property is subject to any lease to which Seller is a party, Seller shall deliver to Buyer copies of the lease(s) and any move-in condition form signed by the tenant within 7 days after the Effective Date of the contract.

Initialed for identification by Buyer_____ _____ and Seller _____ _____   TREC NO. 25-10

Farm and Ranch Contract (continued)

Contract Concerning _____ Page 6 of 9   4-28-2014
(Address of Property)

11. SPECIAL PROVISIONS: (Insert only factual statements and business details applicable to the sale. TREC rules prohibit licensees from adding factual statements or business details for which a contract addendum or other form has been promulgated by TREC for mandatory use.)

12. SETTLEMENT AND OTHER EXPENSES:
   A. The following expenses must be paid at or prior to closing:
      (1) Expenses payable by Seller (Seller's Expenses):
         (a) Releases of existing liens, including prepayment penalties and recording fees; release of Seller's loan liability; tax statements or certificates; preparation of deed; one-half of escrow fee; and other expenses payable by Seller under this contract.
         (b) Seller shall also pay an amount not to exceed $ _____ to be applied in the following order: Buyer's Expenses which Buyer is prohibited from paying by FHA, VA, Texas Veterans Land Board or other governmental loan programs, and then to other Buyer's Expenses as allowed by the lender.
      (2) Expenses payable by Buyer (Buyer's Expenses) Appraisal fees; loan application fees; adjusted origination charges; credit reports; preparation of loan documents; interest on the notes from date of disbursement to one month prior to dates of first monthly payments; recording fees; copies of easements and restrictions; loan title policy with endorsements required by lender; loan-related inspection fees; photos; amortization schedules; one-half of escrow fee; all prepaid items, including required premiums for flood and hazard insurance, reserve deposits for insurance, ad valorem taxes and special governmental assessments; final compliance inspection; courier fee; repair inspection; underwriting fee; wire transfer fee; expenses incident to any loan; Private Mortgage Insurance Premium (PMI), VA Loan Funding Fee, or FHA Mortgage Insurance Premium (MIP) as required by the lender; and other expenses payable by Buyer under this contract.
   B. If any expense exceeds an amount expressly stated in this contract for such expense to be paid by a party, that party may terminate this contract unless the other party agrees to pay such excess. Buyer may not pay charges and fees expressly prohibited by FHA, VA, Texas Veterans Land Board or other governmental loan program regulations.

13. PRORATIONS AND ROLLBACK TAXES:
   A. PRORATIONS: Taxes for the current year, interest, maintenance fees, assessments, dues and rents will be prorated through the Closing Date. The tax proration may be calculated taking into consideration any change in exemptions that will affect the current year's taxes. If taxes for the current year vary from the amount prorated at closing, the parties shall adjust the prorations when tax statements for the current year are available. If taxes are not paid at or prior to closing, Buyer shall pay taxes for the current year. Rentals which are unknown at time of closing will be prorated between Buyer and Seller when they become known.
   B. ROLLBACK TAXES: If this sale or Buyer's use of the Property after closing results in the assessment of additional taxes, penalties or interest (Assessments) for periods prior to closing, the Assessments will be the obligation of Buyer. If Seller's change in use of the Property prior to closing or denial of a special use valuation on the Property claimed by Seller results in Assessments for periods prior to closing, the Assessments will be the obligation of Seller. Obligations imposed by this paragraph will survive closing.

14. CASUALTY LOSS: If any part of the Property is damaged or destroyed by fire or other casualty after the effective date of this contract, Seller shall restore the Property to its previous condition as soon as reasonably possible, but in any event by the Closing Date. If Seller fails to do so due to factors beyond Seller's control, Buyer may (a) terminate this contract and the earnest money will be refunded to Buyer, (b) extend the time for performance up to 15 days and the Closing Date will be extended as necessary or (c) accept the Property in its damaged condition with an assignment of insurance proceeds and receive credit from Seller at closing in the amount of the deductible under the insurance policy. Seller's obligations under this paragraph are independent of any other obligations of Seller under this contract.

15. DEFAULT: If Buyer fails to comply with this contract, Buyer will be in default, and Seller may (a) enforce specific performance, seek such other relief as may be provided by law, or both, or (b) terminate this contract and receive the earnest money as liquidated damages, thereby releasing both parties from this contract. If Seller fails to comply with this contract for any other reason, Seller will be in default and Buyer may (a) enforce specific performance, seek such other relief as may be provided by law, or both, or (b) terminate this contract and receive the earnest money, thereby releasing both parties from this contract.

16. MEDIATION: It is the policy of the State of Texas to encourage resolution of disputes through alternative dispute resolution procedures such as mediation. Any dispute between Seller and Buyer related to this contract which is not resolved through informal discussion will be submitted to a mutually acceptable mediation service or provider. The parties to the mediation shall bear

Initialed for identification by Buyer_____ _____ and Seller _____ _____   TREC NO. 25-10

F I G U R E   4

Farm and Ranch Contract (continued)

Contract Concerning _____ Page 7 of 9   4-28-2014
(Address of Property)

the mediation costs equally. This paragraph does not preclude a party from seeking equitable relief from a court of competent jurisdiction.

17.ATTORNEY'S FEES: A Buyer, Seller, Listing Broker, Other Broker, or escrow agent who prevails in any legal proceeding related to this contract is entitled to recover reasonable attorney's fees and all costs of such proceeding.

18.ESCROW:
  A. ESCROW: The escrow agent is not (i) a party to this contract and does not have liability for the performance or nonperformance of any party to this contract, (ii) liable for interest on the earnest money and (iii) liable for the loss of any earnest money caused by the failure of any financial institution in which the earnest money has been deposited unless the financial institution is acting as escrow agent.
  B. EXPENSES: At closing, the earnest money must be applied first to any cash down payment, then to Buyer's Expenses and any excess refunded to Buyer. If no closing occurs, escrow agent may: (i) require a written release of liability of the escrow agent from all parties, (ii) require payment of unpaid expenses incurred on behalf of a party, and (iii) only deduct from the earnest money the amount of unpaid expenses incurred on behalf of the party receiving the earnest money.
  C. DEMAND: Upon termination of this contract, either party or the escrow agent may send a release of earnest money to each party and the parties shall execute counterparts of the release and deliver same to the escrow agent. If either party fails to execute the release, either party may make a written demand to the escrow agent for the earnest money. If only one party makes written demand for the earnest money, escrow agent shall promptly provide a copy of the demand to the other party. If escrow agent does not receive written objection to the demand from the other party within 15 days, escrow agent may disburse the earnest money to the party making demand reduced by the amount of unpaid expenses incurred on behalf of the party receiving the earnest money and escrow agent may pay the same to the creditors. If escrow agent complies with the provisions of this paragraph, each party hereby releases escrow agent from all adverse claims related to the disbursal of the earnest money.
  D. DAMAGES: Any party who wrongfully fails or refuses to sign a release acceptable to the escrow agent within 7 days of receipt of the request will be liable to the other party for liquidated damages in an amount equal to the sum of: (i) three times the amount of the earnest money; (ii) the earnest money; (iii) reasonable attorney's fees; and (iv) all costs of suit.
  E. NOTICES: Escrow agent's notices will be effective when sent in compliance with Paragraph 21. Notice of objection to the demand will be deemed effective upon receipt by escrow agent.

19.REPRESENTATIONS: All covenants, representations and warranties in this contract survive closing. If any representation of Seller in this contract is untrue on the Closing Date, Seller will be in default. Unless expressly prohibited by written agreement, Seller may continue to show the Property and receive, negotiate and accept back up offers.

20.FEDERAL TAX REQUIREMENTS: If Seller is a "foreign person," as defined by applicable law, or if Seller fails to deliver an affidavit to Buyer that Seller is not a "foreign person," then Buyer shall withhold from the sales proceeds an amount sufficient to comply with applicable tax law and deliver the same to the Internal Revenue Service together with appropriate tax forms. Internal Revenue Service regulations require filing written reports if currency in excess of specified amounts is received in the transaction.

21.NOTICES: All notices from one party to the other must be in writing and are effective when mailed to, hand-delivered at, or transmitted by facsimile or electronic transmission as follows:

To Buyer at: **To Seller at:**

_____   _____

_____   _____

Telephone: ( )_____   Telephone: ( )_____

Facsimile: ( )_____   Facsimile: ( )_____

E-mail: _____   E-mail: _____

Initialed for identification by Buyer_____ _____ and Seller _____ _____   TREC NO. 25-10

FIGURE 4

Farm and Ranch Contract (continued)

Contract Concerning _____ Page 8 of 9   4-28-2014
(Address of Property)

22. AGREEMENT OF PARTIES: This contract contains the entire agreement of the parties and cannot be changed except by their written agreement. Addenda which are a part of this contract are (check all applicable boxes):

❏ Third Party Financing Addendum for Credit Approval

❏ Seller Financing Addendum

❏ Addendum for Property Subject to Mandatory Membership in a Property Owners Association

❏ Buyer's Temporary Residential Lease

❏ Loan Assumption Addendum

❏ Addendum for Sale of Other Property by Buyer

❏ Addendum for "Back-Up" Contract

❏ Addendum for Coastal Area Property

❏ Environmental Assessment, Threatened or Endangered Species and Wetlands Addendum

❏ Seller's Temporary Residential Lease

❏ Short Sale Addendum

❏ Addendum for Property Located Seaward of the Gulf Intracoastal Waterway

❏ Addendum for Seller's Disclosure of Information on Lead-based Paint and Lead-based Paint Hazards as Required by Federal Law

❏ Addendum for Property in a Propane Gas System Service Area

❏ Other (list):_____
_____

23. TERMINATION OPTION: For nominal consideration, the receipt of which is hereby acknowledged by Seller, and Buyer's agreement to pay Seller $_____ (Option Fee) within 3 days after the effective date of this contract, Seller grants Buyer the unrestricted right to terminate this contract by giving notice of termination to Seller within _____ days after the effective date of this contract (Option Period).   If no dollar amount is stated as the Option Fee or if Buyer fails to pay the Option Fee to Seller within the time prescribed, this paragraph will not be a part of this contract and Buyer shall not have the unrestricted right to terminate this contract. If Buyer gives notice of termination within the time prescribed, the Option Fee will not be refunded; however, any earnest money will be refunded to Buyer. The Option Fee ❏will ❏will not be credited to the Sales Price at closing. **Time is of the essence for this paragraph and strict compliance with the time for performance is required.**

24. CONSULT AN ATTORNEY BEFORE SIGNING: TREC rules prohibit real estate licensees from giving legal advice. READ THIS CONTRACT CAREFULLY.

Buyer's
Attorney is: _____

_____

Telephone: ( )_____

Facsimile: ( )_____

E-mail: _____

Seller's
Attorney is: _____

_____

Telephone: ( )_____

Facsimile: ( )_____

E-mail: _____

EXECUTED the _____ day of _____, 20_____ (EFFECTIVE DATE).
(BROKER: FILL IN THE DATE OF FINAL ACCEPTANCE.)

_____
Buyer

_____
Buyer

_____
Seller

_____
Seller

The form of this contract has been approved by the Texas Real Estate Commission. TREC forms are intended for use only by trained real estate licensees. No representation is made as to the legal validity or adequacy of any provision in any specific transactions. It is not intended for complex transactions. Texas Real Estate Commission, P.O. Box 12188, Austin, TX 78711-2188, (512) 936-3000 (http://www.trec.texas.gov) TREC NO. 25-10. This form replaces TREC NO. 25-9.

TREC NO. 25-10

FIGURE 4

Farm and Ranch Contract (continued)

Contract Concerning _____ Page 9 of 9   4-28-2014
(Address of Property)

RATIFICATION   OF   FEE

Listing Broker has agreed to pay Other Broker_____ of the total Sales Price when Listing Broker's fee is received. Escrow Agent is authorized and directed to pay Other Broker from Listing Broker's fee at closing.

Other Broker: Listing Broker:

By: _____   By: _____

BROKER INFORMATION AND AGREEMENT FOR PAYMENT OF BROKERS' FEES

Other Broker   License No.   Listing or Principal Broker   License No.

Licensed Supervisor of Associate   Telephone   Licensed Supervisor of Associate   Telephone

Associate   Associate

Address   Address

City   State   Zip   City   State   Zip

Telephone   Facsimile   Telephone   Facsimile

E-mail   E-mail

represents ☐ Buyer only as Buyer's agent   represents ☐ Seller only
            ☐ Seller as Listing Broker's subagent   ☐ Buyer only
                                                                          ☐ Seller and Buyer as an intermediary

Upon closing of the sale by Seller to Buyer of the Property described in the contract to which this fee agreement is attached: (a) ☐Seller ☐ Buyer will pay Listing/Principal Broker ☐a cash fee of $_____ or ☐ _____% of the total Sales Price; and (b) ☐Seller ☐ Buyer will pay Other Broker ☐a cash fee of $_____or ☐ _____% of the total Sales Price. Seller/Buyer authorizes and directs Escrow Agent to pay the brokers from the proceeds at closing.

Brokers' fees are negotiable. Brokers' fees or the sharing of fees between brokers are not fixed, controlled, recommended, suggested or maintained by the Texas Real Estate Commission.

Seller   Buyer

Seller   Buyer

OPTION FEE RECEIPT

Receipt of $_____ (Option Fee) in the form of _____ is acknowledged.

Seller or Listing Broker   Date

CONTRACT AND EARNEST MONEY RECEIPT

Receipt of ☐Contract and ☐$_____ Earnest Money in the form of _____ is acknowledged.

Escrow Agent: _____   Date: _____

By: _____

Address   Email Address
                                                             Telephone (_____) _____
City   State   Zip   Facsimile: (_____) _____

TREC NO. 25-10

FIGURE 5

Residential Condominium Contract (Resale)

PROMULGATED BY THE TEXAS REAL ESTATE COMMISSION (TREC)   4-28-2014
NOTICE: Not For Use Where Seller Owns Fee Simple Title To Land Beneath Unit
RESIDENTIAL CONDOMINIUM CONTRACT (RESALE)

1. **PARTIES:** The parties to this contract are _____(Seller) and
_____(Buyer). Seller agrees to
sell and convey to Buyer and Buyer agrees to buy from Seller the Property defined below.
2. **PROPERTY AND CONDOMINIUM DOCUMENTS:**
   A. The Condominium Unit, improvements and accessories described below are collectively referred to as the "Property".
      (1) CONDOMINIUM UNIT: Unit _____, in Building _____,
      of _____, a condominium project, located at
      _____
      _____
      (address/zip code), City of _____,County of _____
      _____,
      Texas, described in the Condominium Declaration and Plat and any amendments thereto of record in said County; together with such Unit's undivided interest in the Common Elements designated by the Declaration, including those areas reserved as Limited Common Elements appurtenant to the Unit and such other rights to use the Common Elements which have been specifically assigned to the Unit in any other manner. Parking areas assigned to the Unit are:_____
      _____.
      (2) IMPROVEMENTS: All fixtures and improvements attached to the above described real property including without limitation, the following **permanently installed and built-in items**, if any: all equipment and appliances, valances, screens, shutters, awnings, wall-to-wall carpeting, mirrors, ceiling fans, attic fans, mail boxes, television antennas, mounts and brackets for televisions and speakers, heating and air conditioning units, security and fire detection equipment, wiring, plumbing and lighting fixtures, chandeliers, shrubbery, landscaping, outdoor cooking equipment, and all other property owned by Seller and attached to the above described Condominium Unit.
      (3) ACCESSORIES: The following described related accessories, if any: window air conditioning units, stove, fireplace screens, curtains and rods, blinds, window shades, draperies and rods, door keys, mailbox keys, above ground pool, swimming pool equipment and maintenance accessories, artificial fireplace logs, and controls for: (i) garage doors, (ii) entry gates, and (iii) other improvements and accessories.
      (4) EXCLUSIONS: The following improvements and accessories will be retained by Seller and must be removed prior to delivery of possession: _____
      _____.
   B. The Declaration, Bylaws and any Rules of the Association are called "Documents". (Check one box only):
   ☐ (1) Buyer has received a copy of the Documents. Buyer is advised to read the Documents before signing the contract.
   ☐ (2) Buyer has not received a copy of the Documents. Seller shall deliver the Documents to Buyer within _____ days after the effective date of the contract. Buyer may cancel the contract before the sixth day after Buyer receives the Documents by hand-delivering or mailing written notice of cancellation to Seller by certified United States mail, return receipt requested. If Buyer cancels the contract pursuant to this paragraph, the contract will terminate and the earnest money will be refunded to Buyer.
   C. The Resale Certificate from the condominium owners association (the Association) is called the "Certificate". The Certificate must be in a form promulgated by TREC or required by the parties. The Certificate must have been prepared no more than 3 months before the date it is delivered to Buyer and must contain at a minimum the information required by Section 82.157, Texas Property Code.
   (Check one box only):
   ☐ (1) Buyer has received the Certificate.
   ☐ (2) Buyer has not received the Certificate. Seller shall deliver the Certificate to Buyer within _____days after the effective date of the contract. Buyer may cancel the contract before the sixth day after the date Buyer receives the Certificate by hand-delivering or mailing written notice of cancellation to Seller by certified United States mail, return receipt requested. If Buyer cancels the contract pursuant to this paragraph, the contract will terminate and the earnest money will be refunded to Buyer.
   ☐ (3) Buyer has received Seller's affidavit that Seller requested information from the Association concerning its financial condition as required by the Texas Property Code, and that the Association did not provide a Certificate or information required in the Certificate. Buyer and Seller agree to waive the requirement to furnish the Certificate.

Initialed for identification by Buyer_____ _____ and Seller _____ _____   TREC NO. 30-11

FIGURE 5

Residential Condominium Contract (Resale) (continued)

Contract Concerning_____Page 2 of 8 4-28-2014
(Address of Property)

3. SALES PRICE:
  A. Cash portion of Sales Price payable by Buyer at closing ....$_____

  B. Sum of all financing described below (excluding any loan funding
     fee or mortgage insurance premium)...$_____
  C. Sales Price (Sum of A and B) ....$_____

4. FINANCING (Not for use with reverse mortgage financing): The portion of Sales Price not
❑ payable in cash will be paid as follows: (Check applicable boxes below)
❑A. THIRD PARTY FINANCING: One or more third party mortgage loans in the total amount of
    $_____ (excluding any loan funding fee or mortgage insurance premium).
    (1)Property Approval: If the Property does not satisfy the lenders' underwriting requirements
       for the loan(s), (including, but not limited to appraisal, insurability and lender required
       repairs), Buyer may terminate this contract by giving notice to Seller prior to closing and
       the earnest money will be refunded to Buyer.
    (2)Credit Approval: (Check one box only)
      ❑ (a) This contract is subject to Buyer being approved for the financing described in the
          attached Third Party Financing Addendum for Credit Approval.
      ❑ (b) This contract is not subject to Buyer being approved for financing and does not involve
          FHA or VA financing.
❑B. ASSUMPTION: The assumption of the unpaid principal balance of one or more promissory
    notes described in the attached TREC Loan Assumption Addendum.
❑C. SELLER FINANCING: A promissory note from Buyer to Seller of $_____, secured
    by vendor's and deed of trust liens, and containing the terms and conditions described in the
    attached TREC Seller Financing Addendum. If an owner policy of title insurance is furnished,
    Buyer shall furnish Seller with a mortgagee policy of title insurance.

5. EARNEST MONEY: Upon execution of this contract by all parties, Buyer shall deposit $ _____
as earnest money with _____, as escrow agent,
at _____
(address). Buyer shall deposit additional earnest money of $_____with escrow agent
within _____ days after the effective date of this contract. If Buyer fails to deposit the earnest
money as required by this contract, Buyer will be in default.

6. TITLE POLICY:
  A. TITLE POLICY: Seller shall furnish to Buyer at ❑Seller's ❑Buyer's expense an owner policy of
    title insurance (Title Policy) issued by _____(Title
    Company) in the amount of the Sales Price, dated at or after closing, insuring Buyer against
    loss under the provisions of the Title Policy, subject to the promulgated exclusions (including
    existing building and zoning ordinances) and the following exceptions:
    (1) Restrictive covenants common to the platted subdivision in which the Property is located.
    (2) The standard printed exception for standby fees, taxes and assessments.
    (3) Liens created as part of the financing described in Paragraph 4.
    (4) Terms and provisions of the Documents including the assessments and platted
       easements.
    (5) Reservations or exceptions otherwise permitted by this contract or as may be approved by
       Buyer in writing.
    (6) The standard printed exception as to marital rights.
    (7) The standard printed exception as to waters, tidelands, beaches, streams, and related
       matters.
    (8) The standard printed exception as to discrepancies, conflicts, shortages in area or boundary
       lines, encroachments or protrusions, or overlapping improvements.
  B. COMMITMENT: Within 20 days after the Title Company receives a copy of this contract, Seller
    shall furnish to Buyer a commitment for title insurance (Commitment) and, at Buyer's
    expense, legible copies of restrictive covenants and documents evidencing exceptions in the
    Commitment (Exception Documents) other than the standard printed exceptions. Seller
    authorizes the Title Company to deliver the Commitment and Exception Documents to Buyer
    at Buyer's address shown in Paragraph 21. If the Commitment and Exception Documents are
    not delivered to Buyer within the specified time, the time for delivery will be automatically
    extended up to 15 days or 3 days before the Closing Date, whichever is earlier. If, due to
    factors beyond Seller's control, the Commitment and Exception Documents are not delivered
    within the time required, Buyer may terminate this contract and the earnest money will be
    refunded to Buyer.
  C. OBJECTIONS: Buyer may object in writing to defects, exceptions, or encumbrances to title:
    disclosed in the Commitment other than items 6A(1) through (8) above; or which prohibit the
    following use or activity: _____
    _____.
    Buyer must object the earlier of (i) the Closing Date or (ii) _____ days after Buyer receives
    the Commitment and Exception Documents. Buyer's failure to object within the time
    allowed will constitute a waiver of Buyer's right to object; except that the requirements in

    Schedule C of the Commitment are not waived by Buyer. Provided Seller is not obligated to

Initialed for identification by Buyer_____ _____ and Seller _____ _____   TREC NO. 30-11

FIGURE 5

Residential Condominium Contract (Resale) (continued)

Contract Concerning_____Page 3 of 8 4-28-2014
(Address of Property)

incur any expense, Seller shall cure the timely objections of Buyer or any third party lender within 15 days after Seller receives the objections and the Closing Date will be extended as necessary. If objections are not cured within such 15 day period, this contract will terminate and the earnest money will be refunded to Buyer unless Buyer waives the objections.

   D. TITLE NOTICES:
     (1) ABSTRACT OR TITLE POLICY: Broker advises Buyer to have an abstract of title covering the Property examined by an attorney of Buyer's selection, or Buyer should be furnished with or obtain a Title Policy. If a Title Policy is furnished, the Commitment should be promptly reviewed by an attorney of Buyer's choice due to the time limitations on Buyer's right to object.
     (2) STATUTORY TAX DISTRICTS: If the Property is situated in a utility or other statutorily created district providing water, sewer, drainage, or flood control facilities and services, Chapter 49, Texas Water Code, requires Seller to deliver and Buyer to sign the statutory notice relating to the tax rate, bonded indebtedness, or standby fee of the district prior to final execution of this contract.
     (3) TIDE WATERS: If the Property abuts the tidally influenced waters of the state, §33.135, Texas Natural Resources Code, requires a notice regarding coastal area property to be included in the contract. An addendum containing the notice promulgated by TREC or required by the parties must be used.
     (4) ANNEXATION: If the Property is located outside the limits of a municipality, Seller notifies Buyer under §5.011, Texas Property Code, that the Property may now or later be included in the extraterritorial jurisdiction of a municipality and may now or later be subject to annexation by the municipality. Each municipality maintains a map that depicts its boundaries and extraterritorial jurisdiction. To determine if the Property is located within a municipality's extraterritorial jurisdiction or is likely to be located within a municipality's extraterritorial jurisdiction, contact all municipalities located in the general proximity of the Property for further information.
     (5) PROPERTY LOCATED IN A CERTIFICATED SERVICE AREA OF A UTILITY SERVICE PROVIDER: Notice required by §13.257, Water Code: The real property, described in Paragraph 2, that you are about to purchase may be located in a certificated water or sewer service area, which is authorized by law to provide water or sewer service to the properties in the certificated area. If your property is located in a certificated area there may be special costs or charges that you will be required to pay before you can receive water or sewer service. There may be a period required to construct lines or other facilities necessary to provide water or sewer service to your property. You are advised to determine if the property is in a certificated area and contact the utility service provider to determine the cost that you will be required to pay and the period, if any, that is required to provide water or sewer service to your property. The undersigned Buyer hereby acknowledges receipt of the foregoing notice at or before the execution of a binding contract for the purchase of the real property described in Paragraph 2 or at closing of purchase of the real property.
     (6) TRANSFER FEES: If the Property is subject to a private transfer fee obligation, §5.205, Property Code, requires Seller to notify Buyer as follows: The private transfer fee obligation may be governed by Chapter 5, Subchapter G of the Texas Property Code.
     (7) PROPANE GAS SYSTEM SERVICE AREA: If the Property is located in a propane gas system service area owned by a distribution system retailer, Seller must give Buyer written notice as required by §141.010, Texas Utilities Code. An addendum containing the notice approved by TREC or required by the parties should be used.

7. PROPERTY CONDITION:
   A. ACCESS, INSPECTIONS AND UTILITIES: Seller shall permit Buyer and Buyer's agents access to the Property at reasonable times. Buyer may have the Property inspected by inspectors selected by Buyer and licensed by TREC or otherwise permitted by law to make inspections. Seller at Seller's expense shall immediately cause existing utilities to be turned on and shall keep the utilities on during the time this contract is in effect .
   B. SELLER'S DISCLOSURE NOTICE PURSUANT TO §5.008, TEXAS PROPERTY CODE (Notice): (Check one box only)
     ❑ (1) Buyer has received the Notice.
     ❑ (2) Buyer has not received the Notice. Within _____ days after the effective date of this contract, Seller shall deliver the Notice to Buyer. If Buyer does not receive the Notice, Buyer may terminate this contract at any time prior to the closing and the earnest money will be refunded to Buyer. If Seller delivers the Notice, Buyer may terminate this contract for any reason within 7 days after Buyer receives the Notice or prior to the closing, whichever first occurs, and the earnest money will be refunded to Buyer.
     ❑ (3) The Texas Property Code does not require this Seller to furnish the Notice.
   C. SELLER'S DISCLOSURE OF LEAD-BASED PAINT AND LEAD-BASED PAINT HAZARDS is required by Federal law for a residential dwelling constructed prior to 1978.
   D. ACCEPTANCE OF PROPERTY CONDITION: "As Is" means the present condition of the Property with any and all defects and without warranty except for the warranties of title and the warranties in this contract. Buyer's agreement to accept the Property As Is under Paragraph 7D(1) or (2) does not preclude Buyer from inspecting the Property under Paragraph 7A, from negotiating repairs or treatments in a subsequent amendment, or from terminating this contract during the Option Period, if any.

Initialed for identification by Buyer_____ _____ and Seller _____ _____   TREC NO. 30-11

FIGURE 5

Residential Condominium Contract (Resale) (continued)

Contract Concerning_____Page 4 of 8   4-28-2014
(Address of Property)

(Check one box only)
☐ (1) Buyer accepts the Property As Is.
☐ (2) Buyer accepts the Property As Is provided Seller, at Seller's expense, shall complete the following specific repairs and treatments: _____
    (Do not insert general phrases, such as "subject to inspections," that do not identify specific repairs and treatments.)
E. LENDER REQUIRED REPAIRS AND TREATMENTS: Unless otherwise agreed in writing, neither party is obligated to pay for lender required repairs, which includes treatment for wood destroying insects. If the parties do not agree to pay for the lender required repairs or treatments, this contract will terminate and the earnest money will be refunded to Buyer. If the cost of lender required repairs and treatments exceeds 5% of the Sales Price, Buyer may terminate this contract and the earnest money will be refunded to Buyer.
F. COMPLETION OF REPAIRS AND TREATMENTS: Unless otherwise agreed in writing: (i) Seller shall complete all agreed repairs and treatments prior to the Closing Date; and (ii) all required permits must be obtained, and repairs and treatments must be performed by persons who are licensed to provide such repairs or treatments or, if no license is required by law, are commercially engaged in the trade of providing such repairs or treatments. At Buyer's election, any transferable warranties received by Seller with respect to the repairs and treatments will be transferred to Buyer at Buyer's expense. If Seller fails to complete any agreed repairs and treatments prior to the Closing Date, Buyer may exercise remedies under Paragraph 15 or extend the Closing Date up to 5 days if necessary for Seller to complete repairs and treatments.
G. ENVIRONMENTAL MATTERS: Buyer is advised that the presence of wetlands, toxic substances, including asbestos and wastes or other environmental hazards or the presence of a threatened or endangered species or its habitat may affect Buyer's intended use of the Property. If Buyer is concerned about these matters, an addendum promulgated by TREC or required by the parties should be used.
H. RESIDENTIAL SERVICE CONTRACTS: Buyer may purchase a residential service contract from a residential service company licensed by TREC. If Buyer purchases a residential service contract, Seller shall reimburse Buyer at closing for the cost of the residential service contract in an amount not exceeding $_____. Buyer should review any residential service contract for the scope of coverage, exclusions and limitations. **The purchase of a residential service contract is optional. Similar coverage may be purchased from various companies authorized to do business in Texas.**

8.BROKERS' FEES: All obligations of the parties for payment of brokers' fees are contained in separate written agreements.

9.CLOSING:
A. The closing of the sale will be on or before _____, 20____, or within 7 days after objections to matters disclosed in the Commitment have been cured, whichever date is later (Closing Date). If either party fails to close the sale by the Closing Date, the non-defaulting party may exercise the remedies contained in Paragraph 15.
B. At closing:
    (1) Seller shall execute and deliver a general warranty deed conveying title to the Property to Buyer and showing no additional exceptions to those permitted in Paragraph 6 and furnish tax statements or certificates showing no delinquent taxes on the Property.
    (2) Buyer shall pay the Sales Price in good funds acceptable to the escrow agent.
    (3) Seller and Buyer shall execute and deliver any notices, statements, certificates, affidavits, releases, loan documents and other documents reasonably required for the closing of the sale and the issuance of the Title Policy.
    (4) There will be no liens, assessments, or security interests against the Property which will not be satisfied out of the sales proceeds unless securing the payment of any loans assumed by Buyer and assumed loans will not be in default.
    (5) If the Property is subject to a residential lease, Seller shall transfer security deposits (as defined under §92.102, Property Code), if any, to Buyer. In such an event, Buyer shall deliver to the tenant a signed statement acknowledging that the Buyer has received the security deposit and is responsible for the return of the security deposit, and specifying the exact dollar amount of the security deposit.

10.POSSESSION:
A. Buyers Possession: Seller shall deliver to Buyer possession of the Property in its present or required condition, ordinary wear and tear excepted: ☐ upon closing and funding ☐ according to a temporary residential lease form promulgated by TREC or other written lease required by the parties. Any possession by Buyer prior to closing or by Seller after closing which is not authorized by a written lease will establish a tenancy at sufferance relationship between the parties. **Consult your insurance agent prior to change of ownership and possession because insurance coverage may be limited or terminated. The absence of a written lease or appropriate insurance coverage may expose the parties to economic loss.**
B. Leases:
    (1) After the Effective Date, Seller may not execute any lease (including but not limited to mineral leases) or convey any interest in the Property without Buyer's written consent.

Initialed for identification by Buyer_____ _____ and Seller _____ _____   TREC NO. 30-11

FIGURE 5

Residential Condominium Contract (Resale) (continued)

Contract Concerning_____Page 5 of 8   4-28-2014
(Address of Property)

    (2) If the Property is subject to any lease to which Seller is a party, Seller shall deliver to Buyer copies of the lease(s) and any move-in condition form signed by the tenant within 7 days after the Effective Date of the contract.

11. SPECIAL PROVISIONS: (Insert only factual statements and business details applicable to the sale. TREC rules prohibit licensees from adding factual statements or business details for which a contract addendum, lease or other form has been promulgated by TREC for mandatory use.)

12. SETTLEMENT AND OTHER EXPENSES:
  A. The following expenses must be paid at or prior to closing:
    (1) Expenses payable by Seller (Seller's Expenses):
      (a) Releases of existing liens, including prepayment penalties and recording fees; lender, FHA, or VA completion requirements; tax statements or certificates; preparation of deed; one-half of escrow fee; and other expenses payable by Seller under this contract.
      (b) Seller shall also pay an amount not to exceed $ _____ to be applied in the following order: Buyer's Expenses which Buyer is prohibited from paying by FHA, VA, Texas Veterans Land Board or other governmental loan programs, and then to other Buyer's Expenses as allowed by the lender.
    (2) Expenses payable by Buyer (Buyer's Expenses): Appraisal fees; loan application fees; adjusted origination charges; credit reports; preparation of loan documents; interest on the notes from date of disbursement to one month prior to dates of first monthly payments; recording fees; copies of easements and restrictions; loan title policy with endorsements required by lender; loan-related inspection fees; photos; amortization schedules; one-half of escrow fee; all prepaid items, including required premiums for flood and hazard insurance, reserve deposits for insurance, ad valorem taxes and special governmental assessments; final compliance inspection; courier fee; repair inspection; underwriting fee; wire transfer fee; expenses incident to any loan; Private Mortgage Insurance Premium (PMI), VA Loan Funding Fee, or FHA Mortgage Insurance Premium (MIP) as required by the lender; and other expenses payable by Buyer under this contract.
    (3) Except as provided by 12(A)(4) below, Buyer shall pay any and all Association fees or other charges resulting from the transfer of the Property not to exceed $___ and Seller shall pay any excess.
    (4) Buyer shall pay any deposits for reserves required at closing by the Association.
  B. If any expense exceeds an amount expressly stated in this contract for such expense to be paid by a party, that party may terminate this contract unless the other party agrees to pay such excess. Buyer may not pay charges and fees expressly prohibited by FHA, VA, Texas Veterans Land Board or other governmental loan program regulations.

13. PRORATIONS: Taxes for the current year, interest, maintenance fees, regular condominium assessments, dues and rents will be prorated through the Closing Date. The tax proration may be calculated taking into consideration any change in exemptions that will affect the current year's taxes. If taxes for the current year vary from the amount prorated at closing, the parties shall adjust the prorations when tax statements for the current year are available. If taxes are not paid at or prior to closing, Buyer shall pay taxes for the current year. Cash reserves from regular condominium assessments for deferred maintenance or capital improvements established by the Association will not be credited to Seller. Any special condominium assessment due and unpaid at closing will be the obligation of Seller.

14. CASUALTY LOSS: If any part of the Unit which Seller is solely obligated to maintain and repair under the terms of the Declaration is damaged or destroyed by fire or other casualty, Seller shall restore the same to its previous condition as soon as reasonably possible, but in any event by the Closing Date. If Seller fails to do so due to factors beyond Seller's control, Buyer may (a) terminate this contract and the earnest money will be refunded to Buyer, (b) extend the time for performance up to 15 days and the Closing Date will be extended as necessary or (c) accept the Property in its damaged condition with an assignment of insurance proceeds and receive credit from Seller at closing in the amount of the deductible under the insurance policy. If any part of the Common Elements or Limited Common Elements appurtenant to the Unit is damaged or destroyed by fire or other casualty loss, Buyer will have 7 days from receipt of notice of such casualty loss within which to notify Seller in writing that the contract will be terminated unless Buyer receives written confirmation from the Association that the damaged condition will be restored to its previous condition within a reasonable time at no cost to Buyer. Unless Buyer gives such notice within such time, Buyer will be deemed to have accepted the Property without confirmation of such restoration. Seller will have 7 days from the date of receipt of Buyer's notice within which to cause to be delivered to Buyer such confirmation. If written confirmation is not delivered to Buyer as required above, Buyer may terminate this contract and the earnest money will be refunded to Buyer. Seller's obligations under this paragraph are independent of any other obligations of Seller under this contract.

Initialed for identification by Buyer_____ _____ and Seller _____ _____   TREC NO. 30-11

FIGURE 5

Residential Condominium Contract (Resale) (continued)

Contract Concerning_____Page 6 of 8 4-28-2014
(Address of Property)

15. **DEFAULT:** If Buyer fails to comply with this contract, Buyer will be in default, and Seller may (a) enforce specific performance, seek such other relief as may be provided by law, or both, or (b) terminate this contract and receive the earnest money as liquidated damages, thereby releasing both parties from this contract. If Seller fails to comply with this contract for any other reason, Seller will be in default and Buyer may (a) enforce specific performance, seek such other relief as may be provided by law, or both, or (b) terminate this contract and receive the earnest money, thereby releasing both parties from this contract.

16. **MEDIATION:** It is the policy of the State of Texas to encourage resolution of disputes through alternative dispute resolution procedures such as mediation. Any dispute between Seller and Buyer related to this contract which is not resolved through informal discussion will be submitted to a mutually acceptable mediation service or provider. The parties to the mediation shall bear the mediation costs equally. This paragraph does not preclude a party from seeking equitable relief from a court of competent jurisdiction.

17. **ATTORNEY'S FEES:** A Buyer, Seller, Listing Broker, Other Broker, or escrow agent who prevails in any legal proceeding related to this contract is entitled to recover reasonable attorney's fees and all costs of such proceeding.

18. **ESCROW:**
    A. ESCROW: The escrow agent is not (i) a party to this contract and does not have liability for the performance or nonperformance of any party to this contract, (ii) liable for interest on the earnest money and (iii) liable for the loss of any earnest money caused by the failure of any financial institution in which the earnest money has been deposited unless the financial institution is acting as escrow agent.
    B. EXPENSES: At closing, the earnest money must be applied first to any cash down payment, then to Buyer's Expenses and any excess refunded to Buyer. If no closing occurs, escrow agent may: (i) require a written release of liability of the escrow agent from all parties, (ii) require payment of unpaid expenses incurred on behalf of a party, and (iii) only deduct from the earnest money the amount of unpaid expenses incurred on behalf of the party receiving the earnest money.
    C. DEMAND: Upon termination of this contract, either party or the escrow agent may send a release of earnest money to each party and the parties shall execute counterparts of the release and deliver same to the escrow agent. If either party fails to execute the release, either party may make a written demand to the escrow agent for the earnest money. If only one party makes written demand for the earnest money, escrow agent shall promptly provide a copy of the demand to the other party. If escrow agent does not receive written objection to the demand from the other party within 15 days, escrow agent may disburse the earnest money to the party making demand reduced by the amount of unpaid expenses incurred on behalf of the party receiving the earnest money and escrow agent may pay the same to the creditors. If escrow agent complies with the provisions of this paragraph, each party hereby releases escrow agent from all adverse claims related to the disbursal of the earnest money.
    D. DAMAGES: Any party who wrongfully fails or refuses to sign a release acceptable to the escrow agent within 7 days of receipt of the request will be liable to the other party for liquidated damages in an amount equal to the sum of: (i) three times the amount of the earnest money; (ii) the earnest money; (iii) reasonable attorney's fees; and (iv) all costs of suit.
    E. NOTICES: Escrow agent's notices will be effective when sent in compliance with Paragraph 21. Notice of objection to the demand will be deemed effective upon receipt by escrow agent.

19. **REPRESENTATIONS:** All covenants, representations and warranties in this contract survive closing. If any representation of Seller in this contract is untrue on the Closing Date, Seller will be in default. Unless expressly prohibited by written agreement, Seller may continue to show the Property and receive, negotiate and accept back up offers.

20. **FEDERAL TAX REQUIREMENTS:** If Seller is a "foreign person," as defined by applicable law, or if Seller fails to deliver an affidavit to Buyer that Seller is not a "foreign person," then Buyer shall withhold from the sales proceeds an amount sufficient to comply with applicable tax law and deliver the same to the Internal Revenue Service together with appropriate tax forms. Internal Revenue Service regulations require filing written reports if currency in excess of specified amounts is received in the transaction.

21. **NOTICES:** All notices from one party to the other must be in writing and are effective when mailed to, hand-delivered at, or transmitted by facsimile or electronic transmission as follows:

To Buyer at: **To Seller at:**

_____   _____

_____   _____

Telephone: (____)_____   Telephone: (____)_____

Facsimile: (____)_____   Facsimile: (____)_____

E-mail: _____   E-mail: _____

Initialed for identification by Buyer_____ _____ and Seller _____ _____   TREC NO. 30-11

FIGURE 5

Residential Condominium Contract (Resale) (continued)

Contract Concerning _____ Page 7 of 8   4-28-2014

(Address of Property)

22. AGREEMENT OF PARTIES: This contract contains the entire agreement of the parties and cannot be changed except by their written agreement. Addenda which are a part of this contract are (check all applicable boxes):

☐ Third Party Financing Addendum for Credit Approval

☐ Loan Assumption Addendum

☐ Buyer's Temporary Residential Lease

☐ Seller's Temporary Residential Lease

☐ Addendum for Sale of Other Property by Buyer

☐ Addendum for "Back-Up" Contract

☐ Seller Financing Addendum

☐ Addendum for Coastal Area Property

☐ Short Sale Addendum

☐ Addendum for Seller's Disclosure of Information on Lead-based Paint and Lead-based Paint Hazards as Required by Federal Law

☐ Environmental Assessment, Threatened or Endangered Species and Wetlands Addendum

☐ Addendum for Property Located Seaward of the Gulf Intracoastal Waterway

☐ Addendum for Release of Liability on Assumption of FHA, VA, or Conventional Loan Restoration of Seller's Entitlement for VA Guaranteed Loan

☐ Addendum for Property in a Propane Gas System Service Area

☐ Other (list): _____

_____

_____

23. TERMINATION OPTION: For nominal consideration, the receipt of which is hereby acknowledged by Seller, and Buyer's agreement to pay Seller $_____ (Option Fee) within 3 days after the effective date of this contract, Seller grants Buyer the unrestricted right to terminate this contract by giving notice of termination to Seller within _____ days after the effective date of this contract (Option Period). If no dollar amount is stated as the Option Fee or if Buyer fails to pay the Option Fee to Seller within the time prescribed, this paragraph will not be a part of this contract and Buyer shall not have the unrestricted right to terminate this contract. If Buyer gives notice of termination within the time prescribed, the Option Fee will not be refunded; however, any earnest money will be refunded to Buyer. The Option Fee ☐will ☐will not be credited to the Sales Price at closing. **Time is of the essence for this paragraph and strict compliance with the time for performance is required.**

24. CONSULT AN ATTORNEY BEFORE SIGNING: TREC rules prohibit real estate licensees from giving legal advice. READ THIS CONTRACT CAREFULLY.

Buyer's
Attorney is: _____

_____

Telephone: (____) _____

Facsimile: (____) _____

E-mail: _____

Seller's
Attorney is: _____

_____

Telephone: (____) _____

Facsimile: (____) _____

E-mail: _____

EXECUTED the _____ day of _____, 20_____ (EFFECTIVE DATE).
(BROKER: FILL IN THE DATE OF FINAL ACCEPTANCE.)

_____   _____
Buyer   Seller

_____   _____
Buyer   Seller

Initialed for identification by Buyer_____ _____ and Seller _____ _____   TREC NO. 30-11

FIGURE 5

Residential Condominium Contract (Resale) (continued)

Contract Concerning_____Page 8 of 8 4-28-2014
(Address of Property)

BROKER INFORMATION
(Print name(s) only. Do not sign)

Other Broker Firm _____ License No.

represents ☐ Buyer only as Buyer's agent
☐ Seller as Listing Broker's subagent

Name of Associate's Licensed Supervisor   Telephone

Associate's Name   Telephone

Other Broker's Address   Facsimile

City   State   Zip

Associate's Email Address

Listing Broker Firm _____ License No.

represents ☐ Seller and Buyer as an intermediary
☐ Seller only as Seller's agent

Name of Associate's Licensed Supervisor   Telephone

Listing Associate's Name   Telephone

Listing Broker's Office Address   Facsimile

City   State   Zip

Listing Associate's Email Address

Selling Associate's Name   Telephone

Name of Selling Associate's Licensed Supervisor   Telephone

Selling Associate's Office Address   Facsimile

City   State   Zip

Selling Associate's Email Address

Listing Broker has agreed to pay Other Broker_____of the total sales price when the Listing Broker's fee is received. Escrow agent is authorized and directed to pay other Broker from Listing Broker's fee at closing.

OPTION FEE RECEIPT

Receipt of $_____ (Option Fee) in the form of _____ is acknowledged.

_____   _____
Seller or Listing Broker   Date

CONTRACT AND EARNEST MONEY RECEIPT

Receipt of ☐ Contract and ☐ $_____ Earnest Money in the form of _____
is acknowledged.
Escrow Agent: _____   Date: _____

By: _____

_____   Telephone (_____) _____
Address

City   State   Zip   Facsimile: (_____) _____

Email Address

TREC NO. 30-11

FIGURE 6

Unimproved Property Contract

UNIMPROVED PROPERTY CONTRACT
NOTICE: Not For Use For Condominium Transactions

1. PARTIES: The parties to this contract are _____(Seller) and _____(Buyer). Seller agrees to sell and convey to Buyer and Buyer agrees to buy from Seller the Property defined below.

2. PROPERTY: Lot _____, Block _____, _____Addition, City of _____, County of_____, Texas, known as_____ (address/zip code), or as described on attached exhibit together with all rights, privileges and appurtenances pertaining thereto, including but not limited to: water rights, claims, permits, strips and gores, easements, and cooperative or association memberships (the Property).

3. SALES PRICE:
   A. Cash portion of Sales Price payable by Buyer at closing .... $_____
   B. Sum of all financing described below (excluding any loan funding fee or mortgage insurance premium).. $_____
   C. Sales Price (Sum of A and B).. $_____

4. FINANCING (Not for use with reverse mortgage financing): The portion of Sales Price not payable in cash will be paid as follows: (Check applicable boxes below)
❑A. THIRD PARTY FINANCING: One or more third party mortgage loans in the total amount of $_____ (excluding any loan funding fee or mortgage insurance premium).
   (1) Property Approval: If the Property does not satisfy the lenders' underwriting requirements for the loan(s) (including, but not limited to appraisal, insurability and lender required repairs), Buyer may terminate this contract by giving notice to Seller prior to closing and the earnest money will be refunded to Buyer.
   (2) Credit Approval: (Check one box only)
      ❑ (a) This contract is subject to Buyer being approved for the financing described in the attached Third Party Financing Addendum for Credit Approval.
      ❑ (b) This contract is not subject to Buyer being approved for financing and does not involve FHA or VA financing.
❑B. ASSUMPTION: The assumption of the unpaid principal balance of one or more promissory notes described in the attached TREC Loan Assumption Addendum.
❑C. SELLER FINANCING: A promissory note from Buyer to Seller of $_____, secured by vendor's and deed of trust liens, and containing the terms and conditions described in the attached TREC Seller Financing Addendum. If an owner policy of title insurance is furnished, Buyer shall furnish Seller with a mortgagee policy of title insurance.

5. EARNEST MONEY: Upon execution of contract by all parties, Buyer shall deposit $_____ as earnest money with _____, as escrow agent, at _____ (address). Buyer shall deposit additional earnest money of $_____ with escrow agent within _____ days after the effective date of this contract. If Buyer fails to deposit the earnest money as required by this contract, Buyer will be in default.

6. TITLE POLICY AND SURVEY:
   A. TITLE POLICY: Seller shall furnish to Buyer at ❑Seller's ❑Buyer's expense an owner's policy of title insurance (Title Policy) issued by_____ (Title Company) in the amount of the Sales Price, dated at or after closing, insuring Buyer against loss under the provisions of the Title Policy, subject to the promulgated exclusions (including existing building and zoning ordinances) and the following exceptions:
   (1) Restrictive covenants common to the platted subdivision in which the Property is located.
   (2) The standard printed exception for standby fees, taxes and assessments.
   (3) Liens created as part of the financing described in Paragraph 4.
   (4) Utility easements created by the dedication deed or plat of the subdivision in which the Property is located.
   (5) Reservations or exceptions otherwise permitted by this contract or as may be approved by Buyer in writing.
   (6) The standard printed exception as to marital rights.
   (7) The standard printed exception as to waters, tidelands, beaches, streams, and related matters.
   (8) The standard printed exception as to discrepancies, conflicts, shortages in area or boundary lines, encroachments or protrusions, or overlapping improvements: ❑ (i) will not be amended or deleted from the title policy; ❑(ii) will be amended to read, "shortages in area" at the expense of ❑Buyer ❑Seller.

Initialed for identification by Buyer_____ _____ and Seller _____ _____   TREC NO. 9-11

FIGURE 6

Unimproved Property Contract (continued)

Contract Concerning _____Page 2 of 8 4-28-2014
(Address of Property)

B. COMMITMENT: Within 20 days after the Title Company receives a copy of this contract, Seller shall furnish to Buyer a commitment for title insurance (Commitment) and, at Buyer's expense, legible copies of restrictive covenants and documents evidencing exceptions in the Commitment (Exception Documents) other than the standard printed exceptions. Seller authorizes the Title Company to deliver the Commitment and Exception Documents to Buyer at Buyer's address shown in Paragraph 21. If the Commitment and Exception Documents are not delivered to Buyer within the specified time, the time for delivery will be automatically extended up to 15 days or 3 days before the Closing Date, whichever is earlier. If, due to factors beyond Seller's control, the Commitment and Exception Documents are not delivered within the time required, Buyer may terminate this contract and the earnest money will be refunded to Buyer.

C. SURVEY: The survey must be made by a registered professional land surveyor acceptable to the Title Company and Buyer's lender(s). (Check one box only)

❑ (1) Within _____ days after the effective date of this contract, Seller shall furnish to Buyer and Title Company Seller's existing survey of the Property and a Residential Real Property Affidavit promulgated by the Texas Department of Insurance (T-47 Affidavit). **If Seller fails to furnish the existing survey or affidavit within the time prescribed, Buyer shall obtain a new survey at Seller's expense no later than 3 days prior to Closing Date.** If the existing survey or affidavit is not acceptable to Title Company or Buyer's lender(s), Buyer shall obtain a new survey at ❑ Seller's ❑Buyer's expense no later than 3 days prior to Closing Date.

❑ (2) Within _____ days after the effective date of this contract, Buyer shall obtain a new survey at Buyer's expense. Buyer is deemed to receive the survey on the date of actual receipt or the date specified in this paragraph, whichever is earlier.

❑ (3) Within _____ days after the effective date of this contract, Seller, at Seller's expense shall furnish a new survey to Buyer.

D. OBJECTIONS: Buyer may object in writing to (i) defects, exceptions, or encumbrances to title: disclosed on the survey other than items 6A(1) through (7) above; or disclosed in the Commitment other than items 6A(1) through (8) above; (ii) any portion of the Property lying in a special flood hazard area (Zone V or A) as shown on the current Federal Emergency Management Agency map; or (iii) any exceptions which prohibit the following use or activity:

_____.
Buyer must object the earlier of (i) the Closing Date or (ii) _____ days after Buyer receives the Commitment, Exception Documents, and the survey. Buyer's failure to object within the time allowed will constitute a waiver of Buyer's right to object; except that the requirements in Schedule C of the Commitment are not waived. Provided Seller is not obligated to incur any expense, Seller shall cure the timely objections of Buyer or any third party lender within 15 days after Seller receives the objections and the Closing Date will be extended as necessary. If objections are not cured within such 15 day period, this contract will terminate and the earnest money will be refunded to Buyer unless Buyer waives the objections.

E. TITLE NOTICES:

(1) ABSTRACT OR TITLE POLICY: Broker advises Buyer to have an abstract of title covering the Property examined by an attorney of Buyer's selection, or Buyer should be furnished with or obtain a Title Policy. If a Title Policy is furnished, the Commitment should be promptly reviewed by an attorney of Buyer's choice due to the time limitations on Buyer's right to object.

(2) MEMBERSHIP IN PROPERTY OWNERS ASSOCIATION(S): The Property ❑is ❑is not subject to mandatory membership in a property owners association(s). If the Property is subject to mandatory membership in a property owners association(s), Seller notifies Buyer under §5.012, Texas Property Code, that, as a purchaser of property in the residential community identified in Paragraph 2 in which the Property is located, you are obligated to be a member of the property owners association(s). Restrictive covenants governing the use and occupancy of the Property and all dedicatory instruments governing the establishment, maintenance, and operation of this residential community have been or will be recorded in the Real Property Records of the county in which the Property is located. Copies of the restrictive covenants and dedicatory instruments may be obtained from the county clerk. <u>**You are obligated to pay assessments to the property owners association(s). The amount of the assessments is subject to change. Your failure to pay assessments could result in enforcement of the association's lien on and the foreclosure of the Property.**</u> Section 207.003, Property Code, entitles an owner to receive copies of any document that governs the establishment, maintenance, or operation of a subdivision, including, but not limited to, restrictions, bylaws, rules and regulations, and a resale certificate from a property owners' association. A resale certificate contains information including, but not limited to, statements specifying the amount and frequency of regular assessments and the style and cause number of lawsuits to which the property owners' association is a party, other than lawsuits relating to unpaid ad valorem taxes of an individual member of the association. These documents must be made available to you by the property owners' association or the association's agent on your request. **If Buyer is concerned about these matters, the TREC promulgated Addendum for**

Initialed for identification by Buyer_____ _____ and Seller _____ _____   TREC NO. 9-11

FIGURE 6

Unimproved Property Contract (continued)

Contract Concerning _____ Page 3 of 8 4-28-2014
(Address of Property)

Property Subject to Mandatory Membership in a Property Owners Association should be used.

(3) STATUTORY TAX DISTRICTS: If the Property is situated in a utility or other statutorily created district providing water, sewer, drainage, or flood control facilities and services, Chapter 49, Texas Water Code, requires Seller to deliver and Buyer to sign the statutory notice relating to the tax rate, bonded indebtedness, or standby fee of the district prior to final execution of this contract.

(4) TIDE WATERS: If the Property abuts the tidally influenced waters of the state, §33.135, Texas Natural Resources Code, requires a notice regarding coastal area property to be included in the contract. An addendum containing the notice promulgated by TREC or required by the parties must be used.

(5) ANNEXATION: If the Property is located outside the limits of a municipality, Seller notifies Buyer under §5.011, Texas Property Code, that the Property may now or later be included in the extraterritorial jurisdiction of a municipality and may now or later be subject to annexation by the municipality. Each municipality maintains a map that depicts its boundaries and extraterritorial jurisdiction. To determine if the Property is located within a municipality's extraterritorial jurisdiction or is likely to be located within a municipality's extraterritorial jurisdiction, contact all municipalities located in the general proximity of the Property for further information.

(6) PROPERTY LOCATED IN A CERTIFICATED SERVICE AREA OF A UTILITY SERVICE PROVIDER: Notice required by §13.257, Water Code: The real property, described in Paragraph 2, that you are about to purchase may be located in a certificated water or sewer service area, which is authorized by law to provide water or sewer service to the properties in the certificated area. If your property is located in a certificated area there may be special costs or charges that you will be required to pay before you can receive water or sewer service. There may be a period required to construct lines or other facilities necessary to provide water or sewer service to your property. You are advised to determine if the property is in a certificated area and contact the utility service provider to determine the cost that you will be required to pay and the period, if any, that is required to provide water or sewer service to your property. The undersigned Buyer hereby acknowledges receipt of the foregoing notice at or before the execution of a binding contract for the purchase of the real property described in Paragraph 2 or at closing of purchase of the real property.

(7) PUBLIC IMPROVEMENT DISTRICTS: If the Property is in a public improvement district, §5.014, Property Code, requires Seller to notify Buyer as follows: As a purchaser of this parcel of real property you are obligated to pay an assessment to a municipality or county for an improvement project undertaken by a public improvement district under Chapter 372, Local Government Code. The assessment may be due annually or in periodic installments. More information concerning the amount of the assessment and the due dates of that assessment may be obtained from the municipality or county levying the assessment. The amount of the assessments is subject to change. Your failure to pay the assessments could result in a lien on and the foreclosure of your property.

(8) TEXAS AGRICULTURAL DEVELOPMENT DISTRICT: The Property ❑ is ❑ is not located in a Texas Agricultural Development District. For additional information, contact the Texas Department of Agriculture.

(9) TRANSFER FEES: If the Property is subject to a private transfer fee obligation, §5.205, Property Code requires Seller to notify Buyer as follows: The private transfer fee obligation may be governed by Chapter 5, Subchapter G of the Texas Property Code.

(10) PROPANE GAS SYSTEM SERVICE AREA: If the Property is located in a propane gas system service area owned by a distribution system retailer, Seller must give Buyer written notice as required by §141.010, Texas Utilities Code. An addendum containing the notice approved by TREC or required by the parties should be used.

7. PROPERTY CONDITION:

A. ACCESS, INSPECTIONS AND UTILITIES: Seller shall permit Buyer and Buyer's agents access to the Property at reasonable times. Buyer may have the Property inspected by inspectors selected by Buyer and licensed by TREC or otherwise permitted by law to make inspections. Seller at Seller's expense shall immediately cause existing utilities to be turned on and shall keep the utilities on during the time this contract is in effect.
NOTICE: Buyer should determine the availability of utilities to the Property suitable to satisfy Buyer's needs.

B. ACCEPTANCE OF PROPERTY CONDITION: "As Is" means the present condition of the Property with any and all defects and without warranty except for the warranties of title and the warranties in this contract. Buyer's agreement to accept the Property As Is under Paragraph 7B (1) or (2) does not preclude Buyer from inspecting the Property under Paragraph 7A, from negotiating repairs or treatments in a subsequent amendment, or from terminating this contract during the Option Period, if any.
(Check one box only)
❑ (1) Buyer accepts the Property As Is.
❑ (2) Buyer accepts the Property As Is provided Seller, at Seller's expense, shall complete the

---

Initialed for identification by Buyer_____ _____ and Seller _____ _____   TREC NO. 9-11

FIGURE 6

Unimproved Property Contract (continued)

Contract Concerning _____Page 4 of 8 4-28-2014
(Address of Property)

following specific repairs and treatments: _____
_____.
(Do not insert general phrases, such as "subject to inspections" that do not identify specific repairs and treatments.)

C. COMPLETION OF REPAIRS: Unless otherwise agreed in writing: (i) Seller shall complete all agreed repairs and treatments prior to the Closing Date; and (ii) all required permits must be obtained, and repairs and treatments must be performed by persons who are licensed to provide such repairs or treatments or, if no license is required by law, are commercially engaged in the trade of providing such repairs or treatments.   At Buyer's election, any transferable warranties received by Seller with respect to the repairs and treatments will be transferred to Buyer at Buyer's expense. If Seller fails to complete any agreed repairs and treatments prior to the Closing Date, Buyer may exercise remedies under Paragraph 15 or extend the Closing Date up to 5 days, if necessary, for Seller to complete repairs and treatments.

D. ENVIRONMENTAL MATTERS: Buyer is advised that the presence of wetlands, toxic substances, including asbestos and wastes or other environmental hazards, or the presence of a threatened or endangered species or its habitat may affect Buyer's intended use of the Property. If Buyer is concerned about these matters, an addendum promulgated by TREC or required by the parties should be used.

E. SELLER'S DISCLOSURES: Except as otherwise disclosed in this contract, Seller has no knowledge of the following:
(1) any flooding of the Property which has had a material adverse effect on the use of the Property;
(2) any pending or threatened litigation, condemnation, or special assessment affecting the Property;
(3) any environmental hazards that materially and adversely affect the Property;
(4) any dumpsite, landfill, or underground tanks or containers now or previously located on the Property;
(5) any wetlands, as defined by federal or state law or regulation, affecting the Property; or
(6) any threatened or endangered species or their habitat affecting the Property.

8. BROKERS' FEES: All obligations of the parties for payment of brokers' fees are contained in separate written agreements.

9. CLOSING:
A. The closing of the sale will be on or before _____, 20_____, or within 7 days after objections made under Paragraph 6D have been cured or waived, whichever date is later (Closing Date). If either party fails to close the sale by the Closing Date, the non-defaulting party may exercise the remedies contained in Paragraph 15.
B. At closing:
(1) Seller shall execute and deliver a general warranty deed conveying title to the Property to Buyer and showing no additional exceptions to those permitted in Paragraph 6 and furnish tax statements or certificates showing no delinquent taxes on the Property.
(2) Buyer shall pay the Sales Price in good funds acceptable to the escrow agent.
(3) Seller and Buyer shall execute and deliver any notices, statements, certificates, affidavits, releases, loan documents and other documents reasonably required for the closing of the sale and the issuance of the Title Policy.
(4) There will be no liens, assessments, or security interests against the Property which will not be satisfied out of the sales proceeds unless securing the payment of any loans assumed by Buyer and assumed loans will not be in default.

10. POSSESSION:
A. Buyer's Possession: Seller shall deliver to Buyer possession of the Property in its present or required condition upon closing and funding.
B. Leases:
(1) After the Effective Date, Seller may not execute any lease (including but not limited to mineral leases) or convey any interest in the Property without Buyer's written consent.
(2) If the Property is subject to any lease to which Seller is a party, Seller shall deliver to Buyer copies of the lease(s) and any move-in condition form signed by the tenant within 7 days after the Effective Date of the contract.

11. SPECIAL PROVISIONS: (Insert only factual statements and business details applicable to the sale. TREC rules prohibit licensees from adding factual statements or business details for which a contract addendum or other form has been promulgated by TREC for mandatory use.)

Initialed for identification by Buyer_____ _____ and Seller _____ _____   TREC NO. 9-11

FIGURE 6

Unimproved Property Contract (continued)

Contract Concerning _____ Page 5 of 8 4-28-2014
_____(Address of Property)_____

12. SETTLEMENT AND OTHER EXPENSES:
  A. The following expenses must be paid at or prior to closing:
    (1) Expenses payable by Seller (Seller's Expenses):
      (a) Releases of existing liens, including prepayment penalties and recording fees; release of Seller's loan liability; tax statements or certificates; preparation of deed; one-half of escrow fee; and other expenses payable by Seller under this contract.
      (b) Seller shall also pay an amount not to exceed $ _____ to be applied in the following order: Buyer's Expenses which Buyer is prohibited from paying by FHA, VA, Texas Veterans Land Board or other governmental loan programs, and then to other Buyer's Expenses as allowed by the lender.
    (2) Expenses payable by Buyer (Buyer's Expenses): Appraisal fees; loan application fees; adjusted origination charges; credit reports; preparation of loan documents; interest on the notes from date of disbursement to one month prior to dates of first monthly payments; recording fees; copies of easements and restrictions; loan title policy with endorsements required by lender; loan-related inspection fees; photos; amortization schedules; one-half of escrow fee; all prepaid items, including required premiums for flood and hazard insurance, reserve deposits for insurance, ad valorem taxes and special governmental assessments; final compliance inspection; courier fee; repair inspection; underwriting fee; wire transfer fee; expenses incident to any loan; Private Mortgage Insurance Premium (PMI), VA Loan Funding Fee, or FHA Mortgage Insurance Premium (MIP) as required by the lender; and other expenses payable by Buyer under this contract.
  B. If any expense exceeds an amount expressly stated in this contract for such expense to be paid by a party, that party may terminate this contract unless the other party agrees to pay such excess. Buyer may not pay charges and fees expressly prohibited by FHA, VA, Texas Veterans Land Board or other governmental loan program regulations.

13. PRORATIONS AND ROLLBACK TAXES:
  A. PRORATIONS: Taxes for the current year, interest, maintenance fees, assessments, dues and rents will be prorated through the Closing Date. The tax proration may be calculated taking into consideration any change in exemptions that will affect the current year's taxes. If taxes for the current year vary from the amount prorated at closing, the parties shall adjust the prorations when tax statements for the current year are available. If taxes are not paid at or prior to closing, Buyer shall pay taxes for the current year.
  B. ROLLBACK TAXES: If this sale or Buyer's use of the Property after closing results in the assessment of additional taxes, penalties or interest (Assessments) for periods prior to closing, the Assessments will be the obligation of Buyer. If Seller's change in use of the Property prior to closing or denial of a special use valuation on the Property claimed by Seller results in Assessments for periods prior to closing, the Assessments will be the obligation of Seller. Obligations imposed by this paragraph will survive closing.

14. CASUALTY LOSS: If any part of the Property is damaged or destroyed by fire or other casualty after the effective date of this contract, Seller shall restore the Property to its previous condition as soon as reasonably possible, but in any event by the Closing Date. If Seller fails to do so due to factors beyond Seller's control, Buyer may (a) terminate this contract and the earnest money will be refunded to Buyer (b) extend the time for performance up to 15 days and the Closing Date will be extended as necessary or (c) accept the Property in its damaged condition with an assignment of insurance proceeds and receive credit from Seller at closing in the amount of the deductible under the insurance policy. Seller's obligations under this paragraph are independent of any other obligations of Seller under this contract.

15. DEFAULT: If Buyer fails to comply with this contract, Buyer will be in default, and Seller may (a) enforce specific performance, seek such other relief as may be provided by law, or both, or (b) terminate this contract and receive the earnest money as liquidated damages, thereby releasing both parties from this contract. If Seller fails to comply with this contract, Seller will be in default and Buyer may (a) enforce specific performance, seek such other relief as may be provided by law, or both, or (b) terminate this contract and receive the earnest money, thereby releasing both parties from this contract.

16. MEDIATION: It is the policy of the State of Texas to encourage resolution of disputes through alternative dispute resolution procedures such as mediation. Any dispute between Seller and Buyer related to this contract which is not resolved through informal discussion will be submitted to a mutually acceptable mediation service or provider. The parties to the mediation shall bear the mediation costs equally. This paragraph does not preclude a party from seeking equitable relief from a court of competent jurisdiction.

17. ATTORNEY'S FEES: A Buyer, Seller, Listing Broker, Other Broker, or escrow agent who prevails in any legal proceeding related to this contract is entitled to recover reasonable attorney's fees and all costs of such proceeding.

18. ESCROW:
  A. ESCROW: The escrow agent is not (i) a party to this contract and does not have liability for the performance or nonperformance of any party to this contract, (ii) liable for interest on the earnest money and (iii) liable for the loss of any earnest money caused by the failure of any financial institution in which the earnest money has been deposited unless the financial institution is acting as escrow agent.

Initialed for identification by Buyer_____ _____ and Seller _____ _____   TREC NO. 9-11

FIGURE 6

Unimproved Property Contract (continued)

Contract Concerning _____Page 6 of 8 4-28-2014
(Address of Property)

    B. EXPENSES: At closing, the earnest money must be applied first to any cash down payment, then to Buyer's Expenses and any excess refunded to Buyer. If no closing occurs, escrow agent may: (i) require a written release of liability of the escrow agent from all parties, (ii) require payment of unpaid expenses incurred on behalf of a party, and (iii) only deduct from the earnest money the amount of unpaid expenses incurred on behalf of the party receiving the earnest money.

    C. DEMAND: Upon termination of this contract, either party or the escrow agent may send a release of earnest money to each party and the parties shall execute counterparts of the release and deliver same to the escrow agent. If either party fails to execute the release, either party may make a written demand to the escrow agent for the earnest money. If only one party makes written demand for the earnest money, escrow agent shall promptly provide a copy of the demand to the other party. If escrow agent does not receive written objection to the demand from the other party within 15 days, escrow agent may disburse the earnest money to the party making demand reduced by the amount of unpaid expenses incurred on behalf of the party receiving the earnest money and escrow agent may pay the same to the creditors. If escrow agent complies with the provisions of this paragraph, each party hereby releases escrow agent from all adverse claims related to the disbursal of the earnest money.

    D. DAMAGES: Any party who wrongfully fails or refuses to sign a release acceptable to the escrow agent within 7 days of receipt of the request will be liable to the other party for liquidated damages in an amount equal to the sum of: (i) three times the amount of the earnest money; (ii) the earnest money; (iii) reasonable attorney's fees; and (iv) all costs of suit.

    E. NOTICES: Escrow agent's notices will be effective when sent in compliance with Paragraph 21. Notice of objection to the demand will be deemed effective upon receipt by escrow agent.

19. REPRESENTATIONS: All covenants, representations and warranties in this contract survive closing. If any representation of Seller in this contract is untrue on the Closing Date, Seller will be in default. Unless expressly prohibited by written agreement, Seller may continue to show the Property and receive, negotiate and accept back up offers.

20. FEDERAL TAX REQUIREMENTS: If Seller is a "foreign person," as defined by applicable law, or if Seller fails to deliver an affidavit to Buyer that Seller is not a "foreign person," then Buyer shall withhold from the sales proceeds an amount sufficient to comply with applicable tax law and deliver the same to the Internal Revenue Service together with appropriate tax forms. Internal Revenue Service regulations require filing written reports if currency in excess of specified amounts is received in the transaction.

21. NOTICES: All notices from one party to the other must be in writing and are effective when mailed to, hand-delivered at, or transmitted by facsimile or electronic transmission as follows:

To Buyer at:	**To Seller at:**
_____	_____
_____	_____
_____	_____
Telephone: ( )_____	Telephone: ( )_____
Facsimile: ( )_____	Facsimile: ( )_____
E-mail: _____	E-mail: _____

22. AGREEMENT OF PARTIES: This contract contains the entire agreement of the parties and cannot be changed except by their written agreement. Addenda which are a part of this contract are (check all applicable boxes):

❑ Third Party Financing Addendum for Credit Approval
❑ Seller Financing Addendum
❑ Addendum for Property Subject to Mandatory Membership in a Property Owners Association
❑ Buyer's Temporary Residential Lease
❑ Seller's Temporary Residential Lease
❑ Addendum for Reservation of Oil, Gas and Other Minerals
❑ Addendum for "Back-Up" Contract

❑ Addendum for Coastal Area Property
❑ Environmental Assessment, Threatened or Endangered Species and Wetlands Addendum
❑ Addendum for Property Located Seaward of the Gulf Intracoastal Waterway
❑ Addendum for Sale of Other Property by Buyer
❑ Addendum for Property in a Propane Gas System Service Area
❑ Other (list): _____

Initialed for identification by Buyer_____ _____ and Seller _____ _____   TREC NO. 9-11

FIGURE 6

Unimproved Property Contract (continued)

Contract Concerning _____ Page 7 of 8 4-28-2014
                                    (Address of Property)

23. **TERMINATION OPTION:** For nominal consideration, the receipt of which is hereby acknowledged by Seller, and Buyer's agreement to pay Seller $_____ (Option Fee) which Seller or Listing Broker must receive within 3 days after the effective date of this contract, Seller grants Buyer the unrestricted right to terminate this contract by giving notice of termination to Seller within _____ days after the effective date of this contract (Option Period). If no dollar amount is stated as the Option Fee or if Buyer fails to pay the Option Fee to Seller within the time prescribed, this paragraph will not be a part of this contract and Buyer shall not have the unrestricted right to terminate this contract. If Buyer gives notice of termination within the time prescribed, the Option Fee will not be refunded; however, any earnest money will be refunded to Buyer. The Option Fee ❑will ❑will not be credited to the Sales Price at closing. **Time is of the essence for this paragraph and strict compliance with the time for performance is required.**

24. **CONSULT AN ATTORNEY BEFORE SIGNING:** TREC rules prohibit real estate licensees from giving legal advice. READ THIS CONTRACT CAREFULLY.

Buyer's
Attorney is: _____

Seller's
Attorney is: _____

_____

_____

Telephone: (_____)_____

Telephone: (_____)_____

Facsimile: (_____)_____

Facsimile: (_____)_____

E-mail: _____

E-mail: _____

**EXECUTED the _____day of _____, 20_____ (EFFECTIVE DATE).
(BROKER: FILL IN THE DATE OF FINAL ACCEPTANCE.)**

_____
Buyer

_____
Seller

_____
Buyer

_____
Seller

TREC NO. 9-11

FIGURE 6

Unimproved Property Contract (continued)

Contract Concerning _____ Page 8 of 8 4-28-2014
(Address of Property)

BROKER INFORMATION
(Print name(s) only. Do not sign)

Other Broker Firm _____ License No.	Listing Broker Firm _____ License No.
represents ❑ Buyer only as Buyer's agent ❑ Seller as Listing Broker's subagent	represents ❑ Seller and Buyer as an intermediary ❑ Seller only as Seller's agent
Name of Associate's Licensed Supervisor _____ Telephone	Name of Associate's Licensed Supervisor _____ Telephone
Associate's Name _____ Telephone	Listing Associate's Name _____ Telephone
Other Broker's Address _____ Facsimile	Listing Broker's Office Address _____ Facsimile
City _____ State _____ Zip	City _____ State _____ Zip
Associate's Email Address	Listing Associate's Email Address
	Selling Associate's Name _____ Telephone
	Name of Selling Associate's Licensed Supervisor _____ Telephone
	Selling Associate's Office Address _____ Facsimile
	City _____ State _____ Zip
	Selling Associate's Email Address

Listing Broker has agreed to pay Other Broker_____ of the total sales price when the Listing Broker's fee is received. Escrow agent is authorized and directed to pay other Broker from Listing Broker's fee at closing.

OPTION FEE RECEIPT

Receipt of $_____ (Option Fee) in the form of _____ is acknowledged.

_____   _____
Seller or Listing Broker   Date

CONTRACT AND EARNEST MONEY RECEIPT

Receipt of ❑Contract and ❑$_____ Earnest Money in the form of _____
is acknowledged.
Escrow Agent: _____   Date: _____

By: _____
                                                                         Email Address
_____   Telephone (_____) _____
Address
_____   Facsimile: (_____) _____
City   State   Zip

TREC NO. 9-11

Promulgated Addenda

(including two temporary leases)

FIGURE 7

Addendum for Sale of Other Property by Buyer

PROMULGATED BY THE TEXAS REAL ESTATE COMMISSION (TREC)

12-05-11

ADDENDUM FOR
SALE OF OTHER PROPERTY BY BUYER

TO CONTRACT CONCERNING THE PROPERTY AT

_____
(Address of Property)

A. The contract is contingent upon Buyer's **receipt of the proceeds** from the sale of Buyer's property
at_____
(Address) on or before _____ , 20_____ (the Contingency). If the
Contingency is not satisfied or waived by Buyer by the above date, the contract will terminate
automatically and the earnest money will be refunded to Buyer.

NOTICE: The date inserted in this Paragraph should be no later than the Closing Date specified in
Paragraph 9 of the contract.

B. If Seller accepts a written offer to sell the Property, Seller shall notify Buyer (1) of such acceptance
AND (2) that Seller requires Buyer to waive the Contingency. Buyer must waive the Contingency
on or before the _____ day after Seller's notice to Buyer; otherwise the contract will
terminate automatically and the earnest money will be refunded to Buyer.

C. Buyer may waive the Contingency only by notifying Seller of the waiver and depositing $_____
with escrow agent as additional earnest money. All notices and waivers must be in writing and are
effective when delivered in accordance with the contract.

D. If Buyer waives the Contingency and fails to close and fund solely due to Buyer's non-receipt of
proceeds from Buyer's property described in Paragraph A above, Buyer will be in default. If such
default occurs, Seller may exercise the remedies specified in Paragraph 15 of the contract.

E. For purposes of this Addendum time is of the essence; strict compliance with the times for
performance stated herein is required.

_____   _____
Buyer   Seller

_____   _____
Buyer   Seller

TREC No. 10-6

FIGURE 8

Addendum for Back-up Contract

PROMULGATED BY THE TEXAS REAL ESTATE COMMISSION (TREC)   12-05-11

EQUAL HOUSING
OPPORTUNITY

ADDENDUM FOR
"BACK-UP" CONTRACT

TO CONTRACT CONCERNING THE PROPERTY AT

_____
(Address of Property)

A. The contract to which this Addendum is attached (the Back-Up Contract) is binding upon execution by the parties, and the earnest money and any Option Fee must be paid as provided in the Back-Up Contract. The Back-Up Contract is contingent upon the termination of a previous contract (the First Contract) dated _____, 20_____, for the sale of Property. Except as provided by this Addendum, neither party is required to perform under the Back-Up Contract while it is contingent upon the termination of the First Contract.

B. If the First Contract does not terminate on or before _____, 20_____, the Back-Up Contract terminates and the earnest money will be refunded to Buyer. Seller must notify Buyer immediately of the termination of the First Contract. For purposes of performance, the effective date of the Back-Up Contract changes to the date Buyer receives notice of termination of the First Contract (Amended Effective Date).

C. An amendment or modification of the First Contract will not terminate the First Contract.

D. If Buyer has the unrestricted right to terminate the Back-Up Contract, the time for giving notice of termination begins on the effective date of the Back-Up Contract, continues after the Amended Effective Date and ends upon the expiration of Buyer's unrestricted right to terminate the Back-Up Contract.

E. For purposes of this Addendum, time is of the essence. Strict compliance with the times for performance stated herein is required.

_____   _____
Buyer   Seller

_____   _____
Buyer   Seller

TREC No. 11-7

FIGURE 9

Addendum for Release of Liability on Assumed Loan and/or Restoration of Seller's VA Entitlement

PROMULGATED BY THE TEXAS REAL ESTATE COMMISSION (TREC)   12-05-11

ADDENDUM FOR
RELEASE OF LIABILITY ON ASSUMED LOAN
AND/OR RESTORATION OF SELLER'S VA ENTITLEMENT

TO CONTRACT CONCERNING THE PROPERTY AT

_____

(Address of Property)

❑ **A. RELEASE OF SELLER'S LIABILITY ON LOAN TO BE ASSUMED:**

Within _____ days after the effective date of this contract Seller and Buyer shall apply for release of Seller's liability from (a) any conventional lender, (b) VA and any lender whose loan has been guaranteed by VA, or (c) FHA and any lender whose loan has been insured by FHA. Seller and Buyer shall furnish all required information and documents. If any release of liability has not been approved by the Closing Date: (check one box only)

❑ (1) This contract will terminate and the earnest money will be refunded to Buyer.

❑ (2) Failure to obtain release approval will not delay closing.

❑ **B. RESTORATION OF SELLER'S ENTITLEMENT FOR VA LOAN:**

Within _____ days after the effective date of this contract Seller and Buyer shall apply for restoration of Seller's VA entitlement and shall furnish all information and documents required by VA. If restoration has not been approved by the Closing Date: (check one box only)

❑ (1) This contract will terminate and the earnest money will be refunded to Buyer.

❑ (2) Failure to obtain restoration approval will not delay closing.

NOTICE: VA will not restore Seller's VA entitlement unless Buyer: (a) is a veteran, (b) has sufficient unused VA entitlement and (c) is otherwise qualified. If Seller desires restoration of VA entitlement, paragraphs A and B should be used.

Seller shall pay the cost of securing the release and restoration.

Seller's deed will contain any loan assumption clause required by FHA, VA or any lender.

_____   _____
Buyer   Seller

_____   _____
Buyer   Seller

TREC No. 12-3

F I G U R E 10

Seller's Temporary Residential Lease

PROMULGATED BY THE TEXAS REAL ESTATE COMMISSION (TREC)   12-05-11
(NOTICE: For use only when SELLER occupies the property for no more than 90 days AFTER the closing)

SELLER'S TEMPORARY RESIDENTIAL LEASE

1. **PARTIES:** The parties to this Lease are_____
(Landlord) and _____(Tenant).

2. **LEASE:** Landlord leases to Tenant the Property described in the Contract between Landlord as Buyer and Tenant as Seller known as _____
_____(address).

3. **TERM:** The term of this Lease commences on the date the sale covered by the Contract is closed and funded and terminates _____, unless terminated earlier by reason of other provisions.

4. **RENTAL:** Tenant shall pay to Landlord as rental $_____ per day (excluding the day of closing and funding) with the full amount of rental for the term of the Lease to be paid at the time of funding of the sale. Tenant will not be entitled to a refund of rental if this Lease terminates early due to Tenant's default or voluntary surrender of the Property.

5. **DEPOSIT:** Tenant shall pay to Landlord at the time of funding of the sale $_____ as a deposit to secure performance of this Lease by Tenant. Landlord may use the deposit to satisfy Tenant's obligations under this Lease. Landlord shall refund any unused portion of the deposit to Tenant with an itemized list of all deductions from the deposit within 30 days after Tenant (a) surrenders possession of the Property and (b) provides Landlord written notice of Tenant's forwarding address.

6. **UTILITIES:** Tenant shall pay all utility charges except _____
which Landlord shall pay.

7. **USE OF PROPERTY:** Tenant may use the Property only for residential purposes. Tenant may not assign this Lease or sublet any part of the Property.

8. **PETS:** Tenant may not keep pets on the Property except _____.

9. **CONDITION OF PROPERTY:** Tenant accepts the Property in its present condition and state of repair at the commencement of the Lease. Upon termination, Tenant shall surrender the Property to Landlord in the condition required under the Contract, except normal wear and tear and any casualty loss.

10. **ALTERATIONS:** Tenant may not alter the Property or install improvements or fixtures without the prior written consent of the Landlord. Any improvements or fixtures placed on the Property during the Lease become the Property of Landlord.

11. **SPECIAL PROVISIONS:**

12. **INSPECTIONS:** Landlord may enter at reasonable times to inspect the Property. Tenant shall provide Landlord door keys and access codes to allow access to the Property during the term of Lease.

13. **LAWS:** Tenant shall comply with all applicable laws, restrictions, ordinances, rules and regulations with respect to the Property.

14. **REPAIRS AND MAINTENANCE:** Except as otherwise provided in this Lease, Tenant shall bear all expense of repairing and maintaining the Property, including but not limited to the yard, trees and shrubs, unless otherwise required by the Texas Property Code. Tenant shall promptly repair at Tenant's expense any damage to the Property caused directly or indirectly by any act or omission of the Tenant or any person other than the Landlord, Landlord's agents or invitees.

Initialed for identification by Landlord _____ and Tenant_____   TREC NO. 15-5

F I G U R E   10

Seller's Temporary Residential Lease (continued)

Seller's Temporary Residential Lease _____Page 2 of 2   12-05-11
(Address of Property)

15. **INDEMNITY:** Tenant indemnifies Landlord from the claims of all third parties for injury or damage to the person or property of such third party arising from the use or occupancy of the Property by Tenant. This indemnification includes attorney's fees, costs and expenses incurred by Landlord.

16. **INSURANCE:** Landlord and Tenant shall each maintain such insurance on the contents and Property as each party may deem appropriate during the term of this Lease. <u>NOTE</u>: CONSULT YOUR INSURANCE AGENT; POSSESSION OF THE PROPERTY BY SELLER AS TENANT MAY CHANGE INSURANCE POLICY COVERAGE.

17. **DEFAULT:** If Tenant fails to perform or observe any provision of this Lease and fails, within 24 hours after notice by Landlord, to commence and diligently pursue to remedy such failure, Tenant will be in default.

18. **TERMINATION:** This Lease terminates upon expiration of the term specified in Paragraph 3 or upon Tenant's default under this Lease.

19. **HOLDING OVER:** Tenant shall surrender possession of the Property upon termination of this Lease. Any possession by Tenant after termination creates a tenancy at sufferance and will not operate to renew or extend this Lease. Tenant shall pay $_____ per day during the period of any possession after termination as damages, in addition to any other remedies to which Landlord is entitled.

20. **ATTORNEY'S FEES:** The prevailing party in any legal proceeding brought under or with respect to this Lease is entitled to recover from the non-prevailing party all costs of such proceeding and reasonable attorney's fees.

21. **SMOKE ALARMS:** The Texas Property Code requires Landlord to install smoke alarms in certain locations within the Property at Landlord's expense. <u>Tenant expressly waives Landlord's duty to inspect and repair smoke alarms</u>.

22. **SECURITY DEVICES:** The requirements of the Texas Property Code relating to security devices do not apply to a residential lease for a term of 90 days or less.

23. **CONSULT YOUR ATTORNEY:** Real estate licensees cannot give legal advice. This Lease is intended to be legally binding. READ IT CAREFULLY. If you do not understand the effect of this Lease, consult your attorney BEFORE signing.

24. **NOTICES:** All notices from one party to the other must be in writing and are effective when mailed to, hand-delivered at, or transmitted by facsimile or electronic transmission as follows:

To Landlord: _____   **To Tenant:** _____

_____   _____

_____   _____

_____   _____

Telephone: (   ) _____   Telephone: (   ) _____

Facsimile: (   ) _____   Facsimile: (   ) _____

E-mail: _____   E-mail: _____

_____   _____
Landlord   Tenant

_____   _____
Landlord   Tenant

TREC NO. 15-5

FIGURE 11

Buyer's Temporary Residential Lease

PROMULGATED BY THE TEXAS REAL ESTATE COMMISSION (TREC) 12-05-11
(NOTICE: For use only when BUYER occupies the property for no more than 90 days PRIOR the closing)

BUYER'S TEMPORARY RESIDENTIAL LEASE

1. **PARTIES:** The parties to this Lease are_____
(Landlord) and _____(Tenant).

2. **LEASE:** Landlord leases to Tenant the Property described in the Contract between Landlord as Seller and Tenant as Buyer known as _____
_____(address).

3. **TERM:** The term of this Lease commences _____ and terminates as specified in Paragraph 18.

4. **RENTAL:** Rental will be $_____ per day. Upon commencement of this Lease, Tenant shall pay to Landlord the full amount of rental of $ _____ for the anticipated term of the Lease (commencement date to the Closing Date specified in Paragraph 9 of the Contract). If the actual term of this Lease differs from the anticipated term, any additional rent or reimbursement will be paid at closing. No portion of the rental will be applied to payment of any items covered by the Contract.

5. **DEPOSIT:** Tenant has paid to Landlord $_____ as a deposit to secure performance of this Lease by Tenant. If this Lease is terminated before the Closing Date, Landlord may use the deposit to satisfy Tenant's obligations under this Lease. Landlord shall refund to Tenant any unused portion of the deposit together with an itemized list of all deductions from the deposit within 30 days after Tenant (a) surrenders possession of the Property and (b) provides Landlord written notice of Tenant's forwarding address. If this Lease is terminated by the closing and funding of the sale of the Property, the deposit will be refunded to Tenant at closing and funding.
NOTICE: The deposit must be in addition to the earnest money under the Contract.

6. **UTILITIES:** Tenant shall pay all utility connections, deposits and charges except _____
_____, which Landlord shall pay.

7. **USE OF PROPERTY:** Tenant may use the Property only for residential purposes. Tenant may not assign this Lease or sublet any part of the Property.

8. **PETS:** Tenant may not keep pets on the Property except _____.

9. **CONDITION OF PROPERTY:** Tenant accepts the Property in its present condition and state of repair, but Landlord shall make all repairs and improvements required by the Contract. If this Lease is terminated prior to closing, Tenant shall surrender possession of the Property to Landlord in its present condition, as improved by Landlord, except normal wear and tear and any casualty loss.

10. **ALTERATIONS:** Tenant may not: (a) make any holes or drive nails into the woodwork, floors, walls or ceilings (b) alter, paint or decorate the Property or (c) install improvements or fixtures without the prior written consent of Landlord. Any improvements or fixtures placed on the Property during the Lease become a part of the Property.

11. **SPECIAL PROVISIONS:**

12. **INSPECTIONS:** Landlord may enter at reasonable times to inspect, replace, repair or complete the improvements. Tenant shall provide Landlord door keys and access codes to allow access to the Property during the term of the Lease.

13. **LAWS:** Tenant shall comply with all applicable laws, restrictions, ordinances, rules and regulations with respect to the Property.

14. **REPAIRS AND MAINTENANCE:** Except as otherwise provided in this Lease, Tenant shall bear all expense of repairing, replacing and maintaining the Property, including but not limited to the yard, trees, shrubs, and all equipment and appliances, unless otherwise required by the Texas Property Code. Tenant shall promptly repair at Tenant's expense any damage to the Property caused directly or indirectly by any act or omission of the Tenant or any person other than the Landlord, Landlord's agents or invitees.

Initialed for identification by Landlord _____ and Tenant_____   TREC NO. 16-5

FIGURE 11

Buyer's Temporary Residential Lease (continued)

Buyer's Temporary Residential Lease_____ Page 2 of 2 12-05-11
(Address of Property)

15.INDEMNITY: Tenant indemnifies Landlord from the claims of all third parties for injury or damage to the person or property of such third party arising from the use or occupancy of the Property by Tenant. This indemnification includes attorney's fees, costs and expenses incurred by Landlord.

16.INSURANCE: Landlord and Tenant shall each maintain such insurance on the contents and Property as each party may deem appropriate during the term of this Lease. <u>NOTE</u>: CONSULT YOUR INSURANCE AGENT; POSSESSION OF THE PROPERTY BY BUYER AS TENANT MAY CHANGE INSURANCE POLICY COVERAGE.

17.DEFAULT: If Tenant fails to perform or observe any provision of this Lease and fails, within 24 hours after notice by Landlord, to commence and diligently pursue to remedy such failure, Tenant will be in default.

18.TERMINATION: This Lease terminates upon (a) closing and funding of the sale under the Contract, (b) termination of the Contract prior to closing, (c) Tenant's default under this Lease, or (d) Tenant's default under the Contract, whichever occurs first. Upon termination other than by closing and funding of the sale, Tenant shall surrender possession of the property.

19.HOLDING OVER: Any possession by Tenant after termination creates a tenancy at sufferance and will not operate to renew or extend this Lease. Tenant shall pay $_____ per day during the period of any possession after termination as damages, in addition to any other remedies to which Landlord is entitled.

20.ATTORNEY'S FEES: The prevailing party in any legal proceeding brought under or with respect to this Lease is entitled to recover from the non-prevailing party all costs of such proceeding and reasonable attorney's fees.

21.SMOKE ALARMS: The Texas Property Code requires Landlord to install smoke alarms in certain locations within the Property at Landlord's expense. <u>Tenant expressly waives Landlord's duty to inspect and repair smoke alarms</u>.

22.SECURITY DEVICES: The requirements of the Texas Property Code relating to security devices do not apply to a residential lease for a term of 90 days or less.

23.CONSULT YOUR ATTORNEY: Real estate licensees cannot give legal advice. This Lease is intended to be legally binding. READ IT CAREFULLY. If you do not understand the effect of this Lease, consult your attorney BEFORE signing.

24.NOTICES: All notices from one party to the other must be in writing and are effective when mailed to, hand-delivered at, or transmitted by facsimile or electronic transmission as follows:

To Landlord: _____   **To Tenant:** _____

Telephone: (___)_____   Telephone: (___)_____
Facsimile: (___)_____   Facsimile: (___)_____
E-mail: _____   E-mail: _____

_____   _____
Landlord   Tenant

_____   _____
Landlord   Tenant

TREC NO. 16-5

FIGURE 12

Seller Financing Addendum

PROMULGATED BY THE TEXAS REAL ESTATE COMMISSION (TREC) 12-05-11

EQUAL HOUSING
OPPORTUNITY

SELLER FINANCING ADDENDUM
TO CONTRACT CONCERNING THE PROPERTY AT

_____
(Address of Property)

A. CREDIT DOCUMENTATION. To establish Buyer's creditworthiness, Buyer shall deliver to Seller within_____days after the effective date of this contract, ❏ credit report ❏ verification of employment, including salary ❏ verification of funds on deposit in financial institutions ❏ current financial statement and ❏ _____
_____. Buyer hereby authorizes any credit reporting agency to furnish copies of Buyer's credit reports to Seller at Buyer's sole expense.

B. CREDIT APPROVAL. If the credit documentation described in Paragraph A is not delivered within the specified time, Seller may terminate this contract by notice to Buyer within 7 days after expiration of the time for delivery, and the earnest money will be paid to Seller. If the credit documentation is timely delivered, and Seller determines in Seller's sole discretion that Buyer's credit is unacceptable, Seller may terminate this contract by notice to Buyer within 7 days after expiration of the time for delivery and the earnest money will be refunded to Buyer. If Seller does not terminate this contract, Seller will be deemed to have approved Buyer's creditworthiness.

C. PROMISSORY NOTE. The promissory note (Note) described in Paragraph 4 of this contract payable by Buyer to the order of Seller will bear interest at the rate of _____% per annum and be payable at the place designated by Seller. Buyer may prepay the Note in whole or in part at any time without penalty. Any prepayments are to be applied to the payment of the installments of principal last maturing and interest will immediately cease on the prepaid principal. The Note will contain a provision for payment of a late fee of 5% of any installment not paid within 10 days of the due date. Matured unpaid amounts will bear interest at the rate of 1½% per month or at the highest lawful rate, whichever is less. The Note will be payable as follows:

❏ (1) In one payment due _____ after the date of the Note with interest payable ❏ at maturity ❏ monthly ❏ quarterly. (check one box only)

❏ (2) In monthly installments of $ _____ ❏ including interest ❏plus interest (check one box only) beginning _____ after the date of the Note and continuing monthly thereafter for_____ months when the balance of the Note will be due and payable.

❏ (3) Interest only in monthly installments for the first _____ month(s) and thereafter in installments of $_____ ❏ including interest ❏ plus interest (check one box only) beginning _____ after the date of the Note and continuing monthly thereafter for _____ months when the balance of the Note will be due and payable.

D. DEED OF TRUST. The deed of trust securing the Note will provide for the following:

(1) PROPERTY TRANSFERS: (check one box only)

❏ (a) Consent Not Required: The Property may be sold, conveyed or leased without the consent of Seller, provided any subsequent buyer assumes the Note.

❏ (b) Consent Required: If all or any part of the Property is sold, conveyed, leased for a period longer than 3 years, leased with an option to purchase, or otherwise sold (including any contract for deed), without Seller's prior written consent, which consent may be withheld in Seller's sole discretion, Seller may declare the balance of the Note to be immediately due and payable. The creation of a subordinate lien, any conveyance

Initialed for identification by Buyer_____ and Seller_____   TREC NO. 26-6

FIGURE 12

Seller Financing Addendum (continued)

_____
(Address of Property)

under threat or order of condemnation, any deed solely between buyers, or the passage of title by reason of the death of a buyer or by operation of law will not entitle Seller to exercise the remedies provided in this paragraph.

NOTE: *Under (a) or (b), Buyer's liability to pay the Note will continue unless Buyer obtains a release of liability from Seller.*

(2) TAX AND INSURANCE ESCROW: (check one box only)

☐ (a) Escrow Not Required: Buyer shall furnish Seller, before each year's ad valorem taxes become delinquent, evidence that all ad valorem taxes on the Property have been paid. Buyer shall annually furnish Seller evidence of paid-up casualty insurance naming Seller as a mortgagee loss payee.

☐ (b) Escrow Required: With each installment Buyer shall deposit in escrow with Seller a pro rata part of the estimated annual ad valorem taxes and casualty insurance premiums for the Property. Buyer shall pay any deficiency within 30 days after notice from Seller. Buyer's failure to pay the deficiency will be a default under the deed of trust. Buyer is not required to deposit any escrow payments for taxes and insurance that are deposited with a superior lienholder. The casualty insurance must name Seller as a mortgagee loss payee.

(3) PRIOR LIENS: Any default under any lien superior to the lien securing the Note will be a default under the deed of trust securing the Note.

_____   _____
Buyer   Seller

_____   _____
Buyer   Seller

TREC NO. 26-6

F I G U R E   13

Environmental Assessment, Threatened or Endangered Species, and Wetlands Addendum

PROMULGATED BY THE TEXAS REAL ESTATE COMMISSION (TREC)   12-05-11

EQUAL HOUSING OPPORTUNITY

ENVIRONMENTAL ASSESSMENT, THREATENED OR ENDANGERED SPECIES, AND WETLANDS ADDENDUM

TO CONTRACT CONCERNING THE PROPERTY AT

_____
(Address of Property)

❑ A. ENVIRONMENTAL ASSESSMENT: Buyer, at Buyer's expense, may obtain an environmental assessment report prepared by an environmental specialist.

❑ B. THREATENED OR ENDANGERED SPECIES: Buyer, at Buyer's expense, may obtain a report from a natural resources professional to determine if there are any threatened or endangered species or their habitats as defined by the Texas Parks and Wildlife Department or the U.S. Fish and Wildlife Service.

❑ C. WETLANDS: Buyer, at Buyer's expense, may obtain a report from an environmental specialist to determine if there are wetlands, as defined by federal or state law or regulation.

Within _____ days after the effective date of the contract, Buyer may terminate the contract by furnishing Seller a copy of any report noted above that adversely affects the use of the Property and a notice of termination of the contract. Upon termination, the earnest money will be refunded to Buyer.

_____   _____
Buyer   Seller

_____   _____
Buyer   Seller

This form has been approved by the Texas Real Estate Commission for use with similarly approved or promulgated contract forms. Such approval relates to this form only. TREC forms are intended for use only by trained real estate licensees. No representation is made as to the legal validity or adequacy of any provision in any specific transactions. It is not suitable for complex transactions. Texas Real Estate Commission, P.O. Box 12188, Austin, TX 78711-2188, 512-936-3000 (http://www.trec.texas.gov) TREC No. 28-2. This form replaces TREC No. 28-1.

TREC No. 28-2

FIGURE 14

Addendum for Coastal Area Property

PROMULGATED BY THE TEXAS REAL ESTATE COMMISSION (TREC)   12-05-11

ADDENDUM FOR
COASTAL AREA PROPERTY
(SECTION 33.135, TEXAS NATURAL RESOURCES CODE)

TO CONTRACT CONCERNING THE PROPERTY AT

_____

(Address of Property)

NOTICE REGARDING COASTAL AREA PROPERTY

1. The real property described in and subject to this contract adjoins and shares a common boundary with the tidally influenced submerged lands of the state. The boundary is subject to change and can be determined accurately only by a survey on the ground made by a licensed state land surveyor in accordance with the original grant from the sovereign. The owner of the property described in this contract may gain or lose portions of the tract because of changes in the boundary.

2. The seller, transferor, or grantor has no knowledge of any prior fill as it relates to the property described in and subject to this contract except:_____ _____ _____.

3. State law prohibits the use, encumbrance, construction, or placing of any structure in, on, or over state-owned submerged lands below the applicable tide line, without proper permission.

4. The purchaser or grantee is hereby advised to seek the advice of an attorney or other qualified person as to the legal nature and effect of the facts set forth in this notice on the property described in and subject to this contract. Information regarding the location of the applicable tide line as to the property described in and subject to this contract may be obtained from the surveying division of the General Land Office in Austin.

_____   _____
Buyer   Seller

_____   _____
Buyer   Seller

TREC No. 33-2

FIGURE 15

Addendum for Property Located Seaward of the Gulf Intracoastal Waterway

PROMULGATED BY THE TEXAS REAL ESTATE COMMISSION (TREC) 12-05-11

EQUAL HOUSING
OPPORTUNITY

ADDENDUM FOR
PROPERTY LOCATED SEAWARD OF THE
GULF INTRACOASTAL WATERWAY
(SECTION 61.025, TEXAS NATURAL RESOURCES CODE)

TO CONTRACT CONCERNING THE PROPERTY AT

_____

(Address of Property)

**DISCLOSURE NOTICE CONCERNING LEGAL AND ECONOMIC RISKS OF PURCHASING
COASTAL REAL PROPERTY NEAR A BEACH**

WARNING: THE FOLLOWING NOTICE OF POTENTIAL RISKS OF ECONOMIC LOSS TO YOU AS THE
PURCHASER OF COASTAL REAL PROPERTY IS REQUIRED BY STATE LAW.

- READ THIS NOTICE CAREFULLY. DO NOT SIGN THIS CONTRACT UNTIL YOU FULLY UNDERSTAND
THE RISKS YOU ARE ASSUMING.

- BY PURCHASING THIS PROPERTY, YOU MAY BE ASSUMING ECONOMIC RISKS OVER AND ABOVE THE
RISKS INVOLVED IN PURCHASING INLAND REAL PROPERTY.

- IF YOU OWN A STRUCTURE LOCATED ON COASTAL REAL PROPERTY NEAR A GULF COAST BEACH, IT
MAY COME TO BE LOCATED ON THE PUBLIC BEACH BECAUSE OF COASTAL EROSION AND STORM
EVENTS.

- AS THE OWNER OF A STRUCTURE LOCATED ON THE PUBLIC BEACH, YOU COULD BE SUED BY THE
STATE OF TEXAS AND ORDERED TO REMOVE THE STRUCTURE.

- THE COSTS OF REMOVING A STRUCTURE FROM THE PUBLIC BEACH AND ANY OTHER ECONOMIC
LOSS INCURRED BECAUSE OF A REMOVAL ORDER WOULD BE SOLELY YOUR RESPONSIBILITY.

The real property described in this contract is located seaward of the Gulf Intracoastal Waterway to its
southernmost point and then seaward of the longitudinal line also known as 97 degrees, 12', 19" which
runs southerly to the international boundary from the intersection of the centerline of the Gulf
Intracoastal Waterway and the Brownsville Ship Channel. If the property is in close proximity to a beach
fronting the Gulf of Mexico, the purchaser is hereby advised that the public has acquired a right of use or
easement to or over the area of any public beach by prescription, dedication, or presumption, or has
retained a right by virtue of continuous right in the public since time immemorial, as recognized in law
and custom.

The extreme seaward boundary of natural vegetation that spreads continuously inland customarily
marks the landward boundary of the public easement. If there is no clearly marked natural vegetation
line, the landward boundary of the easement is as provided by Sections 61.016 and 61.017, Natural
Resources Code.

Much of the Gulf of Mexico coastline is eroding at rates of more than five feet per year. Erosion rates for
all Texas Gulf property subject to the open beaches act are available from the Texas General Land
Office.

State law prohibits any obstruction, barrier, restraint, or interference with the use of the public
easement, including the placement of structures seaward of the landward boundary of the easement.
OWNERS OF STRUCTURES ERECTED SEAWARD OF THE VEGETATION LINE (OR OTHER APPLICABLE
EASEMENT BOUNDARY) OR THAT BECOME SEAWARD OF THE VEGETATION LINE AS A RESULT OF
PROCESSES SUCH AS SHORELINE EROSION ARE SUBJECT TO A LAWSUIT BY THE STATE OF TEXAS TO
REMOVE THE STRUCTURES.

The purchaser is hereby notified that the purchaser should: (1) determine the rate of shoreline erosion
in the vicinity of the real property; and (2) seek the advice of an attorney or other qualified person
before executing this contract or instrument of conveyance as to the relevance of these statutes and
facts to the value of the property the purchaser is hereby purchasing or contracting to purchase.

_____   _____
Buyer   Seller

_____   _____
Buyer   Seller

This form has been approved by the Texas Real Estate Commission for use with similarly approved or promulgated contract forms. Such approval
relates to this form only. TREC forms are intended for use only by trained real estate licensees. No representation is made as to the legal validity
or adequacy of any provision in any specific transactions. It is not suitable for complex transactions. Texas Real Estate Commission, P.O. Box
12188, Austin, TX 78711-2188, 512-936-3000 (http://www.trec.texas.gov) TREC No. 34-4. This form replaces TREC No. 34-3.

TREC No. 34-4

F I G U R E   16

Addendum for Property Subject to Mandatory Membership in an Owners' Association

PROMULGATED BY THE TEXAS REAL ESTATE COMMISSION (TREC)   08-18-2014

ADDENDUM FOR PROPERTY SUBJECT TO MANDATORY MEMBERSHIP IN A PROPERTY OWNERS ASSOCIATION
(NOT FOR USE WITH CONDOMINIUMS)
ADDENDUM TO CONTRACT CONCERNING THE PROPERTY AT

_____

(Street Address and City)

_____

(Name of Property Owners Association, (Association) and Phone Number)

A. SUBDIVISION INFORMATION: "Subdivision Information" means: (i) a current copy of the restrictions applying to the subdivision and bylaws and rules of the Association, and (ii) a resale certificate, all of which are described by Section 207.003 of the Texas Property Code.

(Check only one box):

❏ 1. Within _____ days after the effective date of the contract, Seller shall obtain, pay for, and deliver the Subdivision Information to the Buyer. If Seller delivers the Subdivision Information, Buyer may terminate the contract within 3 days after Buyer receives the Subdivision Information or prior to closing, whichever occurs first, and the earnest money will be refunded to Buyer. If Buyer does not receive the Subdivision Information, Buyer, as Buyer's sole remedy, may terminate the contract at any time prior to closing and the earnest money will be refunded to Buyer.

❏ 2. Within _____ days after the effective date of the contract, Buyer shall obtain, pay for, and deliver a copy of the Subdivision Information to the Seller.   If Buyer obtains the Subdivision Information within the time required, Buyer may terminate the contract within 3 days after Buyer receives the Subdivision Information or prior to closing, whichever occurs first, and the earnest money will be refunded to Buyer.   If Buyer, due to factors beyond Buyer's control, is not able to obtain the Subdivision Information within the time required, Buyer may, as Buyer's sole remedy, terminate the contract within 3 days after the time required or prior to closing, whichever occurs first, and the earnest money will be refunded to Buyer.

❏ 3. Buyer has received and approved the Subdivision Information before signing the contract. Buyer ❏ does ❏ does not require an updated resale certificate. If Buyer requires an updated resale certificate, Seller, at Buyer's expense, shall deliver it to Buyer within 10 days after receiving payment for the updated resale certificate from Buyer. Buyer may terminate this contract and the earnest money will be refunded to Buyer if Seller fails to deliver the updated resale certificate within the time required.

❏ 4. Buyer does not require delivery of the Subdivision Information.

The title company or its agent is authorized to act on behalf of the parties to obtain the Subdivision Information ONLY upon receipt of the required fee for the Subdivision Information from the party obligated to pay.

B. MATERIAL CHANGES. If Seller becomes aware of any material changes in the Subdivision Information, Seller shall promptly give notice to Buyer. Buyer may terminate the contract prior to closing by giving written notice to Seller if: (i) any of the Subdivision Information provided was not true; or (ii) any material adverse change in the Subdivision Information occurs prior to closing, and the earnest money will be refunded to Buyer.

C FEES: Except as provided by Paragraphs A, D and E, Buyer shall pay any and all Association fees or other charges associated with the transfer of the Property not to exceed $_____ and Seller shall pay any excess.

D. DEPOSITS FOR RESERVES: Buyer shall pay any deposits for reserves required at closing by the Association.

E. AUTHORIZATION: Seller authorizes the Association to release and provide the Subdivision Information and any updated resale certificate if requested by the Buyer, the Title Company, or any broker to this sale. If Buyer does not require the Subdivision Information or an updated resale certificate, and the Title Company requires information from the Association (such as the status of dues, special assessments, violations of covenants and restrictions, and a waiver of any right of first refusal), ❏ Buyer ❏ Seller shall pay the Title Company the cost of obtaining the information prior to the Title Company ordering the information.

NOTICE TO BUYER REGARDING REPAIRS BY THE ASSOCIATION: The Association may have the sole responsibility to make certain repairs to the Property. If you are concerned about the condition of any part of the Property which the Association is required to repair, you should not sign the contract unless you are satisfied that the Association will make the desired repairs.

_____   _____
Buyer   Seller

_____   _____
Buyer   Seller

TREC NO. 36-8

FIGURE 17

Third Party Financing Addendum for Credit Approval

2-10-2014

PROMULGATED BY THE TEXAS REAL ESTATE COMMISSION (TREC)

THIRD PARTY FINANCING ADDENDUM FOR CREDIT APPROVAL
(Not for use with Reverse Mortgage Financing)

TO CONTRACT CONCERNING THE PROPERTY AT

_____

(Street Address and City)

Buyer shall apply promptly for all financing described below and make every reasonable effort to obtain credit approval for the financing (Credit Approval). Buyer shall furnish all information and documents required by lender for Credit Approval. Credit Approval will be deemed to have been obtained when (1) the terms of the loan(s) described below are available and (2) lender determines that Buyer has satisfied all of lender's requirements related to Buyer's assets, income and credit history. If Buyer cannot obtain Credit Approval, Buyer may give written notice to Seller within _____ days after the effective date of this contract and this contract will terminate and the earnest money will be refunded to Buyer. **If Buyer does not give such notice within the time required, this contract will no longer be subject to Credit Approval. Time is of the essence for this paragraph and strict compliance with the time for performance is required.**

NOTE: Credit Approval does not include approval of lender's underwriting requirements for the Property, as specified in Paragraph 4.A.(1) of the contract.

Each note must be secured by vendor's and deed of trust liens.

CHECK APPLICABLE BOXES:

❏ A. CONVENTIONAL FINANCING:

❏ (1) A first mortgage loan in the principal amount of $ _____ (excluding any financed PMI premium), due in full in _____ year(s), with interest not to exceed _____% per annum for the first _____year(s) of the loan with Adjusted Origination Charges as shown on Buyer's Good Faith Estimate for the loan not to exceed _____% of the loan.

❏ (2) A second mortgage loan in the principal amount of $_____(excluding any financed PMI premium), due in full in _____year(s), with interest not to exceed _____% per annum for the first _____year(s) of the loan with Adjusted Origination Charges as shown on Buyer's Good Faith Estimate for the loan not to exceed _____ % of the loan.

❏ B. TEXAS VETERANS LOAN: A loan(s) from the Texas Veterans Land Board of $_____ for a period in the total amount of _____years at the interest rate established by the Texas Veterans Land Board.

❏C. FHA INSURED FINANCING: A Section _____ FHA insured loan of not less than $_____ (excluding any financed MIP), amortizable monthly for not less than _____years, with interest not to exceed _____% per annum for the first _____year(s) of the loan with Adjusted Origination Charges as shown on Buyer's Good Faith Estimate for the loan not to exceed _____ % of the loan. As required by HUD-FHA, if FHA valuation is unknown, "*It is expressly agreed that, notwithstanding any other provision of this contract, the purchaser (Buyer) shall not be obligated to complete the purchase of the Property described herein or to incur any penalty by forfeiture of earnest money deposits or otherwise unless the purchaser (Buyer) has been given in accordance with HUD/FHA or VA requirements a written statement issued by the Federal Housing Commissioner, Department of Veterans Affairs, or a Direct Endorsement Lender setting forth the appraised value of the Property of not less than $_____. The purchaser (Buyer) shall have the privilege and option of proceeding with consummation of the contract without regard to the amount of the appraised valuation. The appraised valuation is arrived at to determine the*

Initialed for identification by Buyer_____ _____ and Seller_____ _____   TREC NO. 40-6

FIGURE 17

Third Party Financing Addendum for Credit Approval (continued)

Third Party Financing Condition Addendum Concerning   Page 2 of 2   2-10-2014

_____
(Address of Property)

maximum mortgage the Department of Housing and Urban Development will insure. HUD does not warrant the value or the condition of the Property. The purchaser (Buyer) should satisfy himself/herself that the price and the condition of the Property are acceptable."

❏ D. VA GUARANTEED FINANCING: A VA guaranteed loan of not less than $_____
(excluding any financed Funding Fee), amortizable monthly for not less than_____years, with interest not to exceed_____% per annum for the first _____year(s) of the loan with Adjusted Origination Charges as shown on Buyer's Good Faith Estimate for the loan not to exceed _____% of the loan.

VA NOTICE TO BUYER: *"It is expressly agreed that, notwithstanding any other provisions of this contract, the Buyer shall not incur any penalty by forfeiture of earnest money or otherwise or be obligated to complete the purchase of the Property described herein, if the contract purchase price or cost exceeds the reasonable value of the Property established by the Department of Veterans Affairs. The Buyer shall, however, have the privilege and option of proceeding with the consummation of this contract without regard to the amount of the reasonable value established by the Department of Veterans Affairs."*

If Buyer elects to complete the purchase at an amount in excess of the reasonable value established by VA, Buyer shall pay such excess amount in cash from a source which Buyer agrees to disclose to the VA and which Buyer represents will not be from borrowed funds except as approved by VA. If VA reasonable value of the Property is less than the Sales Price, Seller may reduce the Sales Price to an amount equal to the VA reasonable value and the sale will be closed at the lower Sales Price with proportionate adjustments to the down payment and the loan amount.

❏ E.USDA GUARANTEED FINANCING: A USDA-guaranteed loan of not less than $_____
(excluding any financed Funding Fee), amortizable monthly for not less than_____years, with interest not to exceed ____% per annum for the first ____year(s) of the loan with Adjusted Origination Charges as shown on Buyer's Good Faith Estimate for the loan not to exceed _____% of the loan.

Buyer hereby authorizes any lender to furnish to the Seller or Buyer or their representatives information relating only to the status of Credit Approval of Buyer.

_____   _____
Buyer   Seller

_____   _____
Buyer   Seller

TREC NO. 40-6

FIGURE 18

Loan Assumption Addendum

EQUAL HOUSING
OPPORTUNITY

PROMULGATED BY THE TEXAS REAL ESTATE COMMISSION (TREC)   12-05-11

LOAN ASSUMPTION ADDENDUM
TO CONTRACT CONCERNING THE PROPERTY AT

_____
(Address of Property)

A. CREDIT DOCUMENTATION. To establish Buyer's creditworthiness, Buyer shall deliver to Seller within_____days after the effective date of this contract ❑ credit report ❑ verification of employment, including salary ❑ verification of funds on deposit in financial institutions ❑ current financial statement and ❑_____
_____.
Buyer hereby authorizes any credit reporting agency to furnish copies of Buyer's credit reports to Seller at Buyer's sole expense.

B. CREDIT APPROVAL. If the credit documentation described in Paragraph A is not delivered within the specified time, Seller may terminate this contract by notice to Buyer within 7 days after expiration of the time for delivery, and the earnest money will be paid to Seller. If the credit documentation is timely delivered, and Seller determines in Seller's sole discretion that Buyer's credit is unacceptable, Seller may terminate this contract by notice to Buyer within 7 days after expiration of the time for delivery and the earnest money will be refunded to Buyer. If Seller does not terminate this contract within the time specified, Seller will be deemed to have approved Buyer's creditworthiness.

C. ASSUMPTION. Buyer's assumption of an existing note includes all obligations imposed by the deed of trust securing the note.
❑ (1) The unpaid principal balance of a first lien promissory note payable to_____
_____which unpaid balance at closing will be $ _____.
The total current monthly payment including principal, interest and any reserve deposits is $ _____. Buyer's initial payment will be the first payment due after closing.

❑ (2) The unpaid principal balance of a second lien promissory note payable to _____
_____which unpaid balance at closing will be $ _____.
The total current monthly payment including principal, interest and any reserve deposits is $ _____. Buyer's initial payment will be the first payment due after closing.

If the unpaid principal balance of any assumed loan as of the Closing Date varies from the loan balance stated above, the ❑ cash payable at closing ❑ Sales Price will be adjusted by the amount of any variance. If the total principal balance of all assumed loans varies in an amount greater than $500 at closing, either party may terminate this contract and the earnest money will be refunded to Buyer unless the other party elects to pay the excess of the variance.

D. LOAN ASSUMPTION TERMS. Buyer may terminate this contract and the earnest money will be refunded to Buyer if the noteholder requires:
(1) payment of an assumption fee in excess of $ _____in C(1) or $ _____in C(2) and Seller declines to pay such excess, or
(2) an increase in the interest rate to more than _____% in C(1) or_____% in C(2), or
(3) any other modification of the loan documents.

E. CONSENT BY NOTEHOLDER. If the noteholder fails to consent to the assumption of the loan, either Seller or Buyer may terminate this contract by notice to the other party and the earnest money will be refunded to the Buyer.

F. SELLER'S LIENS. Unless Seller is released from liability on any assumed note, a vendor's lien and deed of trust to secure assumption will be required. The vendor's lien will automatically be released on delivery of an executed release by noteholder.

Initialed for identification by Buyer_____ and Seller_____   TREC NO. 41-2

FIGURE 18

Loan Assumption Addendum (continued)

Loan Assumption Addendum Concerning   Page 2 of 2   10-10-11

_____
(Address of Property)

G. TAX AND INSURANCE ESCROW. If noteholder maintains an escrow account for ad valorem taxes, casualty insurance premiums or mortgage insurance premiums, Seller shall transfer the escrow account to Buyer without any deficiency. Buyer shall reimburse Seller for the amount in the transferred accounts.

NOTICE TO BUYER: If you are concerned about the possibility of future adjustments, monthly payments, interest rates or other terms, do not sign the contract without examining the notes and deeds of trust.

NOTICE TO SELLER: Your liability to pay the notes assumed by Buyer will continue unless you obtain a release of liability from the noteholders. If you are concerned about future liability, you should use the TREC Release of Liability Addendum.

_____   _____
Buyer   Seller

_____   _____
Buyer   Seller

FIGURE 19

Addendum for Reservation of Oil, Gas and Other Minerals

PROMULGATED BY THE TEXAS REAL ESTATE COMMISSION (TREC)   12-05-11

ADDENDUM FOR RESERVATION OF OIL, GAS, AND OTHER MINERALS

ADDENDUM TO CONTRACT CONCERNING THE PROPERTY AT

_____

(Street Address and City)

_____

NOTICE: For use only if Seller reserves all or a portion of the Mineral Estate.

A. "Mineral Estate" means all oil, gas, and other minerals in or under the Property, any royalty under any existing or future lease covering any part of the Property, surface rights (including rights of ingress and egress), production and drilling rights, lease payments, and all related benefits.

B. The Mineral Estate owned by Seller, if any, will be conveyed unless reserved as follows (check one box only):

❑ (1) Seller reserves all of the Mineral Estate owned by Seller.

❑ (2) Seller reserves an undivided _____ % interest in the Mineral Estate owned by Seller. *NOTE: If Seller does not own all of the Mineral Estate, Seller reserves only this percentage of Seller's interest.*

C. Seller ❑ waives ❑ does not waive Seller's surface rights (including rights of ingress and egress). *NOTE: Any waiver of surface rights by Seller does not affect any surface rights that may be held by others.*

D. If B(2) applies, Seller shall, on or before the Closing Date, provide Buyer contact information known to Seller for any existing lessee.

If either party is concerned about the legal rights or impact of the above provisions, that party is advised to consult an attorney BEFORE signing.

TREC rules prohibit real estate licensees from giving legal advice.

_____   _____
Buyer   Seller

_____   _____
Buyer   Seller

The form of this addendum has been approved by the Texas Real Estate Commission for use only with similarly approved or promulgated forms of contracts. Such approval relates to this contract form only. TREC forms are intended for use only by trained real estate licensees. No representation is made as to the legal validity or adequacy of any provision in any specific transactions. It is not intended for complex transactions. Texas Real Estate Commission, P.O. Box 12188, Austin, TX 78711-2188, 512-936-3000 (http://www.trec.texas.gov) TREC No. 44-1. This form replaces TREC No. 44-0.

TREC NO. 44-1

FIGURE 20

Short Sale Addendum

PROMULGATED BY THE TEXAS REAL ESTATE COMMISSION (TREC)   12-05-11

SHORT SALE ADDENDUM

ADDENDUM TO CONTRACT CONCERNING THE PROPERTY AT

_____

(Street Address and City)

A. This contract involves a "short sale" of the Property. As used in this Addendum, "short sale" means that:

(1) Seller's net proceeds at closing will be insufficient to pay the balance of Seller's mortgage loan; and

(2) Seller requires:
(a) the consent of the lienholder to sell the Property pursuant to this contract; and
(b) the lienholder's agreement to:
(i) accept Seller's net proceeds in full satisfaction of Seller's liability under the mortgage loan; and
(ii) provide Seller an executed release of lien against the Property in a recordable format.

B. As used in this Addendum, "Seller's net proceeds" means the Sales Price less Seller's Expenses under Paragraph 12 of the contract and Seller's obligation to pay any brokerage fees.

C. The contract to which this Addendum is attached is binding upon execution by the parties and the earnest money and the Option Fee must be paid as provided in the contract. The contract is contingent on the satisfaction of Seller's requirements under Paragraph A(2) of this Addendum (Lienholder's Consent and Agreement). Seller shall apply promptly for and make every reasonable effort to obtain Lienholder's Consent and Agreement, and shall furnish all information and documents required by the lienholder. Except as provided by this Addendum, neither party is required to perform under the contract while it is contingent upon obtaining Lienholder's Consent and Agreement.

D. If Seller does not notify Buyer that Seller has obtained Lienholder's Consent and Agreement on or before _____, this contract terminates and the earnest money will be refunded to Buyer. Seller must notify Buyer immediately if Lienholder's Consent and Agreement is obtained. For purposes of performance, the effective date of the contract changes to the date Seller provides Buyer notice of the Lienholder's Consent and Agreement (Amended Effective Date).

E. This contract will terminate and the earnest money will be refunded to Buyer if the Lienholder refuses or withdraws its Consent and Agreement prior to closing and funding. Seller shall promptly notify Buyer of any lienholder's refusal to provide or withdrawal of a Lienholder's Consent and Agreement.

F. If Buyer has the unrestricted right to terminate this contract, the time for giving notice of termination begins on the effective date of the contract, continues after the Amended Effective Date and ends upon the expiration of Buyer's unrestricted right to terminate the contract under Paragraph 23.

G. For the purposes of this Addendum, time is of the essence. Strict compliance with the times for performance stated in this Addendum is required.

H. Seller authorizes any lienholder to furnish to Buyer or Buyer's representatives information relating to the status of the request for a Lienholder's Consent and Agreement.

I. If there is more than one lienholder or loan secured by the Property, this Addendum applies to each lienholder.

_____   _____
Buyer   Seller

_____   _____
Buyer   Seller

TREC NO. 45-1

FIGURE 21

Addendum for Property in a Propane Gas System Service Area

PROMULGATED BY THE TEXAS REAL ESTATE COMMISSION (TREC)   2-10-2014

EQUAL HOUSING OPPORTUNITY

ADDENDUM FOR PROPERTY IN A PROPANE GAS SYSTEM SERVICE AREA
(Section 141.010, Utilities Code)

CONCERNING THE PROPERTY AT _____
(Street Address and City)

NOTICE

The above referenced real property that you are about to purchase may be located in a propane gas system service area, which is authorized by law to provide propane gas service to the properties in the area pursuant to Chapter 141, Utilities Code. If your property is located in a propane gas system service area, there may be special costs or charges that you will be required to pay before you can receive propane gas service. There may be a period required to construct lines or other facilities necessary to provide propane gas service to your property. You are advised to determine if the property is in a propane gas system service area and contact the distribution system retailer to determine the cost that you will be required to pay and the period, if any, that is required to provide propane gas service to your property.

Buyer hereby acknowledges receipt of this notice at or before execution of a binding contract for the purchase of the above referenced real property or at the closing of the real property.

Section 141.010(a), Utilities Code, requires this notice to include a copy of the notice the distribution system retailer is required to record in the real property records. A copy of the recorded notice is attached.

NOTE: Seller can obtain a copy of the required recorded notice from the county clerk's office where the property is located or from the distribution system retailer.

_____   _____   _____   _____
Buyer   Date   Seller   Date

_____   _____   _____   _____
Buyer   Date   Seller   Date

TREC NO. 47-0

Promulgated
Amendment

FIGURE 22

Amendment to Contract

PROMULGATED BY THE TEXAS REAL ESTATE COMMISSION (TREC) 12-05-11

AMENDMENT
TO CONTRACT CONCERNING THE PROPERTY AT

_____
(Street Address and City)

Seller and Buyer amend the contract as follows: (check each applicable box)

☐(1) The Sales Price in Paragraph 3 of the contract is:
   A. Cash portion of Sales Price payable by Buyer at closing .... $_____
   B. Sum of financing described in the contract... $_____
   C. Sales Price (Sum of A and B) .... $_____

☐(2) In addition to any repairs and treatments otherwise required by the contract, Seller, at Seller's expense, shall complete the following repairs and treatments:

☐(3) The date in Paragraph 9 of the contract is changed to _____, 20_____.

☐(4) The amount in Paragraph 12A(1)(b) of the contract is changed to $ _____.

☐(5) The cost of lender required repairs and treatment, as itemized on the attached list, will be paid as follows: $ _____ by Seller; $ _____ by Buyer.

☐(6) Buyer has paid Seller an additional Option Fee of $ _____ for an extension of the unrestricted right to terminate the contract on or before _____ , 20_____. This additional Option Fee ☐ will ☐ will not be credited to the Sales Price.

☐(7) Buyer waives the unrestricted right to terminate the contract for which the Option Fee was paid.

☐(8) The date for Buyer to give written notice to Seller that Buyer cannot obtain Credit Approval as set forth in the Third Party Financing Condition Addendum for Credit Approval is changed to _____, 20_____.

☐(9) **Other Modifications**: (Insert only factual statements and business details applicable to this sale.)

EXECUTED the _____**day of** _____, 20_____ . **(BROKER: FILL IN THE DATE OF FINAL ACCEPTANCE.)**

_____   _____
Buyer   Seller

_____   _____
Buyer   Seller

This form has been approved by the Texas Real Estate Commission for use with similarly approved or promulgated contract forms. Such approval relates to this form only. TREC forms are intended for use only by trained real estate licensees. No representation is made as to the legal validity or adequacy of any provision in any specific transactions. It is not intended for complex transactions. Texas Real Estate Commission, P.O. Box 12188, Austin, TX 78711-2188, 512-936-3000 (http://www.trec.texas.gov) TREC No. 39-7. This form replaces TREC No. 39-6..

TREC NO. 39-7

Promulgated
Resale Certificates

FIGURE 23

Condominium Resale Certificate

PROMULGATED BY THE TEXAS REAL ESTATE COMMISSION (TREC)   12-05-11

CONDOMINIUM RESALE CERTIFICATE
(Section 82.157, Texas Property Code)

Condominium Certificate concerning Condominium Unit _____, in Building _____, of _____
_____,a condominium project, located at _____
_____(Address), City of _____,
County of _____, Texas, on behalf of the condominium owners' association
(the Association) by the Association's governing body (the Board).

A. The Declaration ☐does ☐does not contain a right of first refusal or other restraint that restricts the right to transfer the Unit. If a right of first refusal or other restraint exists, see Section _____of the Declaration.

B. The periodic common expense assessment for the Unit is $_____ per _____.

C. There ☐ is ☐is not a common expense or special assessment due and unpaid by the Seller to the Association. The total unpaid amount is $_____ and is for _____.

D. Other amounts ☐are ☐are not payable by Seller to the Association. The total unpaid amount is $_____and is for _____.

E. Capital expenditures approved by the Association for the next 12 months are $_____.

F. Reserves for capital expenditures are $_____;of this amount $_____ has been designated for_____.

G. The current operating budget of the Association is attached.

H. The amount of unsatisfied judgments against the Association is $ _____.

I. There ☐are ☐are not any suits pending against the Association. The nature of the suits is _____.

J. The Association ☐does ☐does not provide insurance coverage for the benefit of unit owners as per the attached summary from the Association's insurance agent.

K. The Board ☐has ☐has no knowledge of alterations or improvements to the Unit or to the limited common elements assigned to the Unit or any portion of the project that violate any provision of the Declaration, by-laws or rules of the Association. Known violations are:_____ _____.

L. The Board ☐has ☐has not received notice from a governmental authority concerning violations of health or building codes with respect to the Unit, the limited common elements assigned to the Unit, or any other portion of the condominium project. Notices received are: _____ _____.

M. The remaining term of any leasehold estate that affects the condominium is _____ and the provisions governing an extension or a renewal of the lease are: _____ _____ _____.

N. The Association's managing agent is _____
(Name of Agent)

_____
(Mailing Address)

_____   _____
(Telephone Number)   (Fax Number)

_____
E-mail Address

TREC NO. 32-3

FIGURE 23

Condominium Resale Certificate (continued)

_____
(Address of Property)

O. Association fees resulting from the transfer of the unit described above $ _____.

P. Required contribution, if any, to the capital reserves account $ _____.

REQUIRED ATTACHMENTS:

1. Operating Budget
2. Insurance Summary

NOTICE: The Certificate must be prepared no more than three months before the date it is delivered to Buyer.

_____
Name of Association

By: _____

Name: _____

Title: _____

Date:_____

Mailing Address: _____

E-mail: _____

FIGURE 24

Subdivision Information, Including Resale Certificate for Property Subject to Membership in a Property Owners' Association

PROMULGATED BY THE TEXAS REAL ESTATE COMMISSION (TREC)   2-10-2014

EQUAL HOUSING
OPPORTUNITY

SUBDIVISION INFORMATION, INCLUDING
RESALE CERTIFICATE FOR PROPERTY SUBJECT TO
MANDATORY MEMBERSHIP IN A PROPERTY OWNERS' ASSOCIATION
(Chapter 207, Texas Property Code)

Resale Certificate concerning the Property (including any common areas assigned to the Property) located at _____ (Street Address), City of _____, County of _____, Texas, prepared by the property owners' association (Association).

A. The Property ❏is ❏ is not subject to a right of first refusal (other than a right of first refusal prohibited by statute) or other restraint contained in the restrictions or restrictive covenants that restricts the owner's right to transfer the owner's property.

B. The current regular assessment for the Property is $_____ per _____.

C. A special assessment for the Property due after this resale certificate is delivered is $_____ payable as follows_____ for the following purpose:_____.

D. The total of all amounts due and unpaid to the Association that are attributable to the Property is $ _____ .

E. The capital expenditures approved by the Association for its current fiscal year are $ _____.

F. The amount of reserves for capital expenditures is $_____.

G. Unsatisfied judgments against the Association total $_____.

H. Other than lawsuits relating to unpaid ad valorem taxes of an individual member of the association, there ❏ are ❏ are not any suits pending in which the Association is a party. The style and cause number of each pending suit is: _____.

I. The Association's board ❏has actual knowledge ❏has no actual knowledge of conditions on the Property in violation of the restrictions applying to the subdivision or the bylaws or rules of the Association. Known violations are: _____.

J. The Association ❏has ❏has not received notice from any governmental authority regarding health or building code violations with respect to the Property or any common areas or common facilities owned or leased by the Association. A summary or copy of each notice is attached.

K. The amount of any administrative transfer fee charged by the Association for a change of ownership of property in the subdivision is $_____. Describe all fees associated with the transfer of ownership (include a description of each fee, to whom each fee is payable and the amount of each fee)._____
_____
_____

TREC NO. 37-5

FIGURE 24

Subdivision Information, Including Resale Certificate for Property Subject to Membership in a Property Owners' Association (continued)

Subdivision Information Concerning _____ Page 2 of 2   2-10-2014
(Address of Property)

L. The Association's managing agent is_____
(Name of Agent)

_____
(Mailing Address)

_____   _____
(Telephone Number)(Fax Number)

_____
(E-mail Address)

M. The restrictions ❏ do ❏ do not allow foreclosure of the Association's lien on the Property for failure to pay assessments.
    REQUIRED ATTACHMENTS:

1.	Restrictions	5.	Current Operating Budget
2.	Rules	6.	Certificate of Insurance concerning Property and Liability Insurance for Common Areas and Facilities
3.	Bylaws		
4.	Current Balance Sheet	7.	Any Governmental Notices of Health or Housing Code Violations

NOTICE: This Subdivision Information may change at any time.

_____
Name of Association

By: _____

Print Name: _____

Title: _____

Date:_____

Mailing Address: _____

E-mail: _____

Promulgated Notice

FIGURE 25

Notice of Buyer's Termination of Contract

12-05-11

PROMULGATED BY THE TEXAS REAL ESTATE COMMISSION (TREC)

NOTICE OF BUYER'S TERMINATION OF CONTRACT

CONCERNING THE CONTRACT FOR THE SALE OF THE PROPERTY AT

_____

(Street Address and City)

BETWEEN THE UNDERSIGNED BUYER AND_____

_____ (SELLER)

Buyer notifies Seller that the contract is terminated pursuant to the following:

❑(1) the unrestricted right of Buyer to terminate the contract under Paragraph 23 of the contract.

❑(2) Buyer cannot obtain Credit Approval in accordance with the Third Party Financing Addendum for Credit Approval to the contract.

❑(3) the Property does not satisfy the lenders' underwriting requirements for the loan under Paragraph 4A(1) of the contract.

❑(4) Buyer elects to terminate under Paragraph A of the Addendum for Property Subject to Mandatory Membership in a Property Owners' Association.

❑(5) Buyer elects to terminate under Paragraph 7B(2) of the contract relating to the Seller's Disclosure Notice.

❑(6) Other _(identify the paragraph number of contract or the addendum)_: _____

_____

_____

_____

_____

NOTE: Release of the earnest money is governed by the terms of the contract.

_____   _____

Buyer   Date   Buyer   Date

This form has been approved by the Texas Real Estate Commission for use with similarly approved or promulgated contract forms. Such approval relates to this form only. TREC forms are intended for use only by trained real estate licensees. No representation is made as to the legal validity or adequacy of any provision in any specific transactions. It is not suitable for complex transactions. Texas Real Estate Commission, P.O. Box 12188, Austin, TX 78711-2188, (512) 936-3000 (http://www.trec.texas.gov) TREC No. 38-4. This form replaces TREC No. 38-3.

TREC No.38-4

Promulgated Consumer Disclosures

FIGURE 26

Consumer Information Form 1-1

THIS FIRM IS

LICENSED AND REGULATED

BY THE

TEXAS REAL ESTATE

COMMISSION (TREC)

TREC ADMINISTERS TWO RECOVERY FUNDS

WHICH MAY BE USED TO SATISFY JUDGMENTS

AGAINST INSPECTORS AND REAL ESTATE

LICENSEES INVOLVING A VIOLATION OF THE LAW.

COMPLAINTS OR INQUIRIES SHOULD

BE DIRECTED TO

TEXAS REAL ESTATE COMMISSION
P.O. BOX 12188
AUSTIN, TEXAS 78711-2188

(512) 936-3005

Consumer Information Form 1-1 (7/11))

F I G U R E 27

Disclosure of Relationship with Residential Service Company

PROMULGATED BY THE TEXAS REAL ESTATE COMMISSION (TREC)   12-01-2010
DISCLOSURE OF RELATIONSHIP
WITH RESIDENTIAL SERVICE COMPANY

RESIDENTIAL SERVICE CONTRACTS. A residential service contract is a product under which a residential service company, for a fee, agrees to repair or replace certain equipment or items in a property. Co-payments typically apply to most service calls. Residential service companies are licensed and regulated by the Texas Real Estate Commission. The extent of coverage and the cost of coverage will vary. Before buying a residential service contract, the buyer should read the contract and consider comparing it with the extent of coverage and costs from several other residential service companies. You may obtain a list of the residential service companies licensed in Texas at http://www.trec.state.tx.us as well as a copy of their respective contracts. **YOU MAY CHOOSE ANY COMPANY.**

THE PURCHASE OF A RESIDENTIAL SERVICE CONTRACT IS OPTIONAL. The TREC promulgated residential contract forms contain a paragraph in which the parties may negotiate whether the seller will reimburse the buyer the cost of a residential service contract. The choice of the residential service company and extent of coverage lies with the buyer. **NEITHER A BROKER/SALESPERSON NOR A SELLER MAY CONDITION THE SALE OF A PROPERTY ON THE BUYER'S PURCHASE OF A RESIDENTIAL SERVICE CONTRACT.**

☐ Other Broker/Salesperson will receive no compensation from a residential service company.

☐ Listing Broker/Salesperson will receive no compensation from a residential service company.

☐ Other Broker/Salesperson receives compensation from the following residential service company:

_____

_____

for providing the following services:

_____

_____

☐ Listing Broker/Salesperson receives compensation from the following residential service company:

_____

_____

for providing the following services:

_____

_____

The compensation is not contingent upon a party to the real estate transaction purchasing a contract or services from the residential service company.

The compensation is the fee for the services that Listing Broker or Other Broker, either directly or through an agent, provides to the company. As required by the Real Estate Settlement Procedures Act and HUD Regulation X, any fees paid to a settlement services provider are limited to the reasonable value of services actually rendered.

Other Broker's Name   License No.   Listing Broker's Name   License No.

By: _____   By: _____

The undersigned acknowledges receipt of this notice:

_____   _____
Buyer   Seller

_____   _____
Buyer   Seller

RSC 1

Approved Optional/
Voluntary Use Forms

FIGURE 28

Notice to Prospective Buyer

APPROVED BY THE TEXAS REAL ESTATE COMMISSION   10-10-11

NOTICE TO PROSPECTIVE BUYER

As required by law, I advise you to have the abstract covering the property known as

_____

_____ (Address) examined by
an attorney of your own selection OR you should be furnished with or obtain a policy of
title insurance.

If the property is situated in a Utility District, Chapter 49 of the Texas Water Code
requires you to sign and acknowledge the statutory notice from the seller of the property
relating to the tax rate, bonded indebtedness or standby fee of the District.

DATED: _____ , _____ .

_____
Brokerage Company Name

_____
Broker or Sales Associate

I have received a copy of this **NOTICE TO PROSPECTIVE BUYER.**

_____
Prospective Buyer

_____
Prospective Buyer

This form has been approved by the Texas Real Estate Commission (TREC) for use when a
contract of sale has not been promulgated by TREC. The form should be presented before an offer
to purchase is signed by the prospective buyer. Texas real Estate Commission, P.O. Box 12188,
Austin, Texas 78711-2188, 512-936-3000 (http://www.trec.texas.gov). TREC Notice to
Prospective Buyer. OP-C replaces MA-C.

TREC NO. OP-C

FIGURE 29

Seller's Disclosure of Property Condition

EQUAL HOUSING OPPORTUNITY

10-23-2013

APPROVED BY THE TEXAS REAL ESTATE COMMISSION (TREC)

SELLER'S DISCLOSURE OF PROPERTY CONDITION

CONCERNING THE PROPERTY AT_____
(Street Address and City)

THIS NOTICE IS A DISCLOSURE OF SELLER'S KNOWLEDGE OF THE CONDITION OF THE PROPERTY AS OF THE DATE SIGNED BY SELLER AND IS NOT A SUBSTITUTE FOR ANY INSPECTIONS OR WARRANTIES THE PURCHASER MAY WISH TO OBTAIN. IT IS NOT A WARRANTY OF ANY KIND BY SELLER OR SELLER'S AGENTS.

Seller ☐ is ☐ is not occupying the Property. If unoccupied, how long since Seller has occupied the Property? _____

1. The Property has the items checked below [Write Yes (Y), No (N), or Unknown (U)]:

_____ Range	_____ Oven	_____ Microwave
_____ Dishwasher	_____ Trash Compactor	_____ Disposal
_____ Washer/Dryer Hookups	_____ Window Screens	_____ Rain Gutters
_____ Security System	_____ Fire Detection Equipment	_____ Intercom System
	_____ Smoke Detector	
	_____ Smoke Detector-Hearing Impaired	
	_____ Carbon Monoxide Alarm	
	_____ Emergency Escape Ladder(s)	
_____ TV Antenna	_____ Cable TV Wiring	_____ Satellite Dish
_____ Ceiling Fan(s)	_____ Attic Fan(s)	_____ Exhaust Fan(s)
_____ Central A/C	_____ Central Heating	_____ Wall/Window Air Conditioning
_____ Plumbing System	_____ Septic System	_____ Public Sewer System
_____ Patio/Decking	_____ Outdoor Grill	_____ Fences
_____ Pool	_____ Sauna	_____ Spa _____ Hot Tub
_____ Pool Equipment	_____ Pool Heater	_____ Automatic Lawn Sprinkler System
_____ Fireplace(s) & Chimney (Wood burning)		_____ Fireplace(s) & Chimney (Mock)
_____ Natural Gas Lines		_____ Gas Fixtures
_____ Liquid Propane Gas	_____ LP Community (Captive)	_____ LP on Property

Garage: _____ Attached   _____ Not Attached   _____ Carport

Garage Door Opener(s):   _____ Electronic   _____ Control(s)

Water Heater: _____ Gas   _____ Electric

Water Supply: _____ City   _____ Well   _____ MUD   _____ Co-op

Roof Type:_____ Age:_____ (approx.)

Are you (Seller) aware of any of the above items that are not in working condition, that have known defects, or that are in need of repair? ☐ Yes   ☐ No   ☐ Unknown. If yes, then describe. (Attach additional sheets if necessary):_____

_____

_____

_____

TREC No. OP-H

F I G U R E 29

Seller's Disclosure of Property Condition (continued)

Seller's Disclosure Notice Concerning the Property at _____ Page 2 10-23-2013
(Street Address and City)

2. Does the property have working smoke detectors installed in accordance with the smoke detector requirements of Chapter 766, Health and Safety Code? ☐ Yes ☐ No ☐ Unknown. If the answer to this question is no or unknown, explain (Attach additional sheets if necessary): _____

_____

_____

*   Chapter 766 of the Health and Safety Code requires one-family or two-family dwellings to have working smoke detectors installed in accordance with the requirements of the building code in effect in the area in which the dwelling is located, including performance, location, and power source requirements. If you do not know the building code requirements in effect in your area, you may check unknown above or contact your local building official for more information. A buyer may require a seller to install smoke detectors for the hearing impaired if: (1) the buyer or a member of the buyer's family who will reside in the dwelling is hearing impaired; (2) the buyer gives the seller written evidence of the hearing impairment from a licensed physician; and (3) within 10 days after the effective date, the buyer makes a written request for the seller to install smoke detectors for the hearing impaired and specifies the locations for the installation. The parties may agree who will bear the cost of installing the smoke detectors and which brand of smoke detectors to install.

3. Are you (Seller) aware of any known defects/malfunctions in any of the following? Write Yes (Y) if you are aware, write No (N) if you are not aware.

____ Interior Walls	____ Ceilings	____ Floors
____ Exterior Walls	____ Doors	____ Windows
____ Roof	____ Foundation/Slab(s)	____ Sidewalks
____ Walls/Fences	____ Driveways	____ Intercom System
____ Plumbing/Sewers/Septics	____ Electrical Systems	____ Lighting Fixtures

____ Other Structural Components (Describe): _____

_____

_____

If the answer to any of the above is yes, explain. (Attach additional sheets if necessary):_____

_____

_____

4. Are you (Seller) aware of any of the following conditions? Write Yes (Y) if you are aware, write No (N) if you are not aware.

____ Active Termites (includes wood destroying insects)	____ Previous Structural or Roof Repair
____ Termite or Wood Rot Damage Needing Repair	____ Hazardous or Toxic Waste
____ Previous Termite Damage	____ Asbestos Components
____ Previous Termite Treatment	____ Urea-formaldehyde Insulation
____ Previous Flooding	____ Radon Gas
____ Improper Drainage	____ Lead Based Paint
____ Water Penetration	____ Aluminum Wiring
____ Located in 100-Year Floodplain	____ Previous Fires
____ Present Flood Insurance Coverage	____ Unplatted Easements
____ Landfill, Settling, Soil Movement, Fault Lines	____ Subsurface Structure or Pits
____ Single Blockable Main Drain in Pool/Hot Tub/Spa	____ Previous Use of Premises for Manufacture of Methamphetamine

If the answer to any of the above is yes, explain. (Attach additional sheets if necessary):_____

_____

_____

* A single blockable main drain may cause a section entrapment hazard for an individual.

TREC No. OP-H

FIGURE 29

Seller's Disclosure of Property Condition (continued)

Seller's Disclosure Notice Concerning the Property at _____ Page 3 10-23-2013

(Street Address and City)

5. Are you (Seller) aware of any item, equipment, or system in or on the Property that is in need of repair? ☐ Yes (if you are aware) ☐ No (if you are not aware) If yes, explain. (Attach additional sheets if necessary): _____

_____

_____

6. Are you (Seller) aware of any of the following? Write Yes (Y) if you are aware, write No (N) if you are not aware.

_____ Room additions, structural modifications, or other alterations or repairs made without necessary permits or not in compliance with building codes in effect at that time.

_____ Homeowners' Association or maintenance fees or assessments.

_____ Any "common area" (facilities such as pools, tennis courts, walkways, or other areas) co-owned in undivided interest with others.

_____ Any notices of violations of deed restrictions or governmental ordinances affecting the condition or use of the Property.

_____ Any lawsuits directly or indirectly affecting the Property.

_____ Any condition on the Property which materially affects the physical health or safety of an individual.

_____ Any rainwater harvesting system located on the property that is larger than 500 gallons and that uses a public water supply as an auxiliary water source.

If the answer to any of the above is yes, explain. (Attach additional sheets if necessary):_____

_____

_____

7. If the property is located in a costal area that is seaward of the Gulf Intracoastal Waterway or within 1,000 feet of the mean high tide bordering the Gulf of Mexico, the property may be subject to the Open Beaches Act or the Dune Protection Act (Chapter 61 or 63, Natural Resources Code, respectively) and a beachfront construction certificate or dune protection permit maybe required for repairs or Improvements. Contact the local government with ordinance authority over construction adjacent to public beaches for more information.

_____ _____   _____ _____
Signature of Seller   Date   Signature of Seller   Date

The undersigned purchaser hereby acknowledges receipt of the foregoing notice.

_____ _____   _____ _____
Signature of Purchaser   Date   Signature of Purchaser   Date

TREC No. OP-H

FIGURE 30

Texas Real Estate Consumer Notice Concerning Hazards or Deficiencies

05-06-13

APPROVED BY THE TEXAS REAL ESTATE COMMISSION (TREC)
P.O. BOX 12188, AUSTIN, TX 78711-2188

TEXAS REAL ESTATE CONSUMER NOTICE CONCERNING HAZARDS OR DEFICIENCIES

Each year, Texans sustain property damage and are injured by accidents in the home. While some accidents may not be avoidable, many other accidents, injuries, and deaths may be avoided through the identification and repair of certain hazardous conditions. Examples of such hazards include:

- malfunctioning, improperly installed, or missing ground fault circuit protection (GFCI) devices for electrical receptacles in garages, bathrooms, kitchens, and exterior areas;

- malfunctioning arc fault protection (AFCI) devices;

- ordinary glass in locations where modern construction techniques call for safety glass;

- malfunctioning or lack of fire safety features such as smoke alarms, fire-rated doors in certain locations, and functional emergency escape and rescue openings in bedrooms;

- malfunctioning carbon monoxide alarms;

- excessive spacing between balusters on stairways and porches;

- improperly installed appliances;

- improperly installed or defective safety devices; and

- lack of electrical bonding and grounding.

To ensure that consumers are informed of hazards such as these, the Texas Real Estate Commission (TREC) has adopted Standards of Practice requiring licensed inspectors to report these conditions as "Deficient" when performing an inspection for a buyer or seller, if they can be reasonably determined.

These conditions may not have violated building codes or common practices at the time of the construction of the home, or they may have been "grandfathered" because they were present prior to the adoption of codes prohibiting such conditions. While the TREC Standards of Practice do not require inspectors to perform a code compliance inspection, TREC considers the potential for injury or property loss from the hazards addressed in the Standards of Practice to be significant enough to warrant this notice.

Contract forms developed by TREC for use by its real estate licensees also inform the buyer of the right to have the home inspected and can provide an option clause permitting the buyer to terminate the contract within a specified time. Neither the Standards of Practice nor the TREC contract forms requires a seller to remedy conditions revealed by an inspection. The decision to correct a hazard or any deficiency identified in an inspection report is left to the parties to the contract for the sale or purchase of the home.

This form has been approved by the Texas Real Estate Commission for voluntary use by its licensees. Copies of TREC rules governing real estate brokers, salesperson and real estate inspectors are available from TREC. Texas Real Estate Commission, P.O. Box 12188, Austin, TX 78711-2188, 512-936-3000 (http://www.trec.texas.gov)

TREC Form No. OP-I

F I G U R E   31

Information About Brokerage Services

10-10-11

Approved by the Texas Real Estate Commission for Voluntary Use
Texas law requires all real estate licensees to give the following information about brokerage services to prospective buyers, tenants, sellers and landlords.

Information About Brokerage Services

Before working with a real estate broker, you should know that the duties of a broker depend on whom the broker represents. If you are a prospective seller or landlord (owner) or a prospective buyer or tenant (buyer), you should know that the broker who lists the property for sale or lease is the owner's agent. A broker who acts as a subagent represents the owner in cooperation with the listing broker. A broker who acts as a buyer's agent represents the buyer. A broker may act as an intermediary between the parties if the parties consent in writing. A broker can assist you in locating a property, preparing a contract or lease, or obtaining financing without representing you. A broker is obligated by law to treat you honestly.

IF THE BROKER REPRESENTS THE OWNER:
The broker becomes the owner's agent by entering into an agreement with the owner, usually through a written - listing agreement, or by agreeing to act as a subagent by accepting an offer of subagency from the listing broker. A subagent may work in a different real estate office. A listing broker or subagent can assist the buyer but does not   represent the buyer and must place the interests of the owner first. The buyer should not tell the owner's agent anything the buyer would not want the owner to know because an owner's agent must disclose to the owner any material information known to the agent.

IF THE BROKER REPRESENTS THE BUYER:
The broker becomes the buyer's agent by entering into an agreement to represent the buyer, usually through a written buyer representation agreement. A buyer's agent can assist the owner but does not represent the owner and must place the interests of the buyer first. The owner should not tell a buyer's agent anything the owner would not want the buyer to know because a buyer's agent must disclose to the buyer any material information known to the agent.

IF THE BROKER ACTS AS AN INTERMEDIARY:
A broker may act as an intermediary between the parties if the broker complies with The Texas Real Estate License Act. The broker must obtain the written consent of each party to the transaction to act as an intermediary. The written consent must state who will pay the broker and, in conspicuous bold or underlined print, set forth the broker's obligations as an intermediary. The broker is required to treat each party honestly and fairly and to comply with The Texas Real Estate License Act.   A broker who acts as an intermediary in a transaction:

(1) shall treat all parties honestly;

(2) may not disclose that the owner will accept a price less that the asking price unless authorized in writing to do so by the owner;

(3) may not disclose that the buyer will pay a price greater than the price submitted in a written offer unless authorized in writing to do so by the buyer; and

(4) may not disclose any confidential information or any information that a party specifically instructs the broker in writing not to disclose unless authorized in writing to disclose the information or required to do so by The Texas Real Estate License Act or a court order or if the information materially relates to the condition of the property.

With the parties' consent, a broker acting as an intermediary between the parties may appoint a person who is licensed under The Texas Real Estate License Act and associated with the broker to communicate with and carry out instructions of one party and another person who is licensed under that Act and associated with the broker to communicate with and carry out instructions of the other party.

If you choose to have a broker represent you, you should enter into a written agreement with the broker that clearly establishes the broker's obligations and your obligations. The agreement should state how and by whom the broker will be paid. You have the right to choose the type of representation, if any, you wish to receive. Your payment of a fee to a broker does not necessarily establish that the broker represents you. If you have any questions regarding the duties and responsibilities of the broker, you should resolve those questions before proceeding.

Real estate licensee asks that you acknowledge receipt of this information about brokerage services for the licensee's records.

_____

Buyer, Seller, Landlord or Tenant   Date

Texas Real Estate Brokers and Salespersons are licensed and regulated by the Texas Real Estate Commission (TREC). If you have a question or complaint regarding a real estate licensee, you should contact TREC at P.O. Box 12188, Austin, Texas 78711-2188 , 512-936-3000 (http://www.trec.texas.gov)

TREC No. OP-K

FIGURE 32

Lead-Based Paint Addendum

APPROVED BY THE TEXAS REAL ESTATE COMMISSION   10-10-11

EQUAL HOUSING OPPORTUNITY

ADDENDUM FOR SELLER'S DISCLOSURE OF INFORMATION ON LEAD-BASED PAINT AND LEAD-BASED PAINT HAZARDS AS REQUIRED BY FEDERAL LAW

CONCERNING THE PROPERTY AT _____
(Street Address and City)

A. LEAD WARNING STATEMENT: "Every purchaser of any interest in residential real property on which a residential dwelling was built prior to 1978 is notified that such property may present exposure to lead from lead-based paint that may place young children at risk of developing lead poisoning. Lead poisoning in young children may produce permanent neurological damage, including learning disabilities, reduced intelligence quotient, behavioral problems, and impaired memory. Lead poisoning also poses a particular risk to pregnant women. The seller of any interest in residential real property is required to provide the buyer with any information on lead-based paint hazards from risk assessments or inspections in the seller's possession and notify the buyer of any known lead-based paint hazards. A risk assessment or inspection for possible lead-paint hazards is recommended prior to purchase."
   NOTICE: Inspector must be properly certified as required by federal law.
B. SELLER'S DISCLOSURE:
   1. PRESENCE OF LEAD-BASED PAINT AND/OR LEAD-BASED PAINT HAZARDS (check one box only):
      ☐(a) Known lead-based paint and/or lead-based paint hazards are present in the Property (explain): _____
      _____ .
      ☐(b) Seller has no actual knowledge of lead-based paint and/or lead-based paint hazards in the Property.
   2. RECORDS AND REPORTS AVAILABLE TO SELLER (check one box only):
      ☐(a) Seller has provided the purchaser with all available records and reports pertaining to lead-based paint and/or lead-based paint hazards in the Property (list documents):_____
      _____ .
      ☐(b) Seller has no reports or records pertaining to lead-based paint and/or lead-based paint hazards in the Property.
C. BUYER'S RIGHTS (check one box only)**:**
   ☐1. Buyer waives the opportunity to conduct a risk assessment or inspection of the Property for the presence of lead-based paint or lead-based paint hazards.
   ☐2. Within ten days after the effective date of this contract, Buyer may have the Property inspected by inspectors selected by Buyer. If lead-based paint or lead-based paint hazards are present, Buyer may terminate this contract by giving Seller written notice within 14 days after the effective date of this contract, and the earnest money will be refunded to Buyer.
D. BUYER'S ACKNOWLEDGMENT (check applicable boxes)**:**
   ☐1. Buyer has received copies of all information listed above.
   ☐2. Buyer has received the pamphlet *Protect Your Family from Lead in Your Home.*
E. BROKERS' ACKNOWLEDGMENT: Brokers have informed Seller of Seller's obligations under 42 U.S.C. 4852d to: (a) provide Buyer with the federally approved pamphlet on lead poisoning prevention; (b) complete this addendum; (c) disclose any known lead-based paint and/or lead-based paint hazards in the Property; (d) deliver all records and reports to Buyer pertaining to lead-based paint and/or lead-based paint hazards in the Property; (e) provide Buyer a period of up to 10 days to have the Property inspected; and (f) retain a completed copy of this addendum for at least 3 years following the sale. Brokers are aware of their responsibility to ensure compliance.
F. CERTIFICATION OF ACCURACY: The following persons have reviewed the information above and certify, to the best of their knowledge, that the information they have provided is true and accurate.

_____   _____   _____   _____
Buyer   Date   Seller   Date

_____   _____   _____   _____
Buyer   Date   Seller   Date

_____   _____   _____   _____
Other Broker   Date   Listing Broker   Date

TREC NO. OP-L

FIGURE 33

Non-Realty Items Addendum

EQUAL HOUSING
OPPORTUNITY

APPROVED BY THE TEXAS REAL ESTATE COMMISSION (TREC)   10-10-11
FOR VOLUNTARY USE

NON-REALTY ITEMS ADDENDUM

TO CONTRACT CONCERNING THE PROPERTY AT

_____
(Address of Property)

A. For an additional sum of $_____and other and good valuable consideration, Seller shall convey to Buyer at closing the following personal property (specify each item carefully, include description, model numbers, serial numbers, location, and other information):

_____

_____

_____

_____

_____

_____

_____

_____

_____

_____

_____

B. Seller represents and warrants that Seller owns the personal property described in Paragraph A free and clear of all encumbrances.

C. Seller does not warrant or guarantee the condition or future performance of the personal property conveyed by this document.

_____   _____
Buyer   Seller

_____   _____
Buyer   Seller

> This form has been approved by the Texas Real Estate Commission for voluntary use by its licensees. Copies of TREC rules governing real estate brokers, salesperson and real estate inspectors are available at nominal cost from TREC. Texas Real Estate Commission, P.O. Box 12188, Austin, TX 78711-2188, 512-936-3000 (http://www.trec.texas.gov)

TREC NO. OP-M

FIGURE 34

Reverse Mortgage Financing Addendum

APPROVED BY THE TEXAS REAL ESTATE COMMISSION (TREC)
FOR VOLUNTARY USE

4-28-2014

EQUAL HOUSING
OPPORTUNITY

REVERSE MORTGAGE FINANCING ADDENDUM

If using this form, do not check any box in Paragraph 4 of the contract

CONCERNING THE PROPERTY AT _____
(Street Address and City)

A. The portion of Sales Price not payable in cash under Paragraph 3B will be paid as follows and the contract is subject to Buyer being approved for the financing described below. Buyer shall apply promptly for the financing and make every reasonable effort to obtain approval for the financing, including but not limited to furnishing all information and documents required by Buyer's lender.

A reverse mortgage loan in the original principal amount of $_____ (excluding any financed mortgage insurance premium or other costs), with:

❑ an interest rate not to exceed _____% per annum for a fixed-rate reverse mortgage; or

❑ an initial interest rate not to exceed _____% per annum for a variable-rate mortgage.

B. The Adjusted Origination Charges as shown on Buyer's Good Faith Estimate for the loan shall not exceed _____% of the loan. The reverse mortgage loan ❑ will ❑ will not be an FHA insured loan.

C. <u>Financing Approval</u>: Approval for the financing described above will be deemed to have been obtained when Approval of Buyer and Property Approval are obtained.

(1) <u>Approval of Buyer</u>: Approval of Buyer will be deemed to have been obtained when (i) the terms of the loan described above are available; and (ii) lender determines that Buyer has satisfied all of lender's requirements. If Approval of Buyer is not obtained, Buyer may give written notice to Seller within _____ days after the effective date of this contract and this contract will terminate and the earnest money will be refunded to Buyer. **If Buyer does not terminate the contract under this provision, the contract shall no longer be subject to Approval of Buyer. Time is of the essence for this paragraph and strict compliance with the time for performance is required.**

(2) <u>Property Approval</u>: Property Approval will be deemed to have been obtained when the Property has satisfied lender's underwriting requirements for the loan, including but not limited to appraisal, insurability, and lender required repairs. If the Property Approval is not obtained by the Closing Date, Buyer may terminate this contract by giving notice to Seller prior to closing and the earnest money will be refunded to Buyer.

D. If the loan involves FHA financing: *"It is expressly agreed that, notwithstanding any other provision of this contract, the purchaser (Buyer) shall not be obligated to complete the purchase of the Property described herein or to incur any penalty by forfeiture of earnest money deposits or otherwise unless the purchaser (Buyer) has been given in accordance with HUD/FHA or VA requirements a written statement issued by the Federal Housing Commissioner, Department of Veterans Affairs, or a Direct Endorsement Lender setting forth the appraised value of the Property of not less than $_____ . The purchaser (Buyer) shall have the privilege and option of proceeding with consummation of the contract without regard to the amount of the appraised valuation. The appraised valuation is arrived at to determine the maximum mortgage the Department of Housing and Urban Development will insure. HUD does not warrant the value or the condition of the Property. The purchaser (Buyer) should satisfy himself/herself that the price and the condition of the Property are acceptable."*

_____   _____   _____   _____
Buyer   Date   Seller   Date

_____   _____   _____   _____
Buyer   Date   Seller   Date

TREC NO. OP-N

Case Studies

Transaction: Strassman to Applewhite
(from Chapter 5 of *Texas Promulgated Forms*)

PROMULGATED BY THE TEXAS REAL ESTATE COMMISSION (TREC)   4-28-2014
ONE TO FOUR FAMILY RESIDENTIAL CONTRACT (RESALE)
NOTICE: Not For Use For Condominium Transactions

1. PARTIES: The parties to this contract are _____
(Seller) and _____(Buyer).
Seller agrees to sell and convey to Buyer and Buyer agrees to buy from Seller the Property defined below.

2. PROPERTY: The land, improvements and accessories are collectively referred to as the "Property".
    A. LAND: Lot _____ Block_____, _____
       Addition, City of _____ , County of _____,
       Texas, known as _____
       (address/zip code), or as described on attached exhibit.
    B. IMPROVEMENTS: The house, garage and all other fixtures and improvements attached to the above-described real property, including without limitation, the following **permanently installed and built-in items,** if any: all equipment and appliances, valances, screens, shutters, awnings, wall-to-wall carpeting, mirrors, ceiling fans, attic fans, mail boxes, television antennas, mounts and brackets for televisions and speakers, heating and air-conditioning units, security and fire detection equipment, wiring, plumbing and lighting fixtures, chandeliers, water softener system, kitchen equipment, garage door openers, cleaning equipment, shrubbery, landscaping, outdoor cooking equipment, and all other property owned by Seller and attached to the above described real property.
    C. ACCESSORIES: The following described related accessories, if any: window air conditioning units, stove, fireplace screens, curtains and rods, blinds, window shades, draperies and rods, door keys, mailbox keys, above ground pool, swimming pool equipment and maintenance accessories, artificial fireplace logs, and controls for: (i) garage doors, (ii) entry gates, and (iii) other improvements and accessories.
    D. EXCLUSIONS: The following improvements and accessories will be retained by Seller and must be removed prior to delivery of possession:_____
       _____.

3. SALES PRICE:
    A. Cash portion of Sales Price payable by Buyer at closing .... $_____
    B. Sum of all financing described below (excluding any loan funding
       fee or mortgage insurance premium) .... $_____
    C. Sales Price (Sum of A and B)... $_____

4. FINANCING (Not for use with reverse mortgage financing): The portion of Sales Price not payable in cash will be paid as follows: (Check applicable boxes below)
❏ A.THIRD PARTY FINANCING: One or more third party mortgage loans in the total amount of
    $_____ (excluding any loan funding fee or mortgage insurance premium).
    (1) Property Approval: If the Property does not satisfy the lenders' underwriting requirements for the loan(s) (including, but not limited to appraisal, insurability and lender required repairs), Buyer may terminate this contract by giving notice to Seller prior to closing and the earnest money will be refunded to Buyer.
    (2) Credit Approval: (Check one box only)
    ❏   (a) This contract is subject to Buyer being approved for the financing described in the attached Third Party Financing Addendum for Credit Approval.
    ❏   (b) This contract is not subject to Buyer being approved for financing and does not involve FHA or VA financing.
❏ B. ASSUMPTION: The assumption of the unpaid principal balance of one or more promissory notes described in the attached TREC Loan Assumption Addendum.
❏ C. SELLER FINANCING: A promissory note from Buyer to Seller of $_____, secured by vendor's and deed of trust liens, and containing the terms and conditions described in the attached TREC Seller Financing Addendum. If an owner policy of title insurance is furnished, Buyer shall furnish Seller with a mortgagee policy of title insurance.

Initialed for identification by Buyer_____ _____ and Seller _____ _____   TREC NO. 20-12

Contract Concerning _____Page 2 of 9   4-28-2014
(Address of Property)

5. EARNEST MONEY: Upon execution of this contract by all parties, Buyer shall deposit
$_____ as earnest money with _____, as escrow
agent, at _____ (address). Buyer
shall deposit additional earnest money of $_____ with escrow agent within
_____days after the effective date of this contract. If Buyer fails to deposit the earnest money as
required by this contract, Buyer will be in default.

6. TITLE POLICY AND SURVEY:
A. TITLE POLICY: Seller shall furnish to Buyer at ❑ Seller's ❑ Buyer's expense an owner policy
   of title insurance (Title Policy) issued by _____ (Title
   Company) in the amount of the Sales Price, dated at or after closing, insuring Buyer against
   loss under the provisions of the Title Policy, subject to the promulgated exclusions (including
   existing building and zoning ordinances) and the following exceptions:
   (1) Restrictive covenants common to the platted subdivision in which the Property is located.
   (2) The standard printed exception for standby fees, taxes and assessments.
   (3) Liens created as part of the financing described in Paragraph 4.
   (4) Utility easements created by the dedication deed or plat of the subdivision in which the
       Property is located.
   (5) Reservations or exceptions otherwise permitted by this contract or as may be approved
       by Buyer in writing.
   (6) The standard printed exception as to marital rights.
   (7) The standard printed exception as to waters, tidelands, beaches, streams, and related
       matters.
   (8) The standard printed exception as to discrepancies, conflicts, shortages in area or boundary
       lines, encroachments or protrusions, or overlapping improvements: ❑(i) will not be
       amended or deleted from the title policy; ❑(ii) will be amended to read, "shortages in area"
       at the expense of ❑Buyer ❑Seller.
B. COMMITMENT: Within 20 days after the Title Company receives a copy of this contract,
   Seller shall furnish to Buyer a commitment for title insurance (Commitment) and, at Buyer's
   expense, legible copies of restrictive covenants and documents evidencing exceptions in the
   Commitment (Exception Documents) other than the standard printed exceptions. Seller
   authorizes the Title Company to deliver the Commitment and Exception Documents to Buyer
   at Buyer's address shown in Paragraph 21. If the Commitment and Exception Documents are
   not delivered to Buyer within the specified time, the time for delivery will be automatically
   extended up to 15 days or 3 days before the Closing Date, whichever is earlier. If, due to
   factors beyond Seller's control, the Commitment and Exception Documents are not delivered
   within the time required, Buyer may terminate this contract and the earnest money will be
   refunded to Buyer.
C. SURVEY: The survey must be made by a registered professional land surveyor acceptable to
   the Title Company and Buyer's lender(s). (Check one box only)
❑(1) Within _____ days after the effective date of this contract, Seller shall furnish to Buyer
      and Title Company Seller's existing survey of the Property and a Residential Real Property
      Affidavit promulgated by the Texas Department of Insurance (T-47 Affidavit). **If Seller
      fails to furnish the existing survey or affidavit within the time prescribed, Buyer
      shall obtain a new survey at Seller's expense no later than 3 days prior to Closing
      Date.** If the existing survey or affidavit is not acceptable to Title Company or Buyer's
      lender(s), Buyer shall obtain a new survey at ❑Seller's ❑Buyer's expense no later than 3
      days prior to Closing Date.
❑(2) Within _____ days after the effective date of this contract, Buyer shall obtain a new
      survey at Buyer's expense. Buyer is deemed to receive the survey on the date of actual
      receipt or the date specified in this paragraph, whichever is earlier.
❑(3) Within _____ days after the effective date of this contract, Seller, at Seller's expense
      shall furnish a new survey to Buyer.
D. OBJECTIONS: Buyer may object in writing to defects, exceptions, or encumbrances to title:
   disclosed on the survey other than items 6A(1) through (7) above; disclosed in the
   Commitment other than items 6A(1) through (8) above; or which prohibit the following use
   or activity: _____
   _____.
   Buyer must object the earlier of (i) the Closing Date or (ii) _____ days after Buyer receives
   the Commitment, Exception Documents, and the survey. Buyer's failure to object within the
   time allowed will constitute a waiver of Buyer's right to object; except that the requirements
   in Schedule C of the Commitment are not waived by Buyer. Provided Seller is not obligated
   to incur any expense, Seller shall cure the timely objections of Buyer or any third party lender

Initialed for identification by Buyer_____ _____ and Seller _____ _____   TREC NO. 20-12

Contract Concerning _____ Page 3 of 9   4-28-2014
                                (Address of Property)

within 15 days after Seller receives the objections and the Closing Date will be extended as necessary. If objections are not cured within such 15 day period, this contract will terminate and the earnest money will be refunded to Buyer unless Buyer waives the objections.

E. TITLE NOTICES:
  (1) ABSTRACT OR TITLE POLICY: Broker advises Buyer to have an abstract of title covering the Property examined by an attorney of Buyer's selection, or Buyer should be furnished with or obtain a Title Policy. If a Title Policy is furnished, the Commitment should be promptly reviewed by an attorney of Buyer's choice due to the time limitations on Buyer's right to object.
  (2) MEMBERSHIP IN PROPERTY OWNERS ASSOCIATION(S): The Property ☐is ☐is not subject to mandatory membership in a property owners association(s). If the Property is subject to mandatory membership in a property owners association(s), Seller notifies Buyer under §5.012, Texas Property Code, that, as a purchaser of property in the residential community identified in Paragraph 2A in which the Property is located, you are obligated to be a member of the property owners association(s). Restrictive covenants governing the use and occupancy of the Property and all dedicatory instruments governing the establishment, maintenance, or operation of this residential community have been or will be recorded in the Real Property Records of the county in which the Property is located. Copies of the restrictive covenants and dedicatory instruments may be obtained from the county clerk. **You are obligated to pay assessments to the property owners association(s). The amount of the assessments is subject to change. Your failure to pay the assessments could result in enforcement of the association's lien on and the foreclosure of the Property.** Section 207.003, Property Code, entitles an owner to receive copies of any document that governs the establishment, maintenance, or operation of a subdivision, including, but not limited to, restrictions, bylaws, rules and regulations, and a resale certificate from a property owners' association. A resale certificate contains information including, but not limited to, statements specifying the amount and frequency of regular assessments and the style and cause number of lawsuits to which the property owners' association is a party, other than lawsuits relating to unpaid ad valorem taxes of an individual member of the association. These documents must be made available to you by the property owners' association or the association's agent on your request.
       If Buyer is concerned about these matters, the TREC promulgated Addendum for Property Subject to Mandatory Membership in a Property Owners Association(s) should be used.
  (3) STATUTORY TAX DISTRICTS: If the Property is situated in a utility or other statutorily created district providing water, sewer, drainage, or flood control facilities and services, Chapter 49, Texas Water Code, requires Seller to deliver and Buyer to sign the statutory notice relating to the tax rate, bonded indebtedness, or standby fee of the district prior to final execution of this contract.
  (4) TIDE WATERS: If the Property abuts the tidally influenced waters of the state, §33.135, Texas Natural Resources Code, requires a notice regarding coastal area property to be included in the contract. An addendum containing the notice promulgated by TREC or required by the parties must be used.
  (5) ANNEXATION: If the Property is located outside the limits of a municipality, Seller notifies Buyer under §5.011, Texas Property Code, that the Property may now or later be included in the extraterritorial jurisdiction of a municipality and may now or later be subject to annexation by the municipality. Each municipality maintains a map that depicts its boundaries and extraterritorial jurisdiction. To determine if the Property is located within a municipality's extraterritorial jurisdiction or is likely to be located within a municipality's extraterritorial jurisdiction, contact all municipalities located in the general proximity of the Property for further information.
  (6) PROPERTY LOCATED IN A CERTIFICATED SERVICE AREA OF A UTILITY SERVICE PROVIDER: Notice required by §13.257, Water Code: The real property, described in Paragraph 2, that you are about to purchase may be located in a certificated water or sewer service area, which is authorized by law to provide water or sewer service to the properties in the certificated area. If your property is located in a certificated area there may be special costs or charges that you will be required to pay before you can receive water or sewer service. There may be a period required to construct lines or other facilities necessary to provide water or sewer service to your property. You are advised to determine if the property is in a certificated area and contact the utility service provider to determine the cost that you will be required to pay and the period, if any, that is required to provide water or sewer service to your property. The undersigned Buyer hereby acknowledges receipt of the foregoing notice at or before the execution of a binding contract for the purchase of the real property described in Paragraph 2 or at closing of purchase of the real property.

Initialed for identification by Buyer_____ _____ and Seller _____ _____   TREC NO. 20-12

Contract Concerning _____ Page 4 of 9   4-28-2014
(Address of Property)

(7) PUBLIC IMPROVEMENT DISTRICTS: If the Property is in a public improvement district, §5.014, Property Code, requires Seller to notify Buyer as follows: As a purchaser of this parcel of real property you are obligated to pay an assessment to a municipality or county for an improvement project undertaken by a public improvement district under Chapter 372, Local Government Code. The assessment may be due annually or in periodic installments. More information concerning the amount of the assessment and the due dates of that assessment may be obtained from the municipality or county levying the assessment. The amount of the assessments is subject to change. Your failure to pay the assessments could result in a lien on and the foreclosure of your property.

(8) TRANSFER FEES: If the Property is subject to a private transfer fee obligation, §5.205, Property Code, requires Seller to notify Buyer as follows: The private transfer fee obligation may be governed by Chapter 5, Subchapter G of the Texas Property Code.

(9) PROPANE GAS SYSTEM SERVICE AREA: If the Property is located in a propane gas system service area owned by a distribution system retailer, Seller must give Buyer written notice as required by §141.010, Texas Utilities Code. An addendum containing the notice approved by TREC or required by the parties should be used.

7. PROPERTY CONDITION:

A. ACCESS, INSPECTIONS AND UTILITIES: Seller shall permit Buyer and Buyer's agents access to the Property at reasonable times. Buyer may have the Property inspected by inspectors selected by Buyer and licensed by TREC or otherwise permitted by law to make inspections. Seller at Seller's expense shall immediately cause existing utilities to be turned on and shall keep the utilities on during the time this contract is in effect.

B. SELLER'S DISCLOSURE NOTICE PURSUANT TO §5.008, TEXAS PROPERTY CODE (Notice): (Check one box only)

❑ (1) Buyer has received the Notice.

❑ (2) Buyer has not received the Notice. Within _____ days after the effective date of this contract, Seller shall deliver the Notice to Buyer. If Buyer does not receive the Notice, Buyer may terminate this contract at any time prior to the closing and the earnest money will be refunded to Buyer. If Seller delivers the Notice, Buyer may terminate this contract for any reason within 7 days after Buyer receives the Notice or prior to the closing, whichever first occurs, and the earnest money will be refunded to Buyer.

❑ (3)The Seller is not required to furnish the notice under the Texas Property Code.

C. SELLER'S DISCLOSURE OF LEAD-BASED PAINT AND LEAD-BASED PAINT HAZARDS is required by Federal law for a residential dwelling constructed prior to 1978.

D. ACCEPTANCE OF PROPERTY CONDITION: "As Is" means the present condition of the Property with any and all defects and without warranty except for the warranties of title and the warranties in this contract. Buyer's agreement to accept the Property As Is under Paragraph 7D(1) or (2) does not preclude Buyer from inspecting the Property under Paragraph 7A, from negotiating repairs or treatments in a subsequent amendment, or from terminating this contract during the Option Period, if any. (Check one box only)

❑ (1) Buyer accepts the Property As Is.

❑ (2) Buyer accepts the Property As Is provided Seller, at Seller's expense, shall complete the following specific repairs and treatments: _____ . _____ (Do not insert general phrases, such as "subject to inspections" that do not identify specific repairs and treatments.)

E. LENDER REQUIRED REPAIRS AND TREATMENTS: Unless otherwise agreed in writing, neither party is obligated to pay for lender required repairs, which includes treatment for wood destroying insects. If the parties do not agree to pay for the lender required repairs or treatments, this contract will terminate and the earnest money will be refunded to Buyer. If the cost of lender required repairs and treatments exceeds 5% of the Sales Price, Buyer may terminate this contract and the earnest money will be refunded to Buyer.

F. COMPLETION OF REPAIRS AND TREATMENTS: Unless otherwise agreed in writing: (i) Seller shall complete all agreed repairs and treatments prior to the Closing Date; and (ii) all required permits must be obtained, and repairs and treatments must be performed by persons who are licensed to provide such repairs or treatments or, if no license is required by law, are commercially engaged in the trade of providing such repairs or treatments. At Buyer's election, any transferable warranties received by Seller with respect to the repairs and treatments will be transferred to Buyer at Buyer's expense. If Seller fails to complete any agreed repairs and treatments prior to the Closing Date, Buyer may exercise remedies under Paragraph 15 or extend the Closing Date up to 5 days if necessary for Seller to complete the repairs and treatments.

G. ENVIRONMENTAL MATTERS: Buyer is advised that the presence of wetlands, toxic substances, including asbestos and wastes or other environmental hazards, or the presence of a threatened or endangered species or its habitat may affect Buyer's intended use of the

Initialed for identification by Buyer_____ _____ and Seller _____ _____   TREC NO. 20-12

Contract Concerning _____ Page 5 of 9   4-28-2014
(Address of Property)

Property. If Buyer is concerned about these matters, an addendum promulgated by TREC or required by the parties should be used.

    H. RESIDENTIAL SERVICE CONTRACTS: Buyer may purchase a residential service contract from a residential service company licensed by TREC. If Buyer purchases a residential service contract, Seller shall reimburse Buyer at closing for the cost of the residential service contract in an amount not exceeding $_____. Buyer should review any residential service contract for the scope of coverage, exclusions and limitations. **The purchase of a residential service contract is optional. Similar coverage may be purchased from various companies authorized to do business in Texas.**

8. BROKERS' FEES: All obligations of the parties for payment of brokers' fees are contained in separate written agreements.

9. CLOSING:

    A. The closing of the sale will be on or before _____, 20_____, or within 7 days after objections made under Paragraph 6D have been cured or waived, whichever date is later (Closing Date). If either party fails to close the sale by the Closing Date, the non-defaulting party may exercise the remedies contained in Paragraph 15.

    B. At closing:

        (1) Seller shall execute and deliver a general warranty deed conveying title to the Property to Buyer and showing no additional exceptions to those permitted in Paragraph 6 and furnish tax statements or certificates showing no delinquent taxes on the Property.

        (2) Buyer shall pay the Sales Price in good funds acceptable to the escrow agent.

        (3) Seller and Buyer shall execute and deliver any notices, statements, certificates, affidavits, releases, loan documents and other documents reasonably required for the closing of the sale and the issuance of the Title Policy.

        (4) There will be no liens, assessments, or security interests against the Property which will not be satisfied out of the sales proceeds unless securing the payment of any loans assumed by Buyer and assumed loans will not be in default.

        (5) If the Property is subject to a residential lease, Seller shall transfer security deposits (as defined under §92.102, Property Code), if any, to Buyer. In such an event, Buyer shall deliver to the tenant a signed statement acknowledging that the Buyer has received the security deposit and is responsible for the return of the security deposit, and specifying the exact dollar amount of the security deposit.

10. POSSESSION:

    A Buyer's Possession: Seller shall deliver to Buyer possession of the Property in its present or required condition, ordinary wear and tear excepted: ❑upon closing and funding ❑according to a temporary residential lease form promulgated by TREC or other written lease required by the parties. Any possession by Buyer prior to closing or by Seller after closing which is not authorized by a written lease will establish a tenancy at sufferance relationship between the parties. **Consult your insurance agent prior to change of ownership and possession because insurance coverage may be limited or terminated. The absence of a written lease or appropriate insurance coverage may expose the parties to economic loss.**

    B. Leases:

        (1) After the Effective Date, Seller may not execute any lease (including but not limited to mineral leases) or convey any interest in the Property without Buyer's written consent.

        (2) If the Property is subject to any lease to which Seller is a party, Seller shall deliver to Buyer copies of the lease(s) and any move-in condition form signed by the tenant within 7 days after the Effective Date of the contract.

11. SPECIAL PROVISIONS: (Insert only factual statements and business details applicable to the sale. TREC rules prohibit licensees from adding factual statements or business details for which a contract addendum, lease or other form has been promulgated by TREC for mandatory use.)

12. SETTLEMENT AND OTHER EXPENSES:

    A. The following expenses must be paid at or prior to closing:

        (1) Expenses payable by Seller (Seller's Expenses):

            (a) Releases of existing liens, including prepayment penalties and recording fees; release of Seller's loan liability; tax statements or certificates; preparation of deed; one-half of escrow fee; and other expenses payable by Seller under this contract.

            (b) Seller shall also pay an amount not to exceed $_____ to be applied in the

Contract Concerning _____Page 6 of 9   4-28-2014
(Address of Property)

following order: Buyer's Expenses which Buyer is prohibited from paying by FHA, VA, Texas Veterans Land Board or other governmental loan programs, and then to other Buyer's Expenses as allowed by the lender.

(2) Expenses payable by Buyer (Buyer's Expenses): Appraisal fees; loan application fees; adjusted origination charges; credit reports; preparation of loan documents; interest on the notes from date of disbursement to one month prior to dates of first monthly payments; recording fees; copies of easements and restrictions; loan title policy with endorsements required by lender; loan-related inspection fees; photos; amortization schedules; one-half of escrow fee; all prepaid items, including required premiums for flood and hazard insurance, reserve deposits for insurance, ad valorem taxes and special governmental assessments; final compliance inspection; courier fee; repair inspection; underwriting fee; wire transfer fee; expenses incident to any loan; Private Mortgage Insurance Premium (PMI), VA Loan Funding Fee, or FHA Mortgage Insurance Premium (MIP) as required by the lender; and other expenses payable by Buyer under this contract.

   B. If any expense exceeds an amount expressly stated in this contract for such expense to be paid by a party, that party may terminate this contract unless the other party agrees to pay such excess. Buyer may not pay charges and fees expressly prohibited by FHA, VA, Texas Veterans Land Board or other governmental loan program regulations.

13. **PRORATIONS:** Taxes for the current year, interest, maintenance fees, assessments, dues and rents will be prorated through the Closing Date. The tax proration may be calculated taking into consideration any change in exemptions that will affect the current year's taxes. If taxes for the current year vary from the amount prorated at closing, the parties shall adjust the prorations when tax statements for the current year are available. If taxes are not paid at or prior to closing, Buyer shall pay taxes for the current year.

14. **CASUALTY LOSS:** If any part of the Property is damaged or destroyed by fire or other casualty after the effective date of this contract, Seller shall restore the Property to its previous condition as soon as reasonably possible, but in any event by the Closing Date. If Seller fails to do so due to factors beyond Seller's control, Buyer may (a) terminate this contract and the earnest money will be refunded to Buyer (b) extend the time for performance up to 15 days and the Closing Date will be extended as necessary or (c) accept the Property in its damaged condition with an assignment of insurance proceeds and receive credit from Seller at closing in the amount of the deductible under the insurance policy. Seller's obligations under this paragraph are independent of any other obligations of Seller under this contract.

15. **DEFAULT:** If Buyer fails to comply with this contract, Buyer will be in default, and Seller may (a) enforce specific performance, seek such other relief as may be provided by law, or both, or (b) terminate this contract and receive the earnest money as liquidated damages, thereby releasing both parties from this contract. If Seller fails to comply with this contract, Seller will be in default and Buyer may (a) enforce specific performance, seek such other relief as may be provided by law, or both, or (b) terminate this contract and receive the earnest money, thereby releasing both parties from this contract.

16. **MEDIATION:** It is the policy of the State of Texas to encourage resolution of disputes through alternative dispute resolution procedures such as mediation. Any dispute between Seller and Buyer related to this contract which is not resolved through informal discussion will be submitted to a mutually acceptable mediation service or provider. The parties to the mediation shall bear the mediation costs equally. This paragraph does not preclude a party from seeking equitable relief from a court of competent jurisdiction.

17. **ATTORNEY'S FEES:** A Buyer, Seller, Listing Broker, Other Broker, or escrow agent who prevails in any legal proceeding related to this contract is entitled to recover reasonable attorney's fees and all costs of such proceeding.

18. **ESCROW:**
   A. ESCROW: The escrow agent is not (i) a party to this contract and does not have liability for the performance or nonperformance of any party to this contract, (ii) liable for interest on the earnest money and (iii) liable for the loss of any earnest money caused by the failure of any financial institution in which the earnest money has been deposited unless the financial institution is acting as escrow agent.
   B. EXPENSES: At closing, the earnest money must be applied first to any cash down payment, then to Buyer's Expenses and any excess refunded to Buyer. If no closing occurs, escrow agent may: (i) require a written release of liability of the escrow agent from all parties, (ii) require payment of unpaid expenses incurred on behalf of a party, and (iii) only deduct from the earnest money the amount of unpaid expenses incurred on behalf of the party receiving the earnest money.
   C. DEMAND: Upon termination of this contract, either party or the escrow agent may send a release of earnest money to each party and the parties shall execute counterparts of

Initialed for identification by Buyer_____ _____ and Seller _____ _____   TREC NO. 20-12

Contract Concerning _____ Page 7 of 9 4-28-2014
(Address of Property)

the release and deliver same to the escrow agent. If either party fails to execute the release, either party may make a written demand to the escrow agent for the earnest money. If only one party makes written demand for the earnest money, escrow agent shall promptly provide a copy of the demand to the other party. If escrow agent does not receive written objection to the demand from the other party within 15 days, escrow agent may disburse the earnest money to the party making demand reduced by the amount of unpaid expenses incurred on behalf of the party receiving the earnest money and escrow agent may pay the same to the creditors. If escrow agent complies with the provisions of this paragraph, each party hereby releases escrow agent from all adverse claims related to the disbursal of the earnest money.

    D. DAMAGES: Any party who wrongfully fails or refuses to sign a release acceptable to the escrow agent within 7 days of receipt of the request will be liable to the other party for liquidated damages in an amount equal to the sum of: (i) three times the amount of the earnest money; (ii) the earnest money; (iii) reasonable attorney's fees; and (iv) all costs of suit.

    E. NOTICES: Escrow agent's notices will be effective when sent in compliance with Paragraph 21. Notice of objection to the demand will be deemed effective upon receipt by escrow agent.

19. REPRESENTATIONS: All covenants, representations and warranties in this contract survive closing. If any representation of Seller in this contract is untrue on the Closing Date, Seller will be in default. Unless expressly prohibited by written agreement, Seller may continue to show the Property and receive, negotiate and accept back up offers.

20. FEDERAL TAX REQUIREMENTS: If Seller is a "foreign person," as defined by applicable law, or if Seller fails to deliver an affidavit to Buyer that Seller is not a "foreign person," then Buyer shall withhold from the sales proceeds an amount sufficient to comply with applicable tax law and deliver the same to the Internal Revenue Service together with appropriate tax forms. Internal Revenue Service regulations require filing written reports if currency in excess of specified amounts is received in the transaction.

21. NOTICES: All notices from one party to the other must be in writing and are effective when mailed to, hand-delivered at, or transmitted by facsimile or electronic transmission as follows:

To Buyer at: _____   **To Seller at:** _____

_____   _____

Telephone: ( ) _____   Telephone: ( ) _____

Facsimile: ( ) _____   Facsimile: ( ) _____

E-mail: _____   E-mail: _____

22. AGREEMENT OF PARTIES: This contract contains the entire agreement of the parties and cannot be changed except by their written agreement. Addenda which are a part of this contract are (Check all applicable boxes):

❑ Third Party Financing Addendum for Credit Approval

❑ Seller Financing Addendum

❑ Addendum for Property Subject to Mandatory Membership in a Property Owners Association

❑ Buyer's Temporary Residential Lease

❑ Loan Assumption Addendum

❑ Addendum for Sale of Other Property by Buyer

❑ Addendum for Reservation of Oil, Gas and Other Minerals

❑ Addendum for "Back-Up" Contract

❑ Addendum for Coastal Area Property

❑ Environmental Assessment, Threatened or Endangered Species and Wetlands Addendum

❑ Seller's Temporary Residential Lease

❑ Short Sale Addendum

❑ Addendum for Property Located Seaward of the Gulf Intracoastal Waterway

❑ Addendum for Seller's Disclosure of Information on Lead-based Paint and Lead-based Paint Hazards as Required by Federal Law

❑ Addendum for Property in a Propane Gas System Service Area

❑ Other (list): _____

_____

_____

Initialed for identification by Buyer_____ _____ and Seller _____ _____   TREC NO. 20-12

Contract Concerning _____Page 8 of 9   4-28-2014
(Address of Property)

23. **TERMINATION OPTION:** For nominal consideration, the receipt of which is hereby acknowledged by Seller, and Buyer's agreement to pay Seller $_____ (Option Fee) within 3 days after the effective date of this contract, Seller grants Buyer the unrestricted right to terminate this contract by giving notice of termination to Seller within _____ days after the effective date of this contract (Option Period). If no dollar amount is stated as the Option Fee or if Buyer fails to pay the Option Fee to Seller within the time prescribed, this paragraph will not be a part of this contract and Buyer shall not have the unrestricted right to terminate this contract. If Buyer gives notice of termination within the time prescribed, the Option Fee will not be refunded; however, any earnest money will be refunded to Buyer. The Option Fee ☐will ☐will not be credited to the Sales Price at closing. **Time is of the essence for this paragraph and strict compliance with the time for performance is required.**

24. **CONSULT AN ATTORNEY BEFORE SIGNING:** TREC rules prohibit real estate licensees from giving legal advice. READ THIS CONTRACT CAREFULLY.

Buyer's
Attorney is: _____

Seller's
Attorney is: _____

_____

_____

Telephone: (   ) _____

Telephone: (   ) _____

Facsimile: (   ) _____

Facsimile: (   ) _____

E-mail: _____

E-mail: _____

EXECUTED the _____day of _____, 20_____ (EFFECTIVE DATE).
(BROKER: FILL IN THE DATE OF FINAL ACCEPTANCE.)

_____
Buyer

_____
Seller

_____
Buyer

_____
Seller

TREC NO. 20-12

Contract Concerning _____ Page 9 of 9   4-28-2014
(Address of Property)

BROKER INFORMATION
(Print name(s) only. Do not sign)

Other Broker Firm   License No.   Listing Broker Firm   License No.

represents   ☐ Buyer only as Buyer's agent   represents   ☐ Seller and Buyer as an intermediary
              ☐ Seller as Listing Broker's subagent   ☐ Seller only as Seller's agent

Name of Associate's Licensed Supervisor   Telephone   Name of Associate's Licensed Supervisor   Telephone

Associate's Name   Telephone   Listing Associate's Name   Telephone

Other Broker's Address   Facsimile   Listing Broker's Office Address   Facsimile

City   State   Zip   City   State   Zip

Associate's Email Address   Listing Associate's Email Address

                                                           Selling Associate's Name   Telephone

                                                           Name of Selling Associate's Licensed Supervisor   Telephone

                                                           Selling Associate's Office Address   Facsimile

                                                           City   State   Zip

                                                           Selling Associate's Email Address

Listing Broker has agreed to pay Other Broker_____of the total sales price when the Listing Broker's fee is received. Escrow agent is authorized and directed to pay other Broker from Listing Broker's fee at closing.

OPTION FEE RECEIPT

Receipt of $_____ (Option Fee) in the form of _____ is acknowledged.

Seller or Listing Broker   Date

CONTRACT AND EARNEST MONEY RECEIPT

Receipt of ☐Contract and ☐$_____Earnest Money in the form of _____
is acknowledged.

Escrow Agent: _____   Date: _____

By: _____   _____
                                         Email Address

_____   Telephone (____)_____
Address

_____   Facsimile: (____) _____
City   State   Zip

TREC NO. 20-12

PROMULGATED BY THE TEXAS REAL ESTATE COMMISSION (TREC) 08-18-2014

ADDENDUM FOR PROPERTY SUBJECT TO MANDATORY MEMBERSHIP IN A PROPERTY OWNERS ASSOCIATION
(NOT FOR USE WITH CONDOMINIUMS)
ADDENDUM TO CONTRACT CONCERNING THE PROPERTY AT

_____
(Street Address and City)

_____
(Name of Property Owners Association, (Association) and Phone Number)

A. SUBDIVISION INFORMATION: "Subdivision Information" means: (i) a current copy of the restrictions applying to the subdivision and bylaws and rules of the Association, and (ii) a resale certificate, all of which are described by Section 207.003 of the Texas Property Code.

(Check only one box):

❑ 1. Within _____ days after the effective date of the contract, Seller shall obtain, pay for, and deliver the Subdivision Information to the Buyer. If Seller delivers the Subdivision Information, Buyer may terminate the contract within 3 days after Buyer receives the Subdivision Information or prior to closing, whichever occurs first, and the earnest money will be refunded to Buyer. If Buyer does not receive the Subdivision Information, Buyer, as Buyer's sole remedy, may terminate the contract at any time prior to closing and the earnest money will be refunded to Buyer.

❑ 2. Within _____ days after the effective date of the contract, Buyer shall obtain, pay for, and deliver a copy of the Subdivision Information to the Seller. If Buyer obtains the Subdivision Information within the time required, Buyer may terminate the contract within 3 days after Buyer receives the Subdivision Information or prior to closing, whichever occurs first, and the earnest money will be refunded to Buyer. If Buyer, due to factors beyond Buyer's control, is not able to obtain the Subdivision Information within the time required, Buyer may, as Buyer's sole remedy, terminate the contract within 3 days after the time required or prior to closing, whichever occurs first, and the earnest money will be refunded to Buyer.

❑ 3. Buyer has received and approved the Subdivision Information before signing the contract. Buyer ❑ does ❑ does not require an updated resale certificate. If Buyer requires an updated resale certificate, Seller, at Buyer's expense, shall deliver it to Buyer within 10 days after receiving payment for the updated resale certificate from Buyer. Buyer may terminate this contract and the earnest money will be refunded to Buyer if Seller fails to deliver the updated resale certificate within the time required.

❑ 4. Buyer does not require delivery of the Subdivision Information.

The title company or its agent is authorized to act on behalf of the parties to obtain the Subdivision Information ONLY upon receipt of the required fee for the Subdivision Information from the party obligated to pay.

B. MATERIAL CHANGES. If Seller becomes aware of any material changes in the Subdivision Information, Seller shall promptly give notice to Buyer. Buyer may terminate the contract prior to closing by giving written notice to Seller if: (i) any of the Subdivision Information provided was not true; or (ii) any material adverse change in the Subdivision Information occurs prior to closing, and the earnest money will be refunded to Buyer.

C FEES: Except as provided by Paragraphs A, D and E, Buyer shall pay any and all Association fees or other charges associated with the transfer of the Property not to exceed $_____ and Seller shall pay any excess.

D. DEPOSITS FOR RESERVES: Buyer shall pay any deposits for reserves required at closing by the Association.

E. AUTHORIZATION: Seller authorizes the Association to release and provide the Subdivision Information and any updated resale certificate if requested by the Buyer, the Title Company, or any broker to this sale. If Buyer does not require the Subdivision Information or an updated resale certificate, and the Title Company requires information from the Association (such as the status of dues, special assessments, violations of covenants and restrictions, and a waiver of any right of first refusal), ❑ Buyer ❑ Seller shall pay the Title Company the cost of obtaining the information prior to the Title Company ordering the information.

NOTICE TO BUYER REGARDING REPAIRS BY THE ASSOCIATION: The Association may have the sole responsibility to make certain repairs to the Property. If you are concerned about the condition of any part of the Property which the Association is required to repair, you should not sign the contract unless you are satisfied that the Association will make the desired repairs.

_____   _____
Buyer   Seller

_____   _____
Buyer   Seller

TREC NO. 36-8

SELLER FINANCING ADDENDUM
TO CONTRACT CONCERNING THE PROPERTY AT

_____

(Address of Property)

A. CREDIT DOCUMENTATION. To establish Buyer's creditworthiness, Buyer shall deliver to Seller within_____days after the effective date of this contract, ❑ credit report ❑ verification of employment, including salary ❑ verification of funds on deposit in financial institutions ❑ current financial statement and ❑ _____
_____. Buyer hereby authorizes any credit reporting agency to furnish copies of Buyer's credit reports to Seller at Buyer's sole expense.

B. CREDIT APPROVAL. If the credit documentation described in Paragraph A is not delivered within the specified time, Seller may terminate this contract by notice to Buyer within 7 days after expiration of the time for delivery, and the earnest money will be paid to Seller. If the credit documentation is timely delivered, and Seller determines in Seller's sole discretion that Buyer's credit is unacceptable, Seller may terminate this contract by notice to Buyer within 7 days after expiration of the time for delivery and the earnest money will be refunded to Buyer. If Seller does not terminate this contract, Seller will be deemed to have approved Buyer's creditworthiness.

C. PROMISSORY NOTE. The promissory note (Note) described in Paragraph 4 of this contract payable by Buyer to the order of Seller will bear interest at the rate of _____% per annum and be payable at the place designated by Seller. Buyer may prepay the Note in whole or in part at any time without penalty. Any prepayments are to be applied to the payment of the installments of principal last maturing and interest will immediately cease on the prepaid principal. The Note will contain a provision for payment of a late fee of 5% of any installment not paid within 10 days of the due date. Matured unpaid amounts will bear interest at the rate of 1½% per month or at the highest lawful rate, whichever is less. The Note will be payable as follows:

❑ (1) In one payment due _____ after the date of the Note with interest payable ❑ at maturity ❑ monthly ❑ quarterly. (check one box only)

❑ (2) In monthly installments of $ _____ ❑ including interest ❑plus interest (check one box only) beginning _____ after the date of the Note and continuing monthly thereafter for_____ months when the balance of the Note will be due and payable.

❑ (3) Interest only in monthly installments for the first _____ month(s) and thereafter in installments of $_____ ❑ including interest ❑ plus interest (check one box only) beginning _____ after the date of the Note and continuing monthly thereafter for _____ months when the balance of the Note will be due and payable.

D. DEED OF TRUST. The deed of trust securing the Note will provide for the following:

(1) PROPERTY TRANSFERS: (check one box only)

❑ (a) Consent Not Required: The Property may be sold, conveyed or leased without the consent of Seller, provided any subsequent buyer assumes the Note.

❑ (b) Consent Required: If all or any part of the Property is sold, conveyed, leased for a period longer than 3 years, leased with an option to purchase, or otherwise sold (including any contract for deed), without Seller's prior written consent, which consent may be withheld in Seller's sole discretion, Seller may declare the balance of the Note to be immediately due and payable. The creation of a subordinate lien, any conveyance

Initialed for identification by Buyer_____ and Seller_____   TREC NO. 26-6

(Address of Property)

under threat or order of condemnation, any deed solely between buyers, or the passage of title by reason of the death of a buyer or by operation of law will not entitle Seller to exercise the remedies provided in this paragraph.

NOTE: *Under (a) or (b), Buyer's liability to pay the Note will continue unless Buyer obtains a release of liability from Seller.*

(2) TAX AND INSURANCE ESCROW: (check one box only)

❑ (a) Escrow Not Required: Buyer shall furnish Seller, before each year's ad valorem taxes become delinquent, evidence that all ad valorem taxes on the Property have been paid. Buyer shall annually furnish Seller evidence of paid-up casualty insurance naming Seller as a mortgagee loss payee.

❑ (b) Escrow Required: With each installment Buyer shall deposit in escrow with Seller a pro rata part of the estimated annual ad valorem taxes and casualty insurance premiums for the Property. Buyer shall pay any deficiency within 30 days after notice from Seller. Buyer's failure to pay the deficiency will be a default under the deed of trust. Buyer is not required to deposit any escrow payments for taxes and insurance that are deposited with a superior lienholder. The casualty insurance must name Seller as a mortgagee loss payee.

(3) PRIOR LIENS: Any default under any lien superior to the lien securing the Note will be a default under the deed of trust securing the Note.

_____   _____
Buyer   Seller

_____   _____
Buyer   Seller

PROMULGATED BY THE TEXAS REAL ESTATE COMMISSION (TREC)   12-05-11
(NOTICE: For use only when SELLER occupies the property for no more than 90 days AFTER the closing)

SELLER'S TEMPORARY RESIDENTIAL LEASE

1. **PARTIES:** The parties to this Lease are_____
   (Landlord) and _____(Tenant).

2. **LEASE:** Landlord leases to Tenant the Property described in the Contract between Landlord as Buyer and Tenant as Seller known as _____
   _____(address).

3. **TERM:** The term of this Lease commences on the date the sale covered by the Contract is closed and funded and terminates _____, unless terminated earlier by reason of other provisions.

4. **RENTAL:** Tenant shall pay to Landlord as rental $_____ per day (excluding the day of closing and funding) with the full amount of rental for the term of the Lease to be paid at the time of funding of the sale. Tenant will not be entitled to a refund of rental if this Lease terminates early due to Tenant's default or voluntary surrender of the Property.

5. **DEPOSIT:** Tenant shall pay to Landlord at the time of funding of the sale $_____ as a deposit to secure performance of this Lease by Tenant. Landlord may use the deposit to satisfy Tenant's obligations under this Lease. Landlord shall refund any unused portion of the deposit to Tenant with an itemized list of all deductions from the deposit within 30 days after Tenant (a) surrenders possession of the Property and (b) provides Landlord written notice of Tenant's forwarding address.

6. **UTILITIES:** Tenant shall pay all utility charges except _____ which Landlord shall pay.

7. **USE OF PROPERTY:** Tenant may use the Property only for residential purposes. Tenant may not assign this Lease or sublet any part of the Property.

8. **PETS:** Tenant may not keep pets on the Property except _____.

9. **CONDITION OF PROPERTY:** Tenant accepts the Property in its present condition and state of repair at the commencement of the Lease. Upon termination, Tenant shall surrender the Property to Landlord in the condition required under the Contract, except normal wear and tear and any casualty loss.

10. **ALTERATIONS:** Tenant may not alter the Property or install improvements or fixtures without the prior written consent of the Landlord. Any improvements or fixtures placed on the Property during the Lease become the Property of Landlord.

11. **SPECIAL PROVISIONS:**

12. **INSPECTIONS:** Landlord may enter at reasonable times to inspect the Property. Tenant shall provide Landlord door keys and access codes to allow access to the Property during the term of Lease.

13. **LAWS:** Tenant shall comply with all applicable laws, restrictions, ordinances, rules and regulations with respect to the Property.

14. **REPAIRS AND MAINTENANCE:** Except as otherwise provided in this Lease, Tenant shall bear all expense of repairing and maintaining the Property, including but not limited to the yard, trees and shrubs, unless otherwise required by the Texas Property Code. Tenant shall promptly repair at Tenant's expense any damage to the Property caused directly or indirectly by any act or omission of the Tenant or any person other than the Landlord, Landlord's agents or invitees.

Initialed for identification by Landlord _____ and Tenant_____   TREC NO. 15-5

15. **INDEMNITY:** Tenant indemnifies Landlord from the claims of all third parties for injury or damage to the person or property of such third party arising from the use or occupancy of the Property by Tenant. This indemnification includes attorney's fees, costs and expenses incurred by Landlord.

16. **INSURANCE:** Landlord and Tenant shall each maintain such insurance on the contents and Property as each party may deem appropriate during the term of this Lease. <u>NOTE: CONSULT YOUR INSURANCE AGENT; POSSESSION OF THE PROPERTY BY SELLER AS TENANT MAY CHANGE INSURANCE POLICY COVERAGE.</u>

17. **DEFAULT:** If Tenant fails to perform or observe any provision of this Lease and fails, within 24 hours after notice by Landlord, to commence and diligently pursue to remedy such failure, Tenant will be in default.

18. **TERMINATION:** This Lease terminates upon expiration of the term specified in Paragraph 3 or upon Tenant's default under this Lease.

19. **HOLDING OVER:** Tenant shall surrender possession of the Property upon termination of this Lease. Any possession by Tenant after termination creates a tenancy at sufferance and will not operate to renew or extend this Lease. Tenant shall pay $_____ per day during the period of any possession after termination as damages, in addition to any other remedies to which Landlord is entitled.

20. **ATTORNEY'S FEES:** The prevailing party in any legal proceeding brought under or with respect to this Lease is entitled to recover from the non-prevailing party all costs of such proceeding and reasonable attorney's fees.

21. **SMOKE ALARMS:** The Texas Property Code requires Landlord to install smoke alarms in certain locations within the Property at Landlord's expense. <u>Tenant expressly waives Landlord's duty to inspect and repair smoke alarms.</u>

22. **SECURITY DEVICES:** The requirements of the Texas Property Code relating to security devices do not apply to a residential lease for a term of 90 days or less.

23. **CONSULT YOUR ATTORNEY:** Real estate licensees cannot give legal advice. This Lease is intended to be legally binding. READ IT CAREFULLY. If you do not understand the effect of this Lease, consult your attorney BEFORE signing.

24. **NOTICES:** All notices from one party to the other must be in writing and are effective when mailed to, hand-delivered at, or transmitted by facsimile or electronic transmission as follows:

To Landlord: _____   **To Tenant:** _____

_____   _____

_____   _____

_____   _____

Telephone: (____) _____   Telephone: (____) _____

Facsimile: (____) _____   Facsimile: (____) _____

E-mail: _____   E-mail: _____

_____   _____
Landlord   Tenant

_____   _____
Landlord   Tenant

PROMULGATED BY THE TEXAS REAL ESTATE COMMISSION (TREC)
4-28-2014

ONE TO FOUR FAMILY RESIDENTIAL CONTRACT (RESALE)

NOTICE: Not For Use For Condominium Transactions

1. PARTIES: The parties to this contract are <u>Robert Strassman, N/A</u>
(Seller) and <u>William Applewhite, and wife Sharon Applewhite</u> (Buyer).
Seller agrees to sell and convey to Buyer and Buyer agrees to buy from Seller the Property defined below.

2. PROPERTY: The land, improvements and accessories are collectively referred to as the "Property".
  A. LAND: Lot <u>20</u> Block <u>15</u>, <u>Edwards Lake Subdivision</u>
     Addition, City of <u>Plano</u>, County of <u>Collin</u>,
     Texas, known as <u>1233 Tree Lane, Plano Tx</u>
     (address/zip code), or as described on attached exhibit.
  B. IMPROVEMENTS: The house, garage and all other fixtures and improvements attached to the above-described real property, including without limitation, the following **permanently installed and built-in items,** if any: all equipment and appliances, valances, screens, shutters, awnings, wall-to-wall carpeting, mirrors, ceiling fans, attic fans, mail boxes, television antennas, mounts and brackets for televisions and speakers, heating and air-conditioning units, security and fire detection equipment, wiring, plumbing and lighting fixtures, chandeliers, water softener system, kitchen equipment, garage door openers, cleaning equipment, shrubbery, landscaping, outdoor cooking equipment, and all other property owned by Seller and attached to the above described real property.
  C. ACCESSORIES: The following described related accessories, if any: window air conditioning units, stove, fireplace screens, curtains and rods, blinds, window shades, draperies and rods, door keys, mailbox keys, above ground pool, swimming pool equipment and maintenance accessories, artificial fireplace logs, and controls for: (i) garage doors, (ii) entry gates, and (iii) other improvements and accessories.
  D. EXCLUSIONS: The following improvements and accessories will be retained by Seller and must be removed prior to delivery of possession: <u>N/A</u>
     <u> </u>.

3. SALES PRICE:
  A. Cash portion of Sales Price payable by Buyer at closing .... $ <u>25,000.00</u>
  B. Sum of all financing described below (excluding any loan funding
     fee or mortgage insurance premium) .... $ <u>225,000.00</u>
  C. Sales Price (Sum of A and B).. $ <u>250,000.00</u>

4. FINANCING (Not for use with reverse mortgage financing): The portion of Sales Price not payable in cash will be paid as follows: (Check applicable boxes below)
☐ A.THIRD PARTY FINANCING: One or more third party mortgage loans in the total amount of
    $_____ (excluding any loan funding fee or mortgage insurance premium).
    (1) Property Approval: If the Property does not satisfy the lenders' underwriting requirements for the loan(s) (including, but not limited to appraisal, insurability and lender required repairs), Buyer may terminate this contract by giving notice to Seller prior to closing and the earnest money will be refunded to Buyer.
    (2) Credit Approval: (Check one box only)
    ☐ (a) This contract is subject to Buyer being approved for the financing described in the attached Third Party Financing Addendum for Credit Approval.
    ☐ (b) This contract is not subject to Buyer being approved for financing and does not involve FHA or VA financing.
☐ B. ASSUMPTION: The assumption of the unpaid principal balance of one or more promissory notes described in the attached TREC Loan Assumption Addendum.
☒ C. SELLER FINANCING: A promissory note from Buyer to Seller of $ <u>225,000.00</u>, secured by vendor's and deed of trust liens, and containing the terms and conditions described in the attached TREC Seller Financing Addendum. If an owner policy of title insurance is furnished, Buyer shall furnish Seller with a mortgagee policy of title insurance.

Initialed for identification by Buyer_____ _____ and Seller _____ _____   TREC NO. 20-12

Contract Concerning __1233 Tree Lane, Plano TX 75093_____ Page 2 of 9   4-28-2014
(Address of Property)

5. **EARNEST MONEY:** Upon execution of this contract by all parties, Buyer shall deposit $ _25,000.00_ as earnest money with _Ticor Title Company_____, as escrow agent, at _____1010 San Pedro Road, Frisco, TX_____ (address). Buyer shall deposit additional earnest money of $_____ with escrow agent within _N/A_days after the effective date of this contract. If Buyer fails to deposit the earnest money as required by this contract, Buyer will be in default.

6. **TITLE POLICY AND SURVEY:**
   A. TITLE POLICY: Seller shall furnish to Buyer at ☒ Seller's ☐ Buyer's expense an owner policy of title insurance (Title Policy) issued by _Ticor Title Company_____ (Title Company) in the amount of the Sales Price, dated at or after closing, insuring Buyer against loss under the provisions of the Title Policy, subject to the promulgated exclusions (including existing building and zoning ordinances) and the following exceptions:
      (1) Restrictive covenants common to the platted subdivision in which the Property is located.
      (2) The standard printed exception for standby fees, taxes and assessments.
      (3) Liens created as part of the financing described in Paragraph 4.
      (4) Utility easements created by the dedication deed or plat of the subdivision in which the Property is located.
      (5) Reservations or exceptions otherwise permitted by this contract or as may be approved by Buyer in writing.
      (6) The standard printed exception as to marital rights.
      (7) The standard printed exception as to waters, tidelands, beaches, streams, and related matters.
      (8) The standard printed exception as to discrepancies, conflicts, shortages in area or boundary lines, encroachments or protrusions, or overlapping improvements: ☐(i) will not be amended or deleted from the title policy; ☒(ii) will be amended to read, "shortages in area" at the expense of ☒Buyer ☐Seller.
   B. COMMITMENT: Within 20 days after the Title Company receives a copy of this contract, Seller shall furnish to Buyer a commitment for title insurance (Commitment) and, at Buyer's expense, legible copies of restrictive covenants and documents evidencing exceptions in the Commitment (Exception Documents) other than the standard printed exceptions. Seller authorizes the Title Company to deliver the Commitment and Exception Documents to Buyer at Buyer's address shown in Paragraph 21. If the Commitment and Exception Documents are not delivered to Buyer within the specified time, the time for delivery will be automatically extended up to 15 days or 3 days before the Closing Date, whichever is earlier. If, due to factors beyond Seller's control, the Commitment and Exception Documents are not delivered within the time required, Buyer may terminate this contract and the earnest money will be refunded to Buyer.
   C. SURVEY: The survey must be made by a registered professional land surveyor acceptable to the Title Company and Buyer's lender(s). (Check one box only)
   ☐(1) Within _N/A___ days after the effective date of this contract, Seller shall furnish to Buyer and Title Company Seller's existing survey of the Property and a Residential Real Property Affidavit promulgated by the Texas Department of Insurance (T-47 Affidavit). **If Seller fails to furnish the existing survey or affidavit within the time prescribed, Buyer shall obtain a new survey at Seller's expense no later than 3 days prior to Closing Date.** If the existing survey or affidavit is not acceptable to Title Company or Buyer's lender(s), Buyer shall obtain a new survey at ☐Seller's ☐Buyer's expense no later than 3 days prior to Closing Date.
   ☐(2) Within _N/A___ days after the effective date of this contract, Buyer shall obtain a new survey at Buyer's expense. Buyer is deemed to receive the survey on the date of actual receipt or the date specified in this paragraph, whichever is earlier.
   ☒(3) Within _10____ days after the effective date of this contract, Seller, at Seller's expense shall furnish a new survey to Buyer.
   D. OBJECTIONS: Buyer may object in writing to defects, exceptions, or encumbrances to title: disclosed on the survey other than items 6A(1) through (7) above; disclosed in the Commitment other than items 6A(1) through (8) above; or which prohibit the following use or activity: _N/A_____.

   Buyer must object the earlier of (i) the Closing Date or (ii) _3____ days after Buyer receives the Commitment, Exception Documents, and the survey. Buyer's failure to object within the time allowed will constitute a waiver of Buyer's right to object; except that the requirements in Schedule C of the Commitment are not waived by Buyer. Provided Seller is not obligated to incur any expense, Seller shall cure the timely objections of Buyer or any third party lender

Initialed for identification by Buyer_____ _____ and Seller _____ _____   TREC NO. 20-12

Contract Concerning ___1233 Tree Lane, Plano, TX 75093___ Page 3 of 9   4-28-2014
(Address of Property)

within 15 days after Seller receives the objections and the Closing Date will be extended as necessary. If objections are not cured within such 15 day period, this contract will terminate and the earnest money will be refunded to Buyer unless Buyer waives the objections.

E. TITLE NOTICES:
(1) ABSTRACT OR TITLE POLICY: Broker advises Buyer to have an abstract of title covering the Property examined by an attorney of Buyer's selection, or Buyer should be furnished with or obtain a Title Policy. If a Title Policy is furnished, the Commitment should be promptly reviewed by an attorney of Buyer's choice due to the time limitations on Buyer's right to object.
(2) MEMBERSHIP IN PROPERTY OWNERS ASSOCIATION(S): The Property ☑is ☐is not subject to mandatory membership in a property owners association(s). If the Property is subject to mandatory membership in a property owners association(s), Seller notifies Buyer under §5.012, Texas Property Code, that, as a purchaser of property in the residential community identified in Paragraph 2A in which the Property is located, you are obligated to be a member of the property owners association(s). Restrictive covenants governing the use and occupancy of the Property and all dedicatory instruments governing the establishment, maintenance, or operation of this residential community have been or will be recorded in the Real Property Records of the county in which the Property is located. Copies of the restrictive covenants and dedicatory instruments may be obtained from the county clerk. **You are obligated to pay assessments to the property owners association(s). The amount of the assessments is subject to change. Your failure to pay the assessments could result in enforcement of the association's lien on and the foreclosure of the Property.**
Section 207.003, Property Code, entitles an owner to receive copies of any document that governs the establishment, maintenance, or operation of a subdivision, including, but not limited to, restrictions, bylaws, rules and regulations, and a resale certificate from a property owners' association. A resale certificate contains information including, but not limited to, statements specifying the amount and frequency of regular assessments and the style and cause number of lawsuits to which the property owners' association is a party, other than lawsuits relating to unpaid ad valorem taxes of an individual member of the association. These documents must be made available to you by the property owners' association or the association's agent on your request.
If Buyer is concerned about these matters, the TREC promulgated Addendum for Property Subject to Mandatory Membership in a Property Owners Association(s) should be used.
(3) STATUTORY TAX DISTRICTS: If the Property is situated in a utility or other statutorily created district providing water, sewer, drainage, or flood control facilities and services, Chapter 49, Texas Water Code, requires Seller to deliver and Buyer to sign the statutory notice relating to the tax rate, bonded indebtedness, or standby fee of the district prior to final execution of this contract.
(4) TIDE WATERS: If the Property abuts the tidally influenced waters of the state, §33.135, Texas Natural Resources Code, requires a notice regarding coastal area property to be included in the contract. An addendum containing the notice promulgated by TREC or required by the parties must be used.
(5) ANNEXATION: If the Property is located outside the limits of a municipality, Seller notifies Buyer under §5.011, Texas Property Code, that the Property may now or later be included in the extraterritorial jurisdiction of a municipality and may now or later be subject to annexation by the municipality. Each municipality maintains a map that depicts its boundaries and extraterritorial jurisdiction. To determine if the Property is located within a municipality's extraterritorial jurisdiction or is likely to be located within a municipality's extraterritorial jurisdiction, contact all municipalities located in the general proximity of the Property for further information.
(6) PROPERTY LOCATED IN A CERTIFICATED SERVICE AREA OF A UTILITY SERVICE PROVIDER: Notice required by §13.257, Water Code: The real property, described in Paragraph 2, that you are about to purchase may be located in a certificated water or sewer service area, which is authorized by law to provide water or sewer service to the properties in the certificated area. If your property is located in a certificated area there may be special costs or charges that you will be required to pay before you can receive water or sewer service. There may be a period required to construct lines or other facilities necessary to provide water or sewer service to your property. You are advised to determine if the property is in a certificated area and contact the utility service provider to determine the cost that you will be required to pay and the period, if any, that is required to provide water or sewer service to your property. The undersigned Buyer hereby acknowledges receipt of the foregoing notice at or before the execution of a binding contract for the purchase of the real property described in Paragraph 2 or at closing of purchase of the real property.

Initialed for identification by Buyer_____ _____ and Seller _____ _____   TREC NO. 20-12

Contract Concerning ___1233 Tree Lane, Plano, TX 75093_____Page 4 of 9   4-28-2014
(Address of Property)

(7) PUBLIC IMPROVEMENT DISTRICTS: If the Property is in a public improvement district, §5.014, Property Code, requires Seller to notify Buyer as follows: As a purchaser of this parcel of real property you are obligated to pay an assessment to a municipality or county for an improvement project undertaken by a public improvement district under Chapter 372, Local Government Code. The assessment may be due annually or in periodic installments. More information concerning the amount of the assessment and the due dates of that assessment may be obtained from the municipality or county levying the assessment. The amount of the assessments is subject to change. Your failure to pay the assessments could result in a lien on and the foreclosure of your property.

(8) TRANSFER FEES: If the Property is subject to a private transfer fee obligation, §5.205, Property Code, requires Seller to notify Buyer as follows: The private transfer fee obligation may be governed by Chapter 5, Subchapter G of the Texas Property Code.

(9) PROPANE GAS SYSTEM SERVICE AREA: If the Property is located in a propane gas system service area owned by a distribution system retailer, Seller must give Buyer written notice as required by §141.010, Texas Utilities Code. An addendum containing the notice approved by TREC or required by the parties should be used.

7. PROPERTY CONDITION:
  A. ACCESS, INSPECTIONS AND UTILITIES: Seller shall permit Buyer and Buyer's agents access to the Property at reasonable times. Buyer may have the Property inspected by inspectors selected by Buyer and licensed by TREC or otherwise permitted by law to make inspections. Seller at Seller's expense shall immediately cause existing utilities to be turned on and shall keep the utilities on during the time this contract is in effect.
  B. SELLER'S DISCLOSURE NOTICE PURSUANT TO §5.008, TEXAS PROPERTY CODE (Notice): (Check one box only)
  ☒ (1) Buyer has received the Notice.
  ☐ (2) Buyer has not received the Notice. Within _N/A___ days after the effective date of this contract, Seller shall deliver the Notice to Buyer. If Buyer does not receive the Notice, Buyer may terminate this contract at any time prior to the closing and the earnest money will be refunded to Buyer. If Seller delivers the Notice, Buyer may terminate this contract for any reason within 7 days after Buyer receives the Notice or prior to the closing, whichever first occurs, and the earnest money will be refunded to Buyer.
  ☐ (3)The Seller is not required to furnish the notice under the Texas Property Code.
  C. SELLER'S DISCLOSURE OF LEAD-BASED PAINT AND LEAD-BASED PAINT HAZARDS is required by Federal law for a residential dwelling constructed prior to 1978.
  D. ACCEPTANCE OF PROPERTY CONDITION: "As Is" means the present condition of the Property with any and all defects and without warranty except for the warranties of title and the warranties in this contract. Buyer's agreement to accept the Property As Is under Paragraph 7D(1) or (2) does not preclude Buyer from inspecting the Property under Paragraph 7A, from negotiating repairs or treatments in a subsequent amendment, or from terminating this contract during the Option Period, if any.
  (Check one box only)
  ☒ (1) Buyer accepts the Property As Is.
  ☐ (2) Buyer accepts the Property As Is provided Seller, at Seller's expense, shall complete the following specific repairs and treatments: _N/A_____
  _____.
  (Do not insert general phrases, such as "subject to inspections" that do not identify specific repairs and treatments.)
  E. LENDER REQUIRED REPAIRS AND TREATMENTS: Unless otherwise agreed in writing, neither party is obligated to pay for lender required repairs, which includes treatment for wood destroying insects. If the parties do not agree to pay for the lender required repairs or treatments, this contract will terminate and the earnest money will be refunded to Buyer. If the cost of lender required repairs and treatments exceeds 5% of the Sales Price, Buyer may terminate this contract and the earnest money will be refunded to Buyer.
  F. COMPLETION OF REPAIRS AND TREATMENTS: Unless otherwise agreed in writing: (i) Seller shall complete all agreed repairs and treatments prior to the Closing Date; and (ii) all required permits must be obtained, and repairs and treatments must be performed by persons who are licensed to provide such repairs or treatments or, if no license is required by law, are commercially engaged in the trade of providing such repairs or treatments. At Buyer's election, any transferable warranties received by Seller with respect to the repairs and treatments will be transferred to Buyer at Buyer's expense. If Seller fails to complete any agreed repairs and treatments prior to the Closing Date, Buyer may exercise remedies under Paragraph 15 or extend the Closing Date up to 5 days if necessary for Seller to complete the repairs and treatments.
  G. ENVIRONMENTAL MATTERS: Buyer is advised that the presence of wetlands, toxic substances, including asbestos and wastes or other environmental hazards, or the presence of a threatened or endangered species or its habitat may affect Buyer's intended use of the

Initialed for identification by Buyer_____ _____ and Seller _____ _____   TREC NO. 20-12

Contract Concerning ___1233 Tree Lane, Plano, TX 75093___ Page 5 of 9   4-28-2014
(Address of Property)

Property. If Buyer is concerned about these matters, an addendum promulgated by TREC or required by the parties should be used.

H. RESIDENTIAL SERVICE CONTRACTS: Buyer may purchase a residential service contract from a residential service company licensed by TREC. If Buyer purchases a residential service contract, Seller shall reimburse Buyer at closing for the cost of the residential service contract in an amount not exceeding $ _375.00_____. Buyer should review any residential service contract for the scope of coverage, exclusions and limitations. **The purchase of a residential service contract is optional. Similar coverage may be purchased from various companies authorized to do business in Texas.**

8. **BROKERS' FEES:** All obligations of the parties for payment of brokers' fees are contained in separate written agreements.

9. **CLOSING:**
   A. The closing of the sale will be on or before _(Next Month)_____, 20_xx_, or within 7 days after objections made under Paragraph 6D have been cured or waived, whichever date is later (Closing Date). If either party fails to close the sale by the Closing Date, the non-defaulting party may exercise the remedies contained in Paragraph 15.
   B. At closing:
      (1) Seller shall execute and deliver a general warranty deed conveying title to the Property to Buyer and showing no additional exceptions to those permitted in Paragraph 6 and furnish tax statements or certificates showing no delinquent taxes on the Property.
      (2) Buyer shall pay the Sales Price in good funds acceptable to the escrow agent.
      (3) Seller and Buyer shall execute and deliver any notices, statements, certificates, affidavits, releases, loan documents and other documents reasonably required for the closing of the sale and the issuance of the Title Policy.
      (4) There will be no liens, assessments, or security interests against the Property which will not be satisfied out of the sales proceeds unless securing the payment of any loans assumed by Buyer and assumed loans will not be in default.
      (5) If the Property is subject to a residential lease, Seller shall transfer security deposits (as defined under §92.102, Property Code), if any, to Buyer. In such an event, Buyer shall deliver to the tenant a signed statement acknowledging that the Buyer has received the security deposit and is responsible for the return of the security deposit, and specifying the exact dollar amount of the security deposit.

10. **POSSESSION:**
    A Buyer's Possession: Seller shall deliver to Buyer possession of the Property in its present or required condition, ordinary wear and tear excepted: ☐ upon closing and funding ☒ according to a temporary residential lease form promulgated by TREC or other written lease required by the parties. Any possession by Buyer prior to closing or by Seller after closing which is not authorized by a written lease will establish a tenancy at sufferance relationship between the parties. **Consult your insurance agent prior to change of ownership and possession because insurance coverage may be limited or terminated. The absence of a written lease or appropriate insurance coverage may expose the parties to economic loss.**
    B. Leases:
       (1) After the Effective Date, Seller may not execute any lease (including but not limited to mineral leases) or convey any interest in the Property without Buyer's written consent.
       (2) If the Property is subject to any lease to which Seller is a party, Seller shall deliver to Buyer copies of the lease(s) and any move-in condition form signed by the tenant within 7 days after the Effective Date of the contract.

11. **SPECIAL PROVISIONS:** (Insert only factual statements and business details applicable to the sale. TREC rules prohibit licensees from adding factual statements or business details for which a contract addendum, lease or other form has been promulgated by TREC for mandatory use.)
The parties agree that the interest on the seller financing will begin
3 days after closing and funding

12. **SETTLEMENT AND OTHER EXPENSES:**
    A. The following expenses must be paid at or prior to closing:
       (1) Expenses payable by Seller (Seller's Expenses):
          (a) Releases of existing liens, including prepayment penalties and recording fees; release of Seller's loan liability; tax statements or certificates; preparation of deed; one-half of escrow fee; and other expenses payable by Seller under this contract.
          (b) Seller shall also pay an amount not to exceed $_____ to be applied in the

Initialed for identification by Buyer_____ _____ and Seller _____ _____   TREC NO. 20-12

Contract Concerning ___1233 Tree Lane, Plano, TX 75093_____Page 6 of 9   4-28-2014
(Address of Property)

following order: Buyer's Expenses which Buyer is prohibited from paying by FHA, VA, Texas Veterans Land Board or other governmental loan programs, and then to other Buyer's Expenses as allowed by the lender.

(2) Expenses payable by Buyer (Buyer's Expenses): Appraisal fees; loan application fees; adjusted origination charges; credit reports; preparation of loan documents; interest on the notes from date of disbursement to one month prior to dates of first monthly payments; recording fees; copies of easements and restrictions; loan title policy with endorsements required by lender; loan-related inspection fees; photos; amortization schedules; one-half of escrow fee; all prepaid items, including required premiums for flood and hazard insurance, reserve deposits for insurance, ad valorem taxes and special governmental assessments; final compliance inspection; courier fee; repair inspection; underwriting fee; wire transfer fee; expenses incident to any loan; Private Mortgage Insurance Premium (PMI), VA Loan Funding Fee, or FHA Mortgage Insurance Premium (MIP) as required by the lender; and other expenses payable by Buyer under this contract.

B. If any expense exceeds an amount expressly stated in this contract for such expense to be paid by a party, that party may terminate this contract unless the other party agrees to pay such excess. Buyer may not pay charges and fees expressly prohibited by FHA, VA, Texas Veterans Land Board or other governmental loan program regulations.

13. **PRORATIONS:** Taxes for the current year, interest, maintenance fees, assessments, dues and rents will be prorated through the Closing Date. The tax proration may be calculated taking into consideration any change in exemptions that will affect the current year's taxes. If taxes for the current year vary from the amount prorated at closing, the parties shall adjust the prorations when tax statements for the current year are available. If taxes are not paid at or prior to closing, Buyer shall pay taxes for the current year.

14. **CASUALTY LOSS:** If any part of the Property is damaged or destroyed by fire or other casualty after the effective date of this contract, Seller shall restore the Property to its previous condition as soon as reasonably possible, but in any event by the Closing Date. If Seller fails to do so due to factors beyond Seller's control, Buyer may (a) terminate this contract and the earnest money will be refunded to Buyer (b) extend the time for performance up to 15 days and the Closing Date will be extended as necessary or (c) accept the Property in its damaged condition with an assignment of insurance proceeds and receive credit from Seller at closing in the amount of the deductible under the insurance policy. Seller's obligations under this paragraph are independent of any other obligations of Seller under this contract.

15. **DEFAULT:** If Buyer fails to comply with this contract, Buyer will be in default, and Seller may (a) enforce specific performance, seek such other relief as may be provided by law, or both, or (b) terminate this contract and receive the earnest money as liquidated damages, thereby releasing both parties from this contract. If Seller fails to comply with this contract, Seller will be in default and Buyer may (a) enforce specific performance, seek such other relief as may be provided by law, or both, or (b) terminate this contract and receive the earnest money, thereby releasing both parties from this contract.

16. **MEDIATION:** It is the policy of the State of Texas to encourage resolution of disputes through alternative dispute resolution procedures such as mediation. Any dispute between Seller and Buyer related to this contract which is not resolved through informal discussion will be submitted to a mutually acceptable mediation service or provider. The parties to the mediation shall bear the mediation costs equally. This paragraph does not preclude a party from seeking equitable relief from a court of competent jurisdiction.

17. **ATTORNEY'S FEES:** A Buyer, Seller, Listing Broker, Other Broker, or escrow agent who prevails in any legal proceeding related to this contract is entitled to recover reasonable attorney's fees and all costs of such proceeding.

18. **ESCROW:**
   A. ESCROW: The escrow agent is not (i) a party to this contract and does not have liability for the performance or nonperformance of any party to this contract, (ii) liable for interest on the earnest money and (iii) liable for the loss of any earnest money caused by the failure of any financial institution in which the earnest money has been deposited unless the financial institution is acting as escrow agent.
   B. EXPENSES: At closing, the earnest money must be applied first to any cash down payment, then to Buyer's Expenses and any excess refunded to Buyer. If no closing occurs, escrow agent may: (i) require a written release of liability of the escrow agent from all parties, (ii) require payment of unpaid expenses incurred on behalf of a party, and (iii) only deduct from the earnest money the amount of unpaid expenses incurred on behalf of the party receiving the earnest money.
   C. DEMAND: Upon termination of this contract, either party or the escrow agent may send a release of earnest money to each party and the parties shall execute counterparts of

Initialed for identification by Buyer_____ _____ and Seller _____ _____   TREC NO. 20-12

Contract Concerning 1233 Tree Lane, Plano, TX 75093   Page 7 of 9   4-28-2014
                                          (Address of Property)

the release and deliver same to the escrow agent. If either party fails to execute the release, either party may make a written demand to the escrow agent for the earnest money. If only one party makes written demand for the earnest money, escrow agent shall promptly provide a copy of the demand to the other party. If escrow agent does not receive written objection to the demand from the other party within 15 days, escrow agent may disburse the earnest money to the party making demand reduced by the amount of unpaid expenses incurred on behalf of the party receiving the earnest money and escrow agent may pay the same to the creditors. If escrow agent complies with the provisions of this paragraph, each party hereby releases escrow agent from all adverse claims related to the disbursal of the earnest money.

    D. DAMAGES: Any party who wrongfully fails or refuses to sign a release acceptable to the escrow agent within 7 days of receipt of the request will be liable to the other party for liquidated damages in an amount equal to the sum of: (i) three times the amount of the earnest money; (ii) the earnest money; (iii) reasonable attorney's fees; and (iv) all costs of suit.

    E. NOTICES: Escrow agent's notices will be effective when sent in compliance with Paragraph 21. Notice of objection to the demand will be deemed effective upon receipt by escrow agent.

19. REPRESENTATIONS: All covenants, representations and warranties in this contract survive closing. If any representation of Seller in this contract is untrue on the Closing Date, Seller will be in default. Unless expressly prohibited by written agreement, Seller may continue to show the Property and receive, negotiate and accept back up offers.

20. FEDERAL TAX REQUIREMENTS: If Seller is a "foreign person," as defined by applicable law, or if Seller fails to deliver an affidavit to Buyer that Seller is not a "foreign person," then Buyer shall withhold from the sales proceeds an amount sufficient to comply with applicable tax law and deliver the same to the Internal Revenue Service together with appropriate tax forms. Internal Revenue Service regulations require filing written reports if currency in excess of specified amounts is received in the transaction.

21. NOTICES: All notices from one party to the other must be in writing and are effective when mailed to, hand-delivered at, or transmitted by facsimile or electronic transmission as follows:

To Buyer at: William Applewhite	**To Seller at:** Robert Strassman
1504 Center CT, APT 1001, Plano	1233 Tree Lane, Plano, TX
Telephone: ( ) N/A	Telephone: ( ) N/A
Facsimile: ( ) N/A	Facsimile: ( ) N/A
E-mail: wapplewhite@verizon.net	E-mail: Robert.strassman@gmail.com

22. AGREEMENT OF PARTIES: This contract contains the entire agreement of the parties and cannot be changed except by their written agreement. Addenda which are a part of this contract are (Check all applicable boxes):

☐ Third Party Financing Addendum for Credit Approval

☒ Seller Financing Addendum

☒ Addendum for Property Subject to Mandatory Membership in a Property Owners Association

☐ Buyer's Temporary Residential Lease

☐ Loan Assumption Addendum

☐ Addendum for Sale of Other Property by Buyer

☐ Addendum for Reservation of Oil, Gas and Other Minerals

☐ Addendum for "Back-Up" Contract

☐ Addendum for Coastal Area Property

☐ Environmental Assessment, Threatened or Endangered Species and Wetlands Addendum

☒ Seller's Temporary Residential Lease

☐ Short Sale Addendum

☐ Addendum for Property Located Seaward of the Gulf Intracoastal Waterway

☐ Addendum for Seller's Disclosure of Information on Lead-based Paint and Lead-based Paint Hazards as Required by Federal Law

☐ Addendum for Property in a Propane Gas System Service Area

☐ Other (list): N/A

Initialed for identification by Buyer_____ _____ and Seller _____ _____   TREC NO. 20-12

Contract Concerning ___1233 Tree Lane, Plano, TX 75093_____ Page 8 of 9   4-28-2014
(Address of Property)

23. TERMINATION OPTION: For nominal consideration, the receipt of which is hereby acknowledged by Seller, and Buyer's agreement to pay Seller $ __275.00__ (Option Fee) within 3 days after the effective date of this contract, Seller grants Buyer the unrestricted right to terminate this contract by giving notice of termination to Seller within __7__ days after the effective date of this contract (Option Period). If no dollar amount is stated as the Option Fee or if Buyer fails to pay the Option Fee to Seller within the time prescribed, this paragraph will not be a part of this contract and Buyer shall not have the unrestricted right to terminate this contract. If Buyer gives notice of termination within the time prescribed, the Option Fee will not be refunded; however, any earnest money will be refunded to Buyer. The Option Fee ☒will ☐will not be credited to the Sales Price at closing. **Time is of the essence for this paragraph and strict compliance with the time for performance is required.**

24. CONSULT AN ATTORNEY BEFORE SIGNING: TREC rules prohibit real estate licensees from giving legal advice. READ THIS CONTRACT CAREFULLY.

Buyer's
Attorney is: _N/A_____

_____N/A_____

Telephone: ( ) ___N/A____

Facsimile: ( ) ___N/A____

E-mail: __N/A_____

Seller's
Attorney is: _N/A_____

_____N/A_____

Telephone: ( ) ___N/A____

Facsimile: ( ) ___N/A____

E-mail: _____N/A_____

**EXECUTED the _____day of _____, 20____ (EFFECTIVE DATE).
(BROKER: FILL IN THE DATE OF FINAL ACCEPTANCE.)**

Buyer William Applewhite

Seller Robert Strassman

Buyer and wife Sharon Applewhite

Seller   N/A

TREC NO. 20-12

Contract Concerning ___1233 Tree Lane, Plano, TX 75093_____ Page 9 of 9   4-28-2014

(Address of Property)

BROKER INFORMATION
(Print name(s) only. Do not sign)

N/A	N/A	Your Firm	N/A
Other Broker Firm	License No.	Listing Broker Firm	License No.

represents ☐ Buyer only as Buyer's agent   represents ☒ Seller and Buyer as an intermediary
          ☐ Seller as Listing Broker's subagent   ☐ Seller only as Seller's agent

N/A	N/A	Your Broker/Supervisor	N/A
Name of Associate's Licensed Supervisor	Telephone	Name of Associate's Licensed Supervisor	Telephone
N/A	N/A	Your name	N/A
Associate's Name	Telephone	Listing Associate's Name	Telephone
N/A	N/A	Your Office	N/A
Other Broker's Address	Facsimile	Listing Broker's Office Address	Facsimile

N/A	N/A	N/A	Your Office City	N/A	N/A
City	State	Zip	City	State	Zip

N/A		N/A
Associate's Email Address		Listing Associate's Email Address

	Your e-mail	N/A
	Selling Associate's Name	Telephone
	Your Name	N/A
	Name of Selling Associate's Licensed Supervisor	Telephone
	Your Broker/Supervisor	N/A
	Selling Associate's Office Address	Facsimile

	N/A	N/A	N/A
	City	State	Zip

	Your e-mail
	Selling Associate's Email Address

Listing Broker has agreed to pay Other Broker_____of the total sales price when the Listing Broker's fee is received. Escrow agent is authorized and directed to pay other Broker from Listing Broker's fee at closing.

OPTION FEE RECEIPT

Receipt of $____275.00_____ (Option Fee) in the form of __check number xx____ is acknowledged.

_____   _____
Seller or Listing Broker Your Signature   Date

CONTRACT AND EARNEST MONEY RECEIPT

Receipt of ☒Contract and ☒$_25,000.00_Earnest Money in the form of __cashiers check_____ is acknowledged.

Escrow Agent: __Ticor Title Company_____   Date: _____

By: _____   __maryjane@ticortitle.com_____
    Mary Jane Smite   Email Address
          1010 San Pedro Road_____   Telephone (___) N/A
Address

Frisco   TX   75093   Facsimile: (___) ___N/A____
City   State   Zip

PROMULGATED BY THE TEXAS REAL ESTATE COMMISSION (TREC)   08-18-2014

ADDENDUM FOR PROPERTY SUBJECT TO MANDATORY MEMBERSHIP IN A PROPERTY OWNERS ASSOCIATION
(NOT FOR USE WITH CONDOMINIUMS)
ADDENDUM TO CONTRACT CONCERNING THE PROPERTY AT

1233 Tree Lane, Plano, TX
_____
(Street Address and City)

Arbor HOA (214) 854-1689
_____
(Name of Property Owners Association, (Association) and Phone Number)

A. SUBDIVISION INFORMATION: "Subdivision Information" means: (i) a current copy of the restrictions applying to the subdivision and bylaws and rules of the Association, and (ii) a resale certificate, all of which are described by Section 207.003 of the Texas Property Code.

(Check only one box):

☒ 1. Within 10_____ days after the effective date of the contract, Seller shall obtain, pay for, and deliver the Subdivision Information to the Buyer. If Seller delivers the Subdivision Information, Buyer may terminate the contract within 3 days after Buyer receives the Subdivision Information or prior to closing, whichever occurs first, and the earnest money will be refunded to Buyer. If Buyer does not receive the Subdivision Information, Buyer, as Buyer's sole remedy, may terminate the contract at any time prior to closing and the earnest money will be refunded to Buyer.

❏ 2. Within _____ days after the effective date of the contract, Buyer shall obtain, pay for, and deliver a copy of the Subdivision Information to the Seller. If Buyer obtains the Subdivision Information within the time required, Buyer may terminate the contract within 3 days after Buyer receives the Subdivision Information or prior to closing, whichever occurs first, and the earnest money will be refunded to Buyer. If Buyer, due to factors beyond Buyer's control, is not able to obtain the Subdivision Information within the time required, Buyer may, as Buyer's sole remedy, terminate the contract within 3 days after the time required or prior to closing, whichever occurs first, and the earnest money will be refunded to Buyer.

❏ 3. Buyer has received and approved the Subdivision Information before signing the contract. Buyer ❏ does ❏ does not require an updated resale certificate. If Buyer requires an updated resale certificate, Seller, at Buyer's expense, shall deliver it to Buyer within 10 days after receiving payment for the updated resale certificate from Buyer. Buyer may terminate this contract and the earnest money will be refunded to Buyer if Seller fails to deliver the updated resale certificate within the time required.

❏ 4. Buyer does not require delivery of the Subdivision Information.

The title company or its agent is authorized to act on behalf of the parties to obtain the Subdivision Information ONLY upon receipt of the required fee for the Subdivision Information from the party obligated to pay.

B. MATERIAL CHANGES. If Seller becomes aware of any material changes in the Subdivision Information, Seller shall promptly give notice to Buyer. Buyer may terminate the contract prior to closing by giving written notice to Seller if: (i) any of the Subdivision Information provided was not true; or (ii) any material adverse change in the Subdivision Information occurs prior to closing, and the earnest money will be refunded to Buyer.

C FEES: Except as provided by Paragraphs A, D and E, Buyer shall pay any and all Association fees or other charges associated with the transfer of the Property not to exceed $_100.00_____ and Seller shall pay any excess.

D. DEPOSITS FOR RESERVES: Buyer shall pay any deposits for reserves required at closing by the Association.

E. AUTHORIZATION: Seller authorizes the Association to release and provide the Subdivision Information and any updated resale certificate if requested by the Buyer, the Title Company, or any broker to this sale. If Buyer does not require the Subdivision Information or an updated resale certificate, and the Title Company requires information from the Association (such as the status of dues, special assessments, violations of covenants and restrictions, and a waiver of any right of first refusal), ❏ Buyer ☒ Seller shall pay the Title Company the cost of obtaining the information prior to the Title Company ordering the information.

NOTICE TO BUYER REGARDING REPAIRS BY THE ASSOCIATION: The Association may have the sole responsibility to make certain repairs to the Property. If you are concerned about the condition of any part of the Property which the Association is required to repair, you should not sign the contract unless you are satisfied that the Association will make the desired repairs.

Buyer William Applewhite   Seller Robert Strassman
_____   _____

Buyer and wife Sharon Applewhite   Seller
_____   _____

TREC NO. 36-8

EQUAL HOUSING OPPORTUNITY

SELLER FINANCING ADDENDUM
TO CONTRACT CONCERNING THE PROPERTY AT

1233 Tree Lane, Plano, TX, Plano, 75093
(Address of Property)

A. CREDIT DOCUMENTATION. To establish Buyer's creditworthiness, Buyer shall deliver to Seller within __3__ days after the effective date of this contract, ☒ credit report ❑ verification of employment, including salary ❑ verification of funds on deposit in financial institutions ❑ current financial statement and ❑ _____ _____. Buyer hereby authorizes any credit reporting agency to furnish copies of Buyer's credit reports to Seller at Buyer's sole expense.

B. CREDIT APPROVAL. If the credit documentation described in Paragraph A is not delivered within the specified time, Seller may terminate this contract by notice to Buyer within 7 days after expiration of the time for delivery, and the earnest money will be paid to Seller. If the credit documentation is timely delivered, and Seller determines in Seller's sole discretion that Buyer's credit is unacceptable, Seller may terminate this contract by notice to Buyer within 7 days after expiration of the time for delivery and the earnest money will be refunded to Buyer. If Seller does not terminate this contract, Seller will be deemed to have approved Buyer's creditworthiness.

C. PROMISSORY NOTE. The promissory note (Note) described in Paragraph 4 of this contract payable by Buyer to the order of Seller will bear interest at the rate of __5.000__% per annum and be payable at the place designated by Seller. Buyer may prepay the Note in whole or in part at any time without penalty. Any prepayments are to be applied to the payment of the installments of principal last maturing and interest will immediately cease on the prepaid principal. The Note will contain a provision for payment of a late fee of 5% of any installment not paid within 10 days of the due date. Matured unpaid amounts will bear interest at the rate of 1½% per month or at the highest lawful rate, whichever is less. The Note will be payable as follows:

❑ (1) In one payment due _____ after the date of the Note with interest payable ❑ at maturity ❑ monthly ❑ quarterly. (check one box only)

☒ (2) In monthly installments of $ __1,779.29__ ❑ including interest ❑plus interest (check one box only) beginning __the 1st of mo.__ after the date of the Note and continuing monthly thereafter for __180__ months when the balance of the Note will be due and payable.

❑ (3) Interest only in monthly installments for the first _____ month(s) and thereafter in installments of $_____ ❑ including interest ❑ plus interest (check one box only) beginning _____ after the date of the Note and continuing monthly thereafter for _____ months when the balance of the Note will be due and payable.

D. DEED OF TRUST. The deed of trust securing the Note will provide for the following:

(1) PROPERTY TRANSFERS: (check one box only)

❑ (a) Consent Not Required: The Property may be sold, conveyed or leased without the consent of Seller, provided any subsequent buyer assumes the Note.

☒ (b) Consent Required: If all or any part of the Property is sold, conveyed, leased for a period longer than 3 years, leased with an option to purchase, or otherwise sold (including any contract for deed), without Seller's prior written consent, which consent may be withheld in Seller's sole discretion, Seller may declare the balance of the Note to be immediately due and payable. The creation of a subordinate lien, any conveyance

Initialed for identification by Buyer_____ and Seller_____   TREC NO. 26-6

Seller Financing Addendum Concerning   Page 2 of 2 12-05-11

<u>   1233 Tree Lane, Plano, TX, 75093   </u>
(Address of Property)

under threat or order of condemnation, any deed solely between buyers, or the passage of title by reason of the death of a buyer or by operation of law will not entitle Seller to exercise the remedies provided in this paragraph.

NOTE: *Under (a) or (b), Buyer's liability to pay the Note will continue unless Buyer obtains a release of liability from Seller.*

(2) TAX AND INSURANCE ESCROW: (check one box only)

☐ (a) Escrow Not Required: Buyer shall furnish Seller, before each year's ad valorem taxes become delinquent, evidence that all ad valorem taxes on the Property have been paid. Buyer shall annually furnish Seller evidence of paid-up casualty insurance naming Seller as a mortgagee loss payee.

☒ (b) Escrow Required: With each installment Buyer shall deposit in escrow with Seller a pro rata part of the estimated annual ad valorem taxes and casualty insurance premiums for the Property. Buyer shall pay any deficiency within 30 days after notice from Seller. Buyer's failure to pay the deficiency will be a default under the deed of trust. Buyer is not required to deposit any escrow payments for taxes and insurance that are deposited with a superior lienholder. The casualty insurance must name Seller as a mortgagee loss payee.

(3) PRIOR LIENS: Any default under any lien superior to the lien securing the Note will be a default under the deed of trust securing the Note.

Buyer William Applewhite   Seller Robert Strassman

Buyer Sharon Applewhite   Seller

TREC NO. 26-6

PROMULGATED BY THE TEXAS REAL ESTATE COMMISSION (TREC)   12-05-11
(NOTICE: For use only when SELLER occupies the property for no more than 90 days AFTER the closing)

SELLER'S TEMPORARY RESIDENTIAL LEASE

1. **PARTIES:** The parties to this Lease are William Applewhite, Sharon Applewhite
(Landlord) and _____ Robert Strassman _____ (Tenant).

2. **LEASE:** Landlord leases to Tenant the Property described in the Contract between Landlord as Buyer and Tenant as Seller known as 1233 Tree Lane, Plano, TX, 75093 _____
_____ (address).

3. **TERM:** The term of this Lease commences on the date the sale covered by the Contract is closed and funded and terminates <u>three days later</u>, unless terminated earlier by reason of other provisions.

4. **RENTAL:** Tenant shall pay to Landlord as rental $_____ per day (excluding the day of closing and funding) with the full amount of rental for the term of the Lease to be paid at the time of funding of the sale. Tenant will not be entitled to a refund of rental if this Lease terminates early due to Tenant's default or voluntary surrender of the Property.

5. **DEPOSIT:** Tenant shall pay to Landlord at the time of funding of the sale $ 2,500.00 as a deposit to secure performance of this Lease by Tenant. Landlord may use the deposit to satisfy Tenant's obligations under this Lease. Landlord shall refund any unused portion of the deposit to Tenant with an itemized list of all deductions from the deposit within 30 days after Tenant (a) surrenders possession of the Property and (b) provides Landlord written notice of Tenant's forwarding address.

6. **UTILITIES:** Tenant shall pay all utility charges except _____ N/A _____
which Landlord shall pay.

7. **USE OF PROPERTY:** Tenant may use the Property only for residential purposes. Tenant may not assign this Lease or sublet any part of the Property.

8. **PETS:** Tenant may not keep pets on the Property except _____ N/A _____.

9. **CONDITION OF PROPERTY:** Tenant accepts the Property in its present condition and state of repair at the commencement of the Lease. Upon termination, Tenant shall surrender the Property to Landlord in the condition required under the Contract, except normal wear and tear and any casualty loss.

10. **ALTERATIONS:** Tenant may not alter the Property or install improvements or fixtures without the prior written consent of the Landlord. Any improvements or fixtures placed on the Property during the Lease become the Property of Landlord.

11. **SPECIAL PROVISIONS:**

12. **INSPECTIONS:** Landlord may enter at reasonable times to inspect the Property. Tenant shall provide Landlord door keys and access codes to allow access to the Property during the term of Lease.

13. **LAWS:** Tenant shall comply with all applicable laws, restrictions, ordinances, rules and regulations with respect to the Property.

14. **REPAIRS AND MAINTENANCE:** <u>Except as otherwise provided in this Lease, Tenant shall bear all expense of repairing and maintaining the Property, including but not limited to the yard, trees and shrubs, unless otherwise required by the Texas Property Code. Tenant shall promptly repair at Tenant's expense any damage to the Property caused directly or indirectly by any act or omission of the Tenant or any person other than the Landlord, Landlord's agents or invitees.</u>

Initialed for identification by Landlord _____ and Tenant_____   TREC NO. 15-5

Seller's Temporary Residential Lease <u>1233 Tree Lane, Plano, TX, 75093</u>   Page 2 of 2   12-05-11
(Address of Property)

15. **INDEMNITY:** Tenant indemnifies Landlord from the claims of all third parties for injury or damage to the person or property of such third party arising from the use or occupancy of the Property by Tenant. This indemnification includes attorney's fees, costs and expenses incurred by Landlord.

16. **INSURANCE:** Landlord and Tenant shall each maintain such insurance on the contents and Property as each party may deem appropriate during the term of this Lease. <u>NOTE</u>: CONSULT YOUR INSURANCE AGENT; POSSESSION OF THE PROPERTY BY SELLER AS TENANT MAY CHANGE INSURANCE POLICY COVERAGE.

17. **DEFAULT:** If Tenant fails to perform or observe any provision of this Lease and fails, within 24 hours after notice by Landlord, to commence and diligently pursue to remedy such failure, Tenant will be in default.

18. **TERMINATION:** This Lease terminates upon expiration of the term specified in Paragraph 3 or upon Tenant's default under this Lease.

19. **HOLDING OVER:** Tenant shall surrender possession of the Property upon termination of this Lease. Any possession by Tenant after termination creates a tenancy at sufferance and will not operate to renew or extend this Lease. Tenant shall pay $<u>1,000.00</u>per day during the period of any possession after termination as damages, in addition to any other remedies to which Landlord is entitled.

20. **ATTORNEY'S FEES:** The prevailing party in any legal proceeding brought under or with respect to this Lease is entitled to recover from the non-prevailing party all costs of such proceeding and reasonable attorney's fees.

21. **SMOKE ALARMS:** The Texas Property Code requires Landlord to install smoke alarms in certain locations within the Property at Landlord's expense. <u>Tenant expressly waives Landlord's duty to inspect and repair smoke alarms</u>.

22. **SECURITY DEVICES:** The requirements of the Texas Property Code relating to security devices do not apply to a residential lease for a term of 90 days or less.

23. **CONSULT YOUR ATTORNEY:** Real estate licensees cannot give legal advice. This Lease is intended to be legally binding. READ IT CAREFULLY. If you do not understand the effect of this Lease, consult your attorney BEFORE signing.

24. **NOTICES:** All notices from one party to the other must be in writing and are effective when mailed to, hand-delivered at, or transmitted by facsimile or electronic transmission as follows:

To Landlord: William Applewhite

1501 Center Court, Apt 1001

Plano, TX

Telephone: (214) 797-6501

Facsimile: (   )

E-mail: wapplewhite@verizon.net

To Tenant: Robert Strassman

1233 Tree Lane, Plano, TX

Telephone: (214) 505-1904

Facsimile: (   )

E-mail: robert.strassman@gmail.com

Landlord William Applewhite

Landlord Sharon Applewhite

Tenant Robert Strassman

Tenant

Transaction: Tomas to Perry
(from Chapter 6 of *Texas Promulgated Forms*)

PROMULGATED BY THE TEXAS REAL ESTATE COMMISSION (TREC)   4-28-2014
FARM AND RANCH CONTRACT

1. PARTIES: The parties to this contract are _____
(Seller) and _____(Buyer). Seller agrees to
sell and convey to Buyer and Buyer agrees to buy from Seller the Property defined below.

2. PROPERTY: The land, improvements, accessories and crops except for the exclusions and reservations, are collectively referred to as the "Property".

A. LAND: The land situated in the County of _____, Texas, described as follows:_____
_____
or as described on attached exhibit, also known as _____
(address/zip code), together with all rights, privileges, and appurtenances pertaining thereto, including but not limited to: water rights, claims, permits, strips and gores, easements, and cooperative or association memberships.

B. IMPROVEMENTS:
   (1) FARM and RANCH IMPROVEMENTS: The following **permanently installed and built-in items**, if any: windmills, tanks, barns, pens, fences, gates, sheds, outbuildings, and corrals.
   (2) RESIDENTIAL IMPROVEMENTS: The house, garage, and all other fixtures and improvements attached to the above-described real property, including without limitation, the following **permanently installed and built-in items,** if any: all equipment and appliances, valances, screens, shutters, awnings, wall-to-wall carpeting, mirrors, ceiling fans, attic fans, mail boxes, television antennas, mounts and brackets for televisions and speakers, heating and air-conditioning units, security and fire detection equipment, wiring, plumbing and lighting fixtures, chandeliers, water softener system, kitchen equipment, garage door openers, cleaning equipment, shrubbery, landscaping, outdoor cooking equipment, and all other property owned by Seller and attached to the above described real property.

C. ACCESSORIES:
   (1) FARM AND RANCH ACCESSORIES: The following described related accessories: (check boxes of conveyed accessories) ❑ portable buildings ❑ hunting blinds ❑ game feeders ❑ livestock feeders and troughs ❑ irrigation equipment ❑ fuel tanks ❑ submersible pumps ❑ pressure tanks ❑ corrals ❑ gates ❑ chutes ❑ other:_____
   _____
   (2) RESIDENTIAL ACCESSORIES: The following described related accessories, if any: window air conditioning units, stove, fireplace screens, curtains and rods, blinds, window shades, draperies and rods, door keys, mailbox keys, above ground pool, swimming pool equipment and maintenance accessories, artificial fireplace logs, and controls for:
   (i) garages, (ii) entry gates, and (iii) other improvements and accessories.

D. CROPS: Unless otherwise agreed in writing, Seller has the right to harvest all growing crops until delivery of possession of the Property.

E. EXCLUSIONS: The following improvements, accessories, and crops will be retained by Seller and must be removed prior to delivery of possession: _____
_____.

F. RESERVATIONS: Any reservation for oil, gas, or other minerals, water, timber, or other interests is made in accordance with an attached addendum or Special Provisions.

3. SALES PRICE:

A. Cash portion of Sales Price payable by Buyer at closing....................$_____
B. Sum of all financing described below (excluding any loan funding
   fee or mortgage insurance premium)...$_____
C. Sales Price (Sum of A and B)..$_____
D. The Sales Price ❑ will ❑ will not be adjusted based on the survey required by Paragraph 6C.
   If the Sales Price is adjusted, the Sales Price will be calculated on the basis of $ _____
   per acre. If the Sales Price is adjusted by more than 10%, either party may terminate this contract by providing written notice to the other party within ____ days after the terminating party receives the survey. If neither party terminates this contract or if the variance is 10% or less, the adjustment will be made to the amount in ❑ 3A ❑ 3B ❑ proportionately to 3A and 3B.

4. FINANCING (Not for use with reverse mortgage financing): The portion of Sales Price not payable in cash will be paid as follows: (Check applicable boxes below)
❑ A. THIRD PARTY FINANCING: One or more third party mortgage loans in the total amount of $_____ (excluding any loan funding fee or mortgage insurance premium).
   (1) Property Approval: If the Property does not satisfy the lenders' underwriting requirements for the loan(s) (including, but not limited to appraisal, insurability and lender required repairs), Buyer may terminate this contract by giving notice to Seller prior to closing and the earnest money will be refunded to Buyer.

Initialed for identification by Buyer_____ _____ and Seller _____ _____   TREC NO. 25-10

Contract Concerning _____Page 2 of 9   4-28-2014
(Address of Property)

(2) Credit Approval: (Check one box only)
☐ (a) This contract is subject to Buyer being approved for the financing described in the attached Third Party Financing Addendum for Credit Approval.
☐ (b) This contract is not subject to Buyer being approved for financing and does not involve FHA or VA financing.

☐ B. ASSUMPTION: The assumption of the unpaid principal balance of one or more promissory notes described in the attached TREC Loan Assumption Addendum.

☐ C. SELLER FINANCING: A promissory note from Buyer to Seller of $_____, secured by vendor's and deed of trust liens, and containing the terms and conditions described in the attached TREC Seller Financing Addendum. If an owner policy of title insurance is furnished, Buyer shall furnish Seller with a mortgagee policy of title insurance.

5. EARNEST MONEY: Upon execution of this contract by all parties, Buyer shall deposit $_____ as earnest money with _____, as escrow agent, at _____ (address). Buyer shall deposit additional earnest money of $_____ with escrow agent within _____ days after the effective date of this contract. If Buyer fails to deposit the earnest money as required by this contract, Buyer will be in default.

6. TITLE POLICY AND SURVEY:
A. TITLE POLICY: Seller shall furnish to Buyer at ☐Seller's ☐Buyer's expense an owner policy of title insurance (Title Policy) issued by: _____ (Title Company) in the amount of the Sales Price, dated at or after closing, insuring Buyer against loss under the provisions of the Title Policy, subject to the promulgated exclusions (including existing building and zoning ordinances) and the following exceptions:
(1) The standard printed exception for standby fees, taxes and assessments.
(2) Liens created as part of the financing described in Paragraph 4.
(3) Reservations or exceptions otherwise permitted by this contract or as may be approved by Buyer in writing.
(4) The standard printed exception as to marital rights.
(5) The standard printed exception as to waters, tidelands, beaches, streams, and related matters.
(6) The standard printed exception as to discrepancies, conflicts, shortages in area or boundary lines, encroachments or protrusions, or overlapping improvements: ☐ (i) will not be amended or deleted from the title policy; ☐(ii) will be amended to read, "shortages in area" at the expense of ☐Buyer ☐Seller.

B. COMMITMENT: Within 20 days after the Title Company receives a copy of this contract, Seller shall furnish to Buyer a commitment for title insurance (Commitment) and, at Buyer's expense, legible copies of restrictive covenants and documents evidencing exceptions in the Commitment (Exception Documents) other than the standard printed exceptions.   Seller authorizes the Title Company to deliver the Commitment and Exception Documents to Buyer at Buyer's address shown in Paragraph 21.   If the Commitment and Exception Documents are not delivered to Buyer within the specified time, the time for delivery will be automatically extended up to 15 days or 3 days before the Closing Date, whichever is earlier. If, due to factors beyond Seller's control, the Commitment and Exception Documents are not delivered within the time required, Buyer may terminate this contract and the earnest money will be refunded to Buyer.

C. SURVEY: The survey must be made by a registered professional land surveyor acceptable to the Title Company and Buyer's lender(s). (Check one box only):
☐ (1) Within _____ days after the effective date of this contract, Seller shall furnish to Buyer and Title Company Seller's existing survey of the Property and a Residential Real Property Affidavit promulgated by the Texas Department of Insurance (T-47 Affidavit). **If Seller fails to furnish the existing survey or affidavit within the time prescribed, Buyer shall obtain a new survey at Seller's expense no later than 3 days prior to Closing Date.** The existing survey ☐ will ☐ will not be recertified to a date subsequent to the effective date of this contract at the expense of ☐ Buyer ☐ Seller. If the existing survey is not approved by the Title Company or Buyer's lender(s), a new survey will be obtained at the expense of ☐ Buyer ☐ Seller no later than 3 days prior to Closing Date.
☐ (2) Within _____ days after the effective date of this contract, Buyer shall obtain a new survey at Buyer's expense. Buyer is deemed to receive the survey on the date of actual receipt or the date specified in this paragraph, whichever is earlier.
☐ (3) Within _____ days after the effective date of this contract, Seller, at Seller's expense shall furnish a new survey to Buyer.
☐ (4) No survey is required.

D. OBJECTIONS: Buyer may object in writing to (i) defects, exceptions, or encumbrances to title disclosed on the survey other than items 6A(1) through (5) above; or disclosed in the Commitment other than items 6A(1) through (6) above; (ii) any portion of the Property lying in a special flood hazard area (Zone V or A) as shown on the current Federal Emergency

Initialed for identification by Buyer_____ _____ and Seller _____ _____   TREC NO. 25-10

Contract Concerning _____Page 3 of 9   4-28-2014
(Address of Property)

Management Agency map; or (iii) any exceptions which prohibit the following use or activity:
_____
_____
Buyer must object the earlier of (i) the Closing Date or (ii) _____ days after Buyer receives the Commitment, Exception Documents, and the survey. Buyer's failure to object within the time allowed will constitute a waiver of Buyer's right to object; except that the requirements in Schedule C of the Commitment are not waived by Buyer. Provided Seller is not obligated to incur any expense, Seller shall cure the timely objections of Buyer or any third party lender within 15 days after Seller receives the objections and the Closing Date will be extended as necessary. If objections are not cured within such 15 day period, this contract will terminate and the earnest money will be refunded to Buyer unless Buyer waives the objections.

E. EXCEPTION DOCUMENTS: Prior to the execution of the contract, Seller has provided Buyer with copies of the Exception Documents listed below or on the attached exhibit. Matters reflected in the Exception Documents listed below or on the attached exhibit will be permitted exceptions in the Title Policy and will not be a basis for objection to title:

Document	Date	Recording Reference
_____	_____	_____
_____	_____	_____
_____	_____	_____

F. SURFACE LEASES: Prior to the execution of the contract, Seller has provided Buyer with copies of written leases and given notice of oral leases (Leases) listed below or on the attached exhibit. The following Leases will be permitted exceptions in the Title Policy and will not be a basis for objection to title:_____
_____

G. TITLE NOTICES:
   (1) ABSTRACT OR TITLE POLICY: Broker advises Buyer to have an abstract of title covering the Property examined by an attorney of Buyer's selection, or Buyer should be furnished with or obtain a Title Policy. If a Title Policy is furnished, the Commitment should be promptly reviewed by an attorney of Buyer's choice due to the time limitations on Buyer's right to object.
   (2) STATUTORY TAX DISTRICTS: If the Property is situated in a utility or other statutorily created district providing water, sewer, drainage, or flood control facilities and services, Chapter 49, Texas Water Code, requires Seller to deliver and Buyer to sign the statutory notice relating to the tax rate, bonded indebtedness, or standby fee of the district prior to final execution of this contract.
   (3) TIDE WATERS: If the Property abuts the tidally influenced waters of the state, §33.135, Texas Natural Resources Code, requires a notice regarding coastal area property to be included in the contract. An addendum containing the notice promulgated by TREC or required by the parties must be used.
   (4) ANNEXATION: If the Property is located outside the limits of a municipality, Seller notifies Buyer under §5.011, Texas Property Code, that the Property may now or later be included in the extraterritorial jurisdiction of a municipality and may now or later be subject to annexation by the municipality. Each municipality maintains a map that depicts its boundaries and extraterritorial jurisdiction. To determine if the Property is located within a municipality's extraterritorial jurisdiction or is likely to be located within a municipality's extraterritorial jurisdiction, contact all municipalities located in the general proximity of the Property for further information.
   (5) PROPERTY LOCATED IN A CERTIFICATED SERVICE AREA OF A UTILITY SERVICE PROVIDER: Notice required by §13.257, Water Code: The real property, described in Paragraph 2, that you are about to purchase may be located in a certificated water or sewer service area, which is authorized by law to provide water or sewer service to the properties in the certificated area. If your property is located in a certificated area there may be special costs or charges that you will be required to pay before you can receive water or sewer service. There may be a period required to construct lines or other facilities necessary to provide water or sewer service to your property. You are advised to determine if the property is in a certificated area and contact the utility service provider to determine the cost that you will be required to pay and the period, if any, that is required to provide water or sewer service to your property. The undersigned Buyer hereby acknowledges receipt of the foregoing notice at or before the execution of a binding contract for the purchase of the real property described in Paragraph 2 or at closing of purchase of the real property.
   (6) PUBLIC IMPROVEMENT DISTRICTS: If the Property is in a public improvement district, §5.014, Property Code, requires Seller to notify Buyer as follows: As a purchaser of this parcel of real property you are obligated to pay an assessment to a municipality or county for an improvement project undertaken by a public improvement district under Chapter 372, Local Government Code. The assessment may be due annually or in periodic

Initialed for identification by Buyer_____ _____ and Seller _____ _____   TREC NO. 25-10

installments. More information concerning the amount of the assessment and the due dates of that assessment may be obtained from the municipality or county levying the assessment. The amount of the assessments is subject to change. Your failure to pay the assessments could result in a lien on and the foreclosure of your property.

(7) TEXAS AGRICULTURAL DEVELOPMENT DISTRICT: The Property ❏ is ❏ is not located in a Texas Agricultural Development District. For additional information contact the Texas Department of Agriculture

(8) TRANSFER FEES: If the Property is subject to a private transfer fee obligation, §5.205, Property Code, requires Seller to notify Buyer as follows: The private transfer fee obligation may be governed by Chapter 5, Subchapter G of the Texas Property Code.

(9) PROPANE GAS SYSTEM SERVICE AREA: If the Property is located in a propane gas system service area owned by a distribution system retailer, Seller must give Buyer written notice as required by §141.010, Texas Utilities Code. An addendum containing the notice approved by TREC or required by the parties should be used.

7. PROPERTY CONDITION:

A. ACCESS, INSPECTIONS AND UTILITIES: Seller shall permit Buyer and Buyer's agents access to the Property at reasonable times. Buyer may have the Property inspected by inspectors selected by Buyer and licensed by TREC or otherwise permitted by law to make inspections. Seller at Seller's expense shall immediately cause existing utilities to be turned on and shall keep the utilities on during the time this contract is in effect .
NOTICE: Buyer should determine the availability of utilities to the Property suitable to satisfy Buyer's needs.

B. SELLER'S DISCLOSURE NOTICE PURSUANT TO §5.008, TEXAS PROPERTY CODE (Notice):
(Check one box only)
❏ (1) Buyer has received the Notice
❏ (2) Buyer has not received the Notice. Within ___ days after the effective date of this contract, Seller shall deliver the Notice to Buyer. If Buyer does not receive the Notice, Buyer may terminate this contract at any time prior to the closing and the earnest money will be refunded to Buyer. If Seller delivers the Notice, Buyer may terminate this contract for any reason within 7 days after Buyer receives the Notice or prior to the closing, whichever first occurs, and the earnest money will be refunded to Buyer.
❏ (3) The Texas Property Code does not require this Seller to furnish the Notice.

C. SELLER'S DISCLOSURE OF LEAD-BASED PAINT AND LEAD-BASED PAINT HAZARDS is required by Federal law for a residential dwelling constructed prior to 1978.

D. ACCEPTANCE OF PROPERTY CONDITION: "As Is" means the present condition of the Property with any and all defects and without warranty except for the warranties of title and the warranties in this contract. Buyer's agreement to accept the Property As Is under Paragraph 7D(1) or (2) does not preclude Buyer from inspecting the Property under Paragraph 7A, from negotiating repairs or treatments in a subsequent amendment, or from terminating this contract during the Option Period, if any.
(Check one box only)
❏ (1) Buyer accepts the Property As Is.
❏ (2) Buyer accepts the Property As Is provided Seller, at Seller's expense, shall complete the following specific repairs and treatments: _____
_____.
(Do not insert general phrases, such as "subject to inspections," that do not identify specific repairs and treatments.)

E. COMPLETION OF REPAIRS: Unless otherwise agreed in writing: (i) Seller shall complete all agreed repairs and treatments prior to the Closing Date; and (ii) all required permits must be obtained, and repairs and treatments must be performed by persons who are licensed to provide such repairs or treatments or, if no license is required by law, are commercially engaged in the trade of providing such repairs or treatments. At Buyer's election, any transferable warranties received by Seller with respect to the repairs will be transferred to Buyer at Buyer's expense. If Seller fails to complete any agreed repairs prior to the Closing Date, Buyer may exercise remedies under Paragraph 15 or extend the Closing Date up to 5 days if necessary for Seller to complete repairs.

F. LENDER REQUIRED REPAIRS AND TREATMENTS: Unless otherwise agreed in writing, neither party is obligated to pay for lender required repairs, which includes treatment for wood destroying insects. If the parties do not agree to pay for the lender required repairs or treatments, this contract will terminate and the earnest money will be refunded to Buyer. If the cost of lender required repairs and treatments exceeds 5% of the Sales Price, Buyer may terminate this contract and the earnest money will be refunded to Buyer.

G. ENVIRONMENTAL MATTERS: Buyer is advised that the presence of wetlands, toxic substances, including asbestos and wastes or other environmental hazards, or the presence of a threatened or endangered species or its habitat may affect Buyer's intended use of the Property. If Buyer is concerned about these matters, an addendum promulgated by TREC or required by the parties should be used.

H. SELLER'S DISCLOSURES: Except as otherwise disclosed in this contract, Seller has no knowledge of the following:
   (1) any flooding of the Property which has had a material adverse effect on the use of the Property;
   (2) any pending or threatened litigation, condemnation, or special assessment affecting the Property;
   (3) any environmental hazards that materially and adversely affect the Property;
   (4) any dumpsite, landfill, or underground tanks or containers now or previously located on the Property;
   (5) any wetlands, as defined by federal or state law or regulation, affecting the Property; or
   (6) any threatened or endangered species or their habitat affecting the Property.
I. RESIDENTIAL SERVICE CONTRACTS: Buyer may purchase a residential service contract from a residential service company licensed by TREC. If Buyer purchases a residential service contract, Seller shall reimburse Buyer at closing for the cost of the residential service contract in an amount not exceeding $_____. Buyer should review any residential service contract for the scope of coverage, exclusions and limitations. **The purchase of a residential service contract is optional. Similar coverage may be purchased from various companies authorized to do business in Texas.**
J. GOVERNMENT PROGRAMS: The Property is subject to the government programs listed below or on the attached exhibit:_____
_____.
Seller shall provide Buyer with copies of all governmental program agreements. Any allocation or proration of payment under governmental programs is made by separate agreement between the parties which will survive closing.

8. **BROKERS' FEES:** All obligations of the parties for payment of brokers' fees are contained in separate written agreements.

9. **CLOSING:**
   A. The closing of the sale will be on or before _____, 20_____, or within 7 days after objections made under Paragraph 6D have been cured or waived, whichever date is later (Closing Date). If either party fails to close the sale by the Closing Date, the non-defaulting party may exercise the remedies contained in Paragraph 15.
   B. At closing:
   (1) Seller shall execute and deliver a general warranty deed conveying title to the Property to Buyer and showing no additional exceptions to those permitted in Paragraph 6, an assignment of Leases, and furnish tax statements or certificates showing no delinquent taxes on the Property.
   (2) Buyer shall pay the Sales Price in good funds acceptable to the escrow agent.
   (3) Seller and Buyer shall execute and deliver any notices, statements, certificates, affidavits, releases, loan documents and other documents reasonably required for the closing of the sale and the issuance of the Title Policy.
   (4) There will be no liens, assessments, or security interests against the Property which will not be satisfied out of the sales proceeds unless securing the payment of any loans assumed by Buyer and assumed loans will not be in default.
   (5) If the Property is subject to a residential lease, Seller shall transfer security deposits (as defined under §92.102, Property Code), if any, to Buyer. In such an event, Buyer shall deliver to the tenant a signed statement acknowledging that the Buyer has received the security deposit and is responsible for the return of the security deposit, and specifying the exact dollar amount of the security deposit.

10. **POSSESSION:**
   A. Buyer's Possession: Seller shall deliver to Buyer possession of the Property in its present or required condition, ordinary wear and tear excepted: ❑ upon closing and funding ❑ according to a temporary residential lease form promulgated by TREC or other written lease required by the parties. Any possession by Buyer prior to closing or by Seller after closing which is not authorized by a written lease will establish a tenancy at sufferance relationship between the parties. **Consult your insurance agent prior to change of ownership and possession because insurance coverage may be limited or terminated. The absence of a written lease or appropriate insurance coverage may expose the parties to economic loss.**
   B. Leases:
   (1) After the Effective Date, Seller may not execute any lease (including but not limited to mineral leases) or convey any interest in the Property without Buyer's written consent.
   (2) If the Property is subject to any lease to which Seller is a party, Seller shall deliver to Buyer copies of the lease(s) and any move-in condition form signed by the tenant within 7 days after the Effective Date of the contract.

Contract Concerning _____ Page 6 of 9   4-28-2014
                                       (Address of Property)

11. SPECIAL PROVISIONS: (Insert only factual statements and business details applicable to the sale. TREC rules prohibit licensees from adding factual statements or business details for which a contract addendum or other form has been promulgated by TREC for mandatory use.)

12. SETTLEMENT AND OTHER EXPENSES:
  A. The following expenses must be paid at or prior to closing:
    (1) Expenses payable by Seller (Seller's Expenses):
      (a) Releases of existing liens, including prepayment penalties and recording fees; release of Seller's loan liability; tax statements or certificates; preparation of deed; one-half of escrow fee; and other expenses payable by Seller under this contract.
      (b) Seller shall also pay an amount not to exceed $ _____ to be applied in the following order: Buyer's Expenses which Buyer is prohibited from paying by FHA, VA, Texas Veterans Land Board or other governmental loan programs, and then to other Buyer's Expenses as allowed by the lender.
    (2) Expenses payable by Buyer (Buyer's Expenses) Appraisal fees; loan application fees; adjusted origination charges; credit reports; preparation of loan documents; interest on the notes from date of disbursement to one month prior to dates of first monthly payments; recording fees; copies of easements and restrictions; loan title policy with endorsements required by lender; loan-related inspection fees; photos; amortization schedules; one-half of escrow fee; all prepaid items, including required premiums for flood and hazard insurance, reserve deposits for insurance, ad valorem taxes and special governmental assessments; final compliance inspection; courier fee; repair inspection; underwriting fee; wire transfer fee; expenses incident to any loan; Private Mortgage Insurance Premium (PMI), VA Loan Funding Fee, or FHA Mortgage Insurance Premium (MIP) as required by the lender; and other expenses payable by Buyer under this contract.
  B. If any expense exceeds an amount expressly stated in this contract for such expense to be paid by a party, that party may terminate this contract unless the other party agrees to pay such excess. Buyer may not pay charges and fees expressly prohibited by FHA, VA, Texas Veterans Land Board or other governmental loan program regulations.

13. PRORATIONS AND ROLLBACK TAXES:
  A. PRORATIONS: Taxes for the current year, interest, maintenance fees, assessments, dues and rents will be prorated through the Closing Date. The tax proration may be calculated taking into consideration any change in exemptions that will affect the current year's taxes. If taxes for the current year vary from the amount prorated at closing, the parties shall adjust the prorations when tax statements for the current year are available. If taxes are not paid at or prior to closing, Buyer shall pay taxes for the current year. Rentals which are unknown at time of closing will be prorated between Buyer and Seller when they become known.
  B. ROLLBACK TAXES: If this sale or Buyer's use of the Property after closing results in the assessment of additional taxes, penalties or interest (Assessments) for periods prior to closing, the Assessments will be the obligation of Buyer. If Seller's change in use of the Property prior to closing or denial of a special use valuation on the Property claimed by Seller results in Assessments for periods prior to closing, the Assessments will be the obligation of Seller. Obligations imposed by this paragraph will survive closing.

14. CASUALTY LOSS: If any part of the Property is damaged or destroyed by fire or other casualty after the effective date of this contract, Seller shall restore the Property to its previous condition as soon as reasonably possible, but in any event by the Closing Date. If Seller fails to do so due to factors beyond Seller's control, Buyer may (a) terminate this contract and the earnest money will be refunded to Buyer, (b) extend the time for performance up to 15 days and the Closing Date will be extended as necessary or (c) accept the Property in its damaged condition with an assignment of insurance proceeds and receive credit from Seller at closing in the amount of the deductible under the insurance policy. Seller's obligations under this paragraph are independent of any other obligations of Seller under this contract.

15. DEFAULT: If Buyer fails to comply with this contract, Buyer will be in default, and Seller may (a) enforce specific performance, seek such other relief as may be provided by law, or both, or (b) terminate this contract and receive the earnest money as liquidated damages, thereby releasing both parties from this contract. If Seller fails to comply with this contract for any other reason, Seller will be in default and Buyer may (a) enforce specific performance, seek such other relief as may be provided by law, or both, or (b) terminate this contract and receive the earnest money, thereby releasing both parties from this contract.

16. MEDIATION: It is the policy of the State of Texas to encourage resolution of disputes through alternative dispute resolution procedures such as mediation. Any dispute between Seller and Buyer related to this contract which is not resolved through informal discussion will be submitted to a mutually acceptable mediation service or provider. The parties to the mediation shall bear

Initialed for identification by Buyer_____ _____ and Seller _____ _____   TREC NO. 25-10

Contract Concerning _____ Page 7 of 9   4-28-2014
(Address of Property)

the mediation costs equally. This paragraph does not preclude a party from seeking equitable relief from a court of competent jurisdiction.

17. ATTORNEY'S FEES: A Buyer, Seller, Listing Broker, Other Broker, or escrow agent who prevails in any legal proceeding related to this contract is entitled to recover reasonable attorney's fees and all costs of such proceeding.

18. ESCROW:
   A. ESCROW: The escrow agent is not (i) a party to this contract and does not have liability for the performance or nonperformance of any party to this contract, (ii) liable for interest on the earnest money and (iii) liable for the loss of any earnest money caused by the failure of any financial institution in which the earnest money has been deposited unless the financial institution is acting as escrow agent.
   B. EXPENSES: At closing, the earnest money must be applied first to any cash down payment, then to Buyer's Expenses and any excess refunded to Buyer. If no closing occurs, escrow agent may: (i) require a written release of liability of the escrow agent from all parties, (ii) require payment of unpaid expenses incurred on behalf of a party, and (iii) only deduct from the earnest money the amount of unpaid expenses incurred on behalf of the party receiving the earnest money.
   C. DEMAND: Upon termination of this contract, either party or the escrow agent may send a release of earnest money to each party and the parties shall execute counterparts of the release and deliver same to the escrow agent. If either party fails to execute the release, either party may make a written demand to the escrow agent for the earnest money. If only one party makes written demand for the earnest money, escrow agent shall promptly provide a copy of the demand to the other party. If escrow agent does not receive written objection to the demand from the other party within 15 days, escrow agent may disburse the earnest money to the party making demand reduced by the amount of unpaid expenses incurred on behalf of the party receiving the earnest money and escrow agent may pay the same to the creditors. If escrow agent complies with the provisions of this paragraph, each party hereby releases escrow agent from all adverse claims related to the disbursal of the earnest money.
   D. DAMAGES: Any party who wrongfully fails or refuses to sign a release acceptable to the escrow agent within 7 days of receipt of the request will be liable to the other party for liquidated damages in an amount equal to the sum of: (i) three times the amount of the earnest money; (ii) the earnest money; (iii) reasonable attorney's fees; and (iv) all costs of suit.
   E. NOTICES: Escrow agent's notices will be effective when sent in compliance with Paragraph 21. Notice of objection to the demand will be deemed effective upon receipt by escrow agent.

19. REPRESENTATIONS: All covenants, representations and warranties in this contract survive closing. If any representation of Seller in this contract is untrue on the Closing Date, Seller will be in default. Unless expressly prohibited by written agreement, Seller may continue to show the Property and receive, negotiate and accept back up offers.

20. FEDERAL TAX REQUIREMENTS: If Seller is a "foreign person," as defined by applicable law, or if Seller fails to deliver an affidavit to Buyer that Seller is not a "foreign person," then Buyer shall withhold from the sales proceeds an amount sufficient to comply with applicable tax law and deliver the same to the Internal Revenue Service together with appropriate tax forms. Internal Revenue Service regulations require filing written reports if currency in excess of specified amounts is received in the transaction.

21. NOTICES: All notices from one party to the other must be in writing and are effective when mailed to, hand-delivered at, or transmitted by facsimile or electronic transmission as follows:

To Buyer at: **To Seller at:**

_____   _____

_____   _____

Telephone: (___) _____   Telephone: (___) _____

Facsimile: (___) _____   Facsimile: (___) _____

E-mail: _____   E-mail: _____

Initialed for identification by Buyer_____ _____ and Seller _____ _____   TREC NO. 25-10

Contract Concerning _____ Page 8 of 9   4-28-2014
(Address of Property)

22.AGREEMENT OF PARTIES: This contract contains the entire agreement of the parties and cannot be changed except by their written agreement. Addenda which are a part of this contract are (check all applicable boxes):

❑ Third Party Financing Addendum for Credit Approval

❑ Seller Financing Addendum

❑ Addendum for Property Subject to Mandatory Membership in a Property Owners Association

❑ Buyer's Temporary Residential Lease

❑ Loan Assumption Addendum

❑ Addendum for Sale of Other Property by Buyer

❑ Addendum for "Back-Up" Contract

❑ Addendum for Coastal Area Property

❑ Environmental Assessment, Threatened or Endangered Species and Wetlands Addendum

❑ Seller's Temporary Residential Lease

❑ Short Sale Addendum

❑ Addendum for Property Located Seaward of the Gulf Intracoastal Waterway

❑ Addendum for Seller's Disclosure of Information on Lead-based Paint and Lead-based Paint Hazards as Required by Federal Law

❑ Addendum for Property in a Propane Gas System Service Area

❑ Other (list):_____
_____

23.TERMINATION OPTION: For nominal consideration, the receipt of which is hereby acknowledged by Seller, and Buyer's agreement to pay Seller $_____ (Option Fee) within 3 days after the effective date of this contract, Seller grants Buyer the unrestricted right to terminate this contract by giving notice of termination to Seller within _____ days after the effective date of this contract (Option Period).   If no dollar amount is stated as the Option Fee or if Buyer fails to pay the Option Fee to Seller within the time prescribed, this paragraph will not be a part of this contract and Buyer shall not have the unrestricted right to terminate this contract. If Buyer gives   notice of termination within the time prescribed, the Option Fee will not be refunded; however, any earnest money will be refunded to Buyer. The Option Fee ❑will ❑will not be credited to the Sales Price at closing. **Time is of the essence for this paragraph and strict compliance with the time for performance is required.**

24.CONSULT AN ATTORNEY BEFORE SIGNING: TREC rules prohibit real estate licensees from giving legal advice. READ THIS CONTRACT CAREFULLY.

Buyer's
Attorney is: _____

Seller's
Attorney is: _____

_____

_____

Telephone: (_____)_____

Telephone: (_____)_____

Facsimile: (_____)_____

Facsimile: (_____)_____

E-mail: _____

E-mail: _____

| **EXECUTED the _____day of _____, 20_____ (EFFECTIVE DATE).** |
| **(BROKER: FILL IN THE DATE OF FINAL ACCEPTANCE.)** |

_____
Buyer

_____
Seller

_____
Buyer

_____
Seller

Contract Concerning _____Page 9 of 9   4-28-2014
(Address of Property)

RATIFICATION OF FEE

Listing Broker has agreed to pay Other Broker_____ of the total Sales Price when Listing Broker's fee is received. Escrow Agent is authorized and directed to pay Other Broker from Listing Broker's fee at closing.

Other Broker: Listing Broker:

By: _____   By: _____

BROKER INFORMATION AND AGREEMENT FOR PAYMENT OF BROKERS' FEES

_____   _____
Other Broker   License No.   Listing or Principal Broker   License No.

_____   _____
Licensed Supervisor of Associate   Telephone   Licensed Supervisor of Associate   Telephone

_____   _____
Associate   Associate

_____   _____
Address   Address

_____   _____
City   State   Zip   City   State   Zip

_____   _____
Telephone   Facsimile   Telephone   Facsimile

_____   _____
E-mail   E-mail

represents   ❏ Buyer only as Buyer's agent   represents   ❏ Seller only
             ❏ Seller as Listing Broker's subagent   ❏ Buyer only
                                                                  ❏ Seller and Buyer as an intermediary

Upon closing of the sale by Seller to Buyer of the Property described in the contract to which this fee agreement is attached: (a) ❏ Seller ❏ Buyer will pay Listing/Principal Broker ❏ a cash fee of $_____ or ❏ _____% of the total Sales Price; and (b) ❏ Seller ❏ Buyer will pay Other Broker ❏ a cash fee of $_____ or ❏ _____% of the total Sales Price. Seller/Buyer authorizes and directs Escrow Agent to pay the brokers from the proceeds at closing.

Brokers' fees are negotiable. Brokers' fees or the sharing of fees between brokers are not fixed, controlled, recommended, suggested or maintained by the Texas Real Estate Commission.

_____   _____
Seller   Buyer

_____   _____
Seller   Buyer

OPTION FEE RECEIPT

Receipt of $_____ (Option Fee) in the form of _____ is acknowledged.

_____   _____
Seller or Listing Broker   Date

CONTRACT AND EARNEST MONEY RECEIPT

Receipt of ❏ Contract and ❏ $_____ Earnest Money in the form of _____ is acknowledged.

Escrow Agent: _____   Date: _____

By: _____

_____   _____
Address   Email Address
                                                     Telephone (_____) _____

_____
City   State   Zip   Facsimile: (_____) _____

PROMULGATED BY THE TEXAS REAL ESTATE COMMISSION (TREC)   12-05-11

ADDENDUM FOR RESERVATION OF OIL, GAS, AND OTHER MINERALS

ADDENDUM TO CONTRACT CONCERNING THE PROPERTY AT

_____

(Street Address and City)

_____

NOTICE: For use only if Seller reserves all or a portion of the Mineral Estate.

A. "Mineral Estate" means all oil, gas, and other minerals in or under the Property, any royalty under any existing or future lease covering any part of the Property, surface rights (including rights of ingress and egress), production and drilling rights, lease payments, and all related benefits.

B. The Mineral Estate owned by Seller, if any, will be conveyed unless reserved as follows (check one box only):

❑ (1) Seller reserves all of the Mineral Estate owned by Seller.

❑ (2) Seller reserves an undivided _____% interest in the Mineral Estate owned by Seller. *NOTE: If Seller does not own all of the Mineral Estate, Seller reserves only this percentage of Seller's interest.*

C. Seller ❑ waives ❑ does not waive Seller's surface rights (including rights of ingress and egress). *NOTE: Any waiver of surface rights by Seller does not affect any surface rights that may be held by others.*

D. If B(2) applies, Seller shall, on or before the Closing Date, provide Buyer contact information known to Seller for any existing lessee.

If either party is concerned about the legal rights or impact of the above provisions, that party is advised to consult an attorney BEFORE signing.

TREC rules prohibit real estate licensees from giving legal advice.

_____   _____
Buyer   Seller

_____   _____
Buyer   Seller

The form of this addendum has been approved by the Texas Real Estate Commission for use only with similarly approved or promulgated forms of contracts. Such approval relates to this contract form only. TREC forms are intended for use only by trained real estate licensees. No representation is made as to the legal validity or adequacy of any provision in any specific transactions. It is not intended for complex transactions. Texas Real Estate Commission, P.O. Box 12188, Austin, TX 78711-2188, 512-936-3000 (http://www.trec.texas.gov) TREC No. 44-1. This form replaces TREC No. 44-0.

APPROVED BY THE TEXAS REAL ESTATE COMMISSION   10-10-11

ADDENDUM FOR SELLER'S DISCLOSURE OF INFORMATION ON LEAD-BASED PAINT AND LEAD-BASED PAINT HAZARDS AS REQUIRED BY FEDERAL LAW

CONCERNING THE PROPERTY AT _____

(Street Address and City)

A. LEAD WARNING STATEMENT: "Every purchaser of any interest in residential real property on which a residential dwelling was built prior to 1978 is notified that such property may present exposure to lead from lead-based paint that may place young children at risk of developing lead poisoning. Lead poisoning in young children may produce permanent neurological damage, including learning disabilities, reduced intelligence quotient, behavioral problems, and impaired memory. Lead poisoning also poses a particular risk to pregnant women. The seller of any interest in residential real property is required to provide the buyer with any information on lead-based paint hazards from risk assessments or inspections in the seller's possession and notify the buyer of any known lead-based paint hazards. A risk assessment or inspection for possible lead-paint hazards is recommended prior to purchase."

NOTICE: Inspector must be properly certified as required by federal law.

B. SELLER'S DISCLOSURE:
1. PRESENCE OF LEAD-BASED PAINT AND/OR LEAD-BASED PAINT HAZARDS (check one box only):
   ❑(a) Known lead-based paint and/or lead-based paint hazards are present in the Property (explain): _____
   _____ .
   ❑(b) Seller has no actual knowledge of lead-based paint and/or lead-based paint hazards in the Property.
2. RECORDS AND REPORTS AVAILABLE TO SELLER (check one box only):
   ❑(a) Seller has provided the purchaser with all available records and reports pertaining to lead-based paint and/or lead-based paint hazards in the Property (list documents):_____
   _____ .
   ❑(b) Seller has no reports or records pertaining to lead-based paint and/or lead-based paint hazards in the Property.

C. BUYER'S RIGHTS (check one box only)**:**
   ❑1. Buyer waives the opportunity to conduct a risk assessment or inspection of the Property for the presence of lead-based paint or lead-based paint hazards.
   ❑2. Within ten days after the effective date of this contract, Buyer may have the Property inspected by inspectors selected by Buyer. If lead-based paint or lead-based paint hazards are present, Buyer may terminate this contract by giving Seller written notice within 14 days after the effective date of this contract, and the earnest money will be refunded to Buyer.

D. BUYER'S ACKNOWLEDGMENT (check applicable boxes)**:**
   ❑1. Buyer has received copies of all information listed above.
   ❑2. Buyer has received the pamphlet *Protect Your Family from Lead in Your Home*.

E. BROKERS' ACKNOWLEDGMENT: Brokers have informed Seller of Seller's obligations under 42 U.S.C. 4852d to: (a) provide Buyer with the federally approved pamphlet on lead poisoning prevention; (b) complete this addendum; (c) disclose any known lead-based paint and/or lead-based paint hazards in the Property; (d) deliver all records and reports to Buyer pertaining to lead-based paint and/or lead-based paint hazards in the Property; (e) provide Buyer a period of up to 10 days to have the Property inspected; and (f) retain a completed copy of this addendum for at least 3 years following the sale. Brokers are aware of their responsibility to ensure compliance.

F. CERTIFICATION OF ACCURACY: The following persons have reviewed the information above and certify, to the best of their knowledge, that the information they have provided is true and accurate.

_____ _____   _____ _____
Buyer   Date   Seller   Date

_____ _____   _____ _____
Buyer   Date   Seller   Date

_____ _____   _____ _____
Other Broker   Date   Listing Broker   Date

TREC NO. OP-L

PROMULGATED BY THE TEXAS REAL ESTATE COMMISSION (TREC)   12-05-11

EQUAL HOUSING
OPPORTUNITY

ENVIRONMENTAL ASSESSMENT, THREATENED OR ENDANGERED SPECIES, AND WETLANDS ADDENDUM

TO CONTRACT CONCERNING THE PROPERTY AT

_____

(Address of Property)

❑ A. ENVIRONMENTAL ASSESSMENT: Buyer, at Buyer's expense, may obtain an environmental assessment report prepared by an environmental specialist.

❑ B. THREATENED OR ENDANGERED SPECIES: Buyer, at Buyer's expense, may obtain a report from a natural resources professional to determine if there are any threatened or endangered species or their habitats as defined by the Texas Parks and Wildlife Department or the U.S. Fish and Wildlife Service.

❑ C. WETLANDS: Buyer, at Buyer's expense, may obtain a report from an environmental specialist to determine if there are wetlands, as defined by federal or state law or regulation.

Within _____ days after the effective date of the contract, Buyer may terminate the contract by furnishing Seller a copy of any report noted above that adversely affects the use of the Property and a notice of termination of the contract. Upon termination, the earnest money will be refunded to Buyer.

_____   _____
Buyer   Seller

_____   _____
Buyer   Seller

TREC No. 28-2

PROMULGATED BY THE TEXAS REAL ESTATE COMMISSION (TREC)

4-28-2014

FARM AND RANCH CONTRACT

1. PARTIES: The parties to this contract are Richard Tomas, a single man
(Seller) and Thomas and Anna Perry, a married couple (Buyer). Seller agrees to
sell and convey to Buyer and Buyer agrees to buy from Seller the Property defined below.

2. PROPERTY: The land, improvements, accessories and crops except for the exclusions and
reservations, are collectively referred to as the "Property".

A. LAND: The land situated in the County of Fannin County , Texas,
described as follows: Approximately 175 acres... see Attachement A

or as described on attached exhibit, also known as 3013 Rural Lane, Paris, TX N/A
(address/zip code), together with all rights, privileges, and appurtenances pertaining thereto,
including but not limited to: water rights, claims, permits, strips and gores, easements, and
cooperative or association memberships.

B. IMPROVEMENTS:

(1) FARM and RANCH IMPROVEMENTS: The following **permanently installed and built-in
items**, if any: windmills, tanks, barns, pens, fences, gates, sheds, outbuildings, and
corrals.

(2) RESIDENTIAL IMPROVEMENTS: The house, garage, and all other fixtures and
improvements attached to the above-described real property, including without limitation,
the following **permanently installed and built-in items,** if any: all equipment and
appliances, valances, screens, shutters, awnings, wall-to-wall carpeting, mirrors, ceiling
fans, attic fans, mail boxes, television antennas, mounts and brackets for televisions and
speakers, heating and air-conditioning units, security and fire detection equipment, wiring,
plumbing and lighting fixtures, chandeliers, water softener system, kitchen equipment,
garage door openers, cleaning equipment, shrubbery, landscaping, outdoor cooking
equipment, and all other property owned by Seller and attached to the above described
real property.

C. ACCESSORIES:

(1) FARM AND RANCH ACCESSORIES: The following described related accessories: (check
boxes of conveyed accessories) ❑ portable buildings ❑ hunting blinds ❑ game feeders
❑ livestock feeders and troughs ❑ irrigation equipment ❑ fuel tanks ❑ submersible
pumps ❑ pressure tanks ❑ corrals ❑ gates ❑ chutes ❑ other: N/A

(2) RESIDENTIAL ACCESSORIES: The following described related accessories, if any: window
air conditioning units, stove, fireplace screens, curtains and rods, blinds, window shades,
draperies and rods, door keys, mailbox keys, above ground pool, swimming pool
equipment and maintenance accessories, artificial fireplace logs, and controls for:
(i) garages, (ii) entry gates, and (iii) other improvements and accessories.

D. CROPS: Unless otherwise agreed in writing, Seller has the right to harvest all growing crops
until delivery of possession of the Property.

E. EXCLUSIONS: The following improvements, accessories, and crops will be retained by Seller
and must be removed prior to delivery of possession: N/A
.

F. RESERVATIONS: Any reservation for oil, gas, or other minerals, water, timber, or other
interests is made in accordance with an attached addendum or Special Provisions.

3. SALES PRICE:

A. Cash portion of Sales Price payable by Buyer at closing.................... $447,500.00

B. Sum of all financing described below (excluding any loan funding
fee or mortgage insurance premium) .... $ N/A

C. Sales Price (Sum of A and B) .... $ 447,500.00

D. The Sales Price ☒ will ❑ will not be adjusted based on the survey required by Paragraph 6C.
If the Sales Price is adjusted, the Sales Price will be calculated on the basis of $ 250.00
per acre. If the Sales Price is adjusted by more than 10%, either party may terminate this
contract by providing written notice to the other party within 3 days after the terminating
party receives the survey. If neither party terminates this contract or if the variance is 10%
or less, the adjustment will be made to the amount in ☒ 3A ❑ 3B ❑ proportionately to 3A
and 3B.

4. FINANCING (Not for use with reverse mortgage financing): The portion of Sales Price not
payable in cash will be paid as follows: (Check applicable boxes below)

❑ A. THIRD PARTY FINANCING: One or more third party mortgage loans in the total amount of
$ N/A (excluding any loan funding fee or mortgage insurance premium).

(1) Property Approval: If the Property does not satisfy the lenders' underwriting requirements
for the loan(s) (including, but not limited to appraisal, insurability and lender required
repairs), Buyer may terminate this contract by giving notice to Seller prior to closing and
the earnest money will be refunded to Buyer.

Contract Concerning ___3013 Rural Lane, Paris, TX_____ Page 2 of 9   4-28-2014
(Address of Property)

(2) Credit Approval: (Check one box only)
❑ (a) This contract is subject to Buyer being approved for the financing described in the attached Third Party Financing Addendum for Credit Approval.
❑ (b) This contract is not subject to Buyer being approved for financing and does not involve FHA or VA financing.
❑ B. ASSUMPTION: The assumption of the unpaid principal balance of one or more promissory notes described in the attached TREC Loan Assumption Addendum.
❑ C. SELLER FINANCING: A promissory note from Buyer to Seller of $ N/A_____, secured by vendor's and deed of trust liens, and containing the terms and conditions described in the attached TREC Seller Financing Addendum. If an owner policy of title insurance is furnished, Buyer shall furnish Seller with a mortgagee policy of title insurance.

5. EARNEST MONEY: Upon execution of this contract by all parties, Buyer shall deposit $100,000.00 as earnest money with _Fannin Co. Title & Abstract_____, as escrow agent, at _1012 Midpoint, Paris, TX_____ (address). Buyer shall deposit additional earnest money of $ N/A_____ with escrow agent within _N/A_ days after the effective date of this contract. If Buyer fails to deposit the earnest money as required by this contract, Buyer will be in default.

6. TITLE POLICY AND SURVEY:
A. TITLE POLICY: Seller shall furnish to Buyer at ☒Seller's ❑Buyer's expense an owner policy of title insurance (Title Policy) issued by: _Fannin Co. Title & Abstract_____ (Title Company) in the amount of the Sales Price, dated at or after closing, insuring Buyer against loss under the provisions of the Title Policy, subject to the promulgated exclusions (including existing building and zoning ordinances) and the following exceptions:
(1) The standard printed exception for standby fees, taxes and assessments.
(2) Liens created as part of the financing described in Paragraph 4.
(3) Reservations or exceptions otherwise permitted by this contract or as may be approved by Buyer in writing.
(4) The standard printed exception as to marital rights.
(5) The standard printed exception as to waters, tidelands, beaches, streams, and related matters.
(6) The standard printed exception as to discrepancies, conflicts, shortages in area or boundary lines, encroachments or protrusions, or overlapping improvements: ❑ (i) wlll not be amended or deleted from the title policy; ☒(ii) will be amended to read, "shortages in area" at the expense of ☒Buyer ❑Seller.
B. COMMITMENT: Within 20 days after the Title Company receives a copy of this contract, Seller shall furnish to Buyer a commitment for title insurance (Commitment) and, at Buyer's expense, legible copies of restrictive covenants and documents evidencing exceptions in the Commitment (Exception Documents) other than the standard printed exceptions.   Seller authorizes the Title Company to deliver the Commitment and Exception Documents to Buyer at Buyer's address shown in Paragraph 21. If the Commitment and Exception Documents are not delivered to Buyer within the specified time, the time for delivery will be automatically extended up to 15 days or 3 days before the Closing Date, whichever is earlier. If, due to factors beyond Seller's control, the Commitment and Exception Documents are not delivered within the time required, Buyer may terminate this contract and the earnest money will be refunded to Buyer.
C. SURVEY: The survey must be made by a registered professional land surveyor acceptable to the Title Company and Buyer's lender(s). (Check one box only):
❑ (1) Within _N/A_ days after the effective date of this contract, Seller shall furnish to Buyer and Title Company Seller's existing survey of the Property and a Residential Real Property Affidavit promulgated by the Texas Department of Insurance (T-47 Affidavit). **If Seller fails to furnish the existing survey or affidavit within the time prescribed, Buyer shall obtain a new survey at Seller's expense no later than 3 days prior to Closing Date.** The existing survey ❑ will ❑ will not be recertified to a date subsequent to the effective date of this contract at the expense of ❑ Buyer ❑ Seller. If the existing survey is not approved by the Title Company or Buyer's lender(s), a new survey will be obtained at the expense of ❑ Buyer ❑ Seller no later than 3 days prior to Closing Date.
❑ (2) Within _N/A_ days after the effective date of this contract, Buyer shall obtain a new survey at Buyer's expense. Buyer is deemed to receive the survey on the date of actual receipt or the date specified in this paragraph, whichever is earlier.
☒ (3) Within __20__ days after the effective date of this contract, Seller, at Seller's expense shall furnish a new survey to Buyer.
❑ (4) No survey is required.
D. OBJECTIONS: Buyer may object in writing to (i) defects, exceptions, or encumbrances to title disclosed on the survey other than items 6A(1) through (5) above; or disclosed in the Commitment other than items 6A(1) through (6) above; (ii) any portion of the Property lying in a special flood hazard area (Zone V or A) as shown on the current Federal Emergency

Initialed for identification by Buyer_____ _____ and Seller _____ _____   TREC NO. 25-10

Contract Concerning __3013 Rural Lane, Paris, TX_____ Page 3 of 9   4-28-2014
(Address of Property)

Management Agency map; or (iii) any exceptions which prohibit the following use or activity: __N/A_____

Buyer must object the earlier of (i) the Closing Date or (ii) __7___ days after Buyer receives the Commitment, Exception Documents, and the survey. Buyer's failure to object within the time allowed will constitute a waiver of Buyer's right to object; except that the requirements in Schedule C of the Commitment are not waived by Buyer. Provided Seller is not obligated to incur any expense, Seller shall cure the timely objections of Buyer or any third party lender within 15 days after Seller receives the objections and the Closing Date will be extended as necessary. If objections are not cured within such 15 day period, this contract will terminate and the earnest money will be refunded to Buyer unless Buyer waives the objections.

E. EXCEPTION DOCUMENTS: Prior to the execution of the contract, Seller has provided Buyer with copies of the Exception Documents listed below or on the attached exhibit. Matters reflected in the Exception Documents listed below or on the attached exhibit will be permitted exceptions in the Title Policy and will not be a basis for objection to title:

Document	Date	Recording Reference
N/A		N/A
N/A		N/A
N/A		N/A

F. SURFACE LEASES: Prior to the execution of the contract, Seller has provided Buyer with copies of written leases and given notice of oral leases (Leases) listed below or on the attached exhibit. The following Leases will be permitted exceptions in the Title Policy and will not be a basis for objection to title: __N/A_____
_____

G. TITLE NOTICES:
(1) ABSTRACT OR TITLE POLICY: Broker advises Buyer to have an abstract of title covering the Property examined by an attorney of Buyer's selection, or Buyer should be furnished with or obtain a Title Policy. If a Title Policy is furnished, the Commitment should be promptly reviewed by an attorney of Buyer's choice due to the time limitations on Buyer's right to object.
(2) STATUTORY TAX DISTRICTS: If the Property is situated in a utility or other statutorily created district providing water, sewer, drainage, or flood control facilities and services, Chapter 49, Texas Water Code, requires Seller to deliver and Buyer to sign the statutory notice relating to the tax rate, bonded indebtedness, or standby fee of the district prior to final execution of this contract.
(3) TIDE WATERS: If the Property abuts the tidally influenced waters of the state, §33.135, Texas Natural Resources Code, requires a notice regarding coastal area property to be included in the contract. An addendum containing the notice promulgated by TREC or required by the parties must be used.
(4) ANNEXATION: If the Property is located outside the limits of a municipality, Seller notifies Buyer under §5.011, Texas Property Code, that the Property may now or later be included in the extraterritorial jurisdiction of a municipality and may now or later be subject to annexation by the municipality. Each municipality maintains a map that depicts its boundaries and extraterritorial jurisdiction. To determine if the Property is located within a municipality's extraterritorial jurisdiction or is likely to be located within a municipality's extraterritorial jurisdiction, contact all municipalities located in the general proximity of the Property for further information.
(5) PROPERTY LOCATED IN A CERTIFICATED SERVICE AREA OF A UTILITY SERVICE PROVIDER: Notice required by §13.257, Water Code: The real property, described in Paragraph 2, that you are about to purchase may be located in a certificated water or sewer service area, which is authorized by law to provide water or sewer service to the properties in the certificated area. If your property is located in a certificated area there may be special costs or charges that you will be required to pay before you can receive water or sewer service. There may be a period required to construct lines or other facilities necessary to provide water or sewer service to your property. You are advised to determine if the property is in a certificated area and contact the utility service provider to determine the cost that you will be required to pay and the period, if any, that is required to provide water or sewer service to your property. The undersigned Buyer hereby acknowledges receipt of the foregoing notice at or before the execution of a binding contract for the purchase of the real property described in Paragraph 2 or at closing of purchase of the real property.
(6) PUBLIC IMPROVEMENT DISTRICTS: If the Property is in a public improvement district, §5.014, Property Code, requires Seller to notify Buyer as follows: As a purchaser of this parcel of real property you are obligated to pay an assessment to a municipality or county for an improvement project undertaken by a public improvement district under Chapter 372, Local Government Code. The assessment may be due annually or in periodic

Initialed for identification by Buyer_____ _____ and Seller _____ _____   TREC NO. 25-10

Contract Concerning _____ 3013 Rural Lane, Paris, TX _____ Page 4 of 9   4-28-2014
(Address of Property)

installments. More information concerning the amount of the assessment and the due dates of that assessment may be obtained from the municipality or county levying the assessment. The amount of the assessments is subject to change. Your failure to pay the assessments could result in a lien on and the foreclosure of your property.
(7) TEXAS AGRICULTURAL DEVELOPMENT DISTRICT: The Property ☐ is ☒ is not located in a Texas Agricultural Development District. For additional information contact the Texas Department of Agriculture
(8) TRANSFER FEES: If the Property is subject to a private transfer fee obligation, §5.205, Property Code, requires Seller to notify Buyer as follows: The private transfer fee obligation may be governed by Chapter 5, Subchapter G of the Texas Property Code.
(9) PROPANE GAS SYSTEM SERVICE AREA: If the Property is located in a propane gas system service area owned by a distribution system retailer, Seller must give Buyer written notice as required by §141.010, Texas Utilities Code. An addendum containing the notice approved by TREC or required by the parties should be used.

7. PROPERTY CONDITION:
  A. ACCESS, INSPECTIONS AND UTILITIES: Seller shall permit Buyer and Buyer's agents access to the Property at reasonable times. Buyer may have the Property inspected by inspectors selected by Buyer and licensed by TREC or otherwise permitted by law to make inspections. Seller at Seller's expense shall immediately cause existing utilities to be turned on and shall keep the utilities on during the time this contract is in effect .
  NOTICE: Buyer should determine the availability of utilities to the Property suitable to satisfy Buyer's needs.
  B. SELLER'S DISCLOSURE NOTICE PURSUANT TO §5.008, TEXAS PROPERTY CODE (Notice):
  (Check one box only)
  ☒ (1) Buyer has received the Notice
  ☐ (2) Buyer has not received the Notice. Within N/A days after the effective date of this contract, Seller shall deliver the Notice to Buyer. If Buyer does not receive the Notice, Buyer may terminate this contract at any time prior to the closing and the earnest money will be refunded to Buyer. If Seller delivers the Notice, Buyer may terminate this contract for any reason within 7 days after Buyer receives the Notice or prior to the closing, whichever first occurs, and the earnest money will be refunded to Buyer.
  ☐ (3) The Texas Property Code does not require this Seller to furnish the Notice.
  C. SELLER'S DISCLOSURE OF LEAD-BASED PAINT AND LEAD-BASED PAINT HAZARDS is required by Federal law for a residential dwelling constructed prior to 1978.
  D. ACCEPTANCE OF PROPERTY CONDITION: "As Is" means the present condition of the Property with any and all defects and without warranty except for the warranties of title and the warranties in this contract. Buyer's agreement to accept the Property As Is under Paragraph 7D(1) or (2) does not preclude Buyer from inspecting the Property under Paragraph 7A, from negotiating repairs or treatments in a subsequent amendment, or from terminating this contract during the Option Period, if any.
  (Check one box only)
  ☒ (1) Buyer accepts the Property As Is.
  ☐ (2) Buyer accepts the Property As Is provided Seller, at Seller's expense, shall complete the following specific repairs and treatments: N/A _____
  _____.
  (Do not insert general phrases, such as "subject to inspections," that do not identify specific repairs and treatments.)
  E. COMPLETION OF REPAIRS: Unless otherwise agreed in writing: (i) Seller shall complete all agreed repairs and treatments prior to the Closing Date; and (ii) all required permits must be obtained, and repairs and treatments must be performed by persons who are licensed to provide such repairs or treatments or, if no license is required by law, are commercially engaged in the trade of providing such repairs or treatments. At Buyer's election, any transferable warranties received by Seller with respect to the repairs will be transferred to Buyer at Buyer's expense. If Seller fails to complete any agreed repairs prior to the Closing Date, Buyer may exercise remedies under Paragraph 15 or extend the Closing Date up to 5 days if necessary for Seller to complete repairs.
  F. LENDER REQUIRED REPAIRS AND TREATMENTS: Unless otherwise agreed in writing, neither party is obligated to pay for lender required repairs, which includes treatment for wood destroying insects. If the parties do not agree to pay for the lender required repairs or treatments, this contract will terminate and the earnest money will be refunded to Buyer. If the cost of lender required repairs and treatments exceeds 5% of the Sales Price, Buyer may terminate this contract and the earnest money will be refunded to Buyer.
  G. ENVIRONMENTAL MATTERS: Buyer is advised that the presence of wetlands, toxic substances, including asbestos and wastes or other environmental hazards, or the presence of a threatened or endangered species or its habitat may affect Buyer's intended use of the Property. If Buyer is concerned about these matters, an addendum promulgated by TREC or required by the parties should be used.

Initialed for identification by Buyer_____ _____ and Seller _____ _____   TREC NO. 25-10

Contract Concerning _____3013 Rural Lane, Paris, TX_____Page 5 of 9   4-28-2014
(Address of Property)

H. SELLER'S DISCLOSURES: Except as otherwise disclosed in this contract, Seller has no knowledge of the following:
   (1) any flooding of the Property which has had a material adverse effect on the use of the Property;
   (2) any pending or threatened litigation, condemnation, or special assessment affecting the Property;
   (3) any environmental hazards that materially and adversely affect the Property;
   (4) any dumpsite, landfill, or underground tanks or containers now or previously located on the Property;
   (5) any wetlands, as defined by federal or state law or regulation, affecting the Property; or
   (6) any threatened or endangered species or their habitat affecting the Property.
I. RESIDENTIAL SERVICE CONTRACTS: Buyer may purchase a residential service contract from a residential service company licensed by TREC. If Buyer purchases a residential service contract, Seller shall reimburse Buyer at closing for the cost of the residential service contract in an amount not exceeding $_500.00_____. Buyer should review any residential service contract for the scope of coverage, exclusions and limitations. **The purchase of a residential service contract is optional. Similar coverage may be purchased from various companies authorized to do business in Texas.**
J. GOVERNMENT PROGRAMS: The Property is subject to the government programs listed below or on the attached exhibit: _N/A_____
_____.
Seller shall provide Buyer with copies of all governmental program agreements. Any allocation or proration of payment under governmental programs is made by separate agreement between the parties which will survive closing.

8. **BROKERS' FEES:** All obligations of the parties for payment of brokers' fees are contained in separate written agreements.

9. **CLOSING:**
   A. The closing of the sale will be on or before _30 days from today_, 20_xx_, or within 7 days after objections made under Paragraph 6D have been cured or waived, whichever date is later (Closing Date). If either party fails to close the sale by the Closing Date, the non-defaulting party may exercise the remedies contained in Paragraph 15.
   B. At closing:
      (1) Seller shall execute and deliver a general warranty deed conveying title to the Property to Buyer and showing no additional exceptions to those permitted in Paragraph 6, an assignment of Leases, and furnish tax statements or certificates showing no delinquent taxes on the Property.
      (2) Buyer shall pay the Sales Price in good funds acceptable to the escrow agent.
      (3) Seller and Buyer shall execute and deliver any notices, statements, certificates, affidavits, releases, loan documents and other documents reasonably required for the closing of the sale and the issuance of the Title Policy.
      (4) There will be no liens, assessments, or security interests against the Property which will not be satisfied out of the sales proceeds unless securing the payment of any loans assumed by Buyer and assumed loans will not be in default.
      (5) If the Property is subject to a residential lease, Seller shall transfer security deposits (as defined under §92.102, Property Code), if any, to Buyer. In such an event, Buyer shall deliver to the tenant a signed statement acknowledging that the Buyer has received the security deposit and is responsible for the return of the security deposit, and specifying the exact dollar amount of the security deposit.

10. **POSSESSION:**
    A. Buyer's Possession: Seller shall deliver to Buyer possession of the Property in its present or required condition, ordinary wear and tear excepted: ☒ upon closing and funding   ☐ according to a temporary residential lease form promulgated by TREC or other written lease required by the parties. Any possession by Buyer prior to closing or by Seller after closing which is not authorized by a written lease will establish a tenancy at sufferance relationship between the parties. **Consult your insurance agent prior to change of ownership and possession because insurance coverage may be limited or terminated. The absence of a written lease or appropriate insurance coverage may expose the parties to economic loss.**
    B. Leases:
       (1) After the Effective Date, Seller may not execute any lease (including but not limited to mineral leases) or convey any interest in the Property without Buyer's written consent.
       (2) If the Property is subject to any lease to which Seller is a party, Seller shall deliver to Buyer copies of the lease(s) and any move-in condition form signed by the tenant within 7 days after the Effective Date of the contract.

Initialed for identification by Buyer_____ _____ and Seller _____ _____   TREC NO. 25-10

Contract Concerning ___3013 Rural Lane, Paris, TX_____ Page 6 of 9   4-28-2014
                                    (Address of Property)

11. SPECIAL PROVISIONS: (Insert only factual statements and business details applicable to the sale. TREC rules prohibit licensees from adding factual statements or business details for which a contract addendum or other form has been promulgated by TREC for mandatory use.)

Attachment A, containing the legal description of the property is a part of this contract

12. SETTLEMENT AND OTHER EXPENSES:
   A. The following expenses must be paid at or prior to closing:
      (1) Expenses payable by Seller (Seller's Expenses):
         (a) Releases of existing liens, including prepayment penalties and recording fees; release of Seller's loan liability; tax statements or certificates; preparation of deed; one-half of escrow fee; and other expenses payable by Seller under this contract.
         (b) Seller shall also pay an amount not to exceed $ _N/A_____ to be applied in the following order: Buyer's Expenses which Buyer is prohibited from paying by FHA, VA, Texas Veterans Land Board or other governmental loan programs, and then to other Buyer's Expenses as allowed by the lender.
      (2) Expenses payable by Buyer (Buyer's Expenses) Appraisal fees; loan application fees; adjusted origination charges; credit reports; preparation of loan documents; interest on the notes from date of disbursement to one month prior to dates of first monthly payments; recording fees; copies of easements and restrictions; loan title policy with endorsements required by lender; loan-related inspection fees; photos; amortization schedules; one-half of escrow fee; all prepaid items, including required premiums for flood and hazard insurance, reserve deposits for insurance, ad valorem taxes and special governmental assessments; final compliance inspection; courier fee; repair inspection; underwriting fee; wire transfer fee; expenses incident to any loan; Private Mortgage Insurance Premium (PMI), VA Loan Funding Fee, or FHA Mortgage Insurance Premium (MIP) as required by the lender; and other expenses payable by Buyer under this contract.
   B. If any expense exceeds an amount expressly stated in this contract for such expense to be paid by a party, that party may terminate this contract unless the other party agrees to pay such excess. Buyer may not pay charges and fees expressly prohibited by FHA, VA, Texas Veterans Land Board or other governmental loan program regulations.

13. PRORATIONS AND ROLLBACK TAXES:
   A. PRORATIONS: Taxes for the current year, interest, maintenance fees, assessments, dues and rents will be prorated through the Closing Date. The tax proration may be calculated taking into consideration any change in exemptions that will affect the current year's taxes. If taxes for the current year vary from the amount prorated at closing, the parties shall adjust the prorations when tax statements for the current year are available. If taxes are not paid at or prior to closing, Buyer shall pay taxes for the current year. Rentals which are unknown at time of closing will be prorated between Buyer and Seller when they become known.
   B. ROLLBACK TAXES: If this sale or Buyer's use of the Property after closing results in the assessment of additional taxes, penalties or interest (Assessments) for periods prior to closing, the Assessments will be the obligation of Buyer. If Seller's change in use of the Property prior to closing or denial of a special use valuation on the Property claimed by Seller results in Assessments for periods prior to closing, the Assessments will be the obligation of Seller. Obligations imposed by this paragraph will survive closing.

14. CASUALTY LOSS: If any part of the Property is damaged or destroyed by fire or other casualty after the effective date of this contract, Seller shall restore the Property to its previous condition as soon as reasonably possible, but in any event by the Closing Date. If Seller fails to do so due to factors beyond Seller's control, Buyer may (a) terminate this contract and the earnest money will be refunded to Buyer, (b) extend the time for performance up to 15 days and the Closing Date will be extended as necessary or (c) accept the Property in its damaged condition with an assignment of insurance proceeds and receive credit from Seller at closing in the amount of the deductible under the insurance policy. Seller's obligations under this paragraph are independent of any other obligations of Seller under this contract.

15. DEFAULT: If Buyer fails to comply with this contract, Buyer will be in default, and Seller may (a) enforce specific performance, seek such other relief as may be provided by law, or both, or (b) terminate this contract and receive the earnest money as liquidated damages, thereby releasing both parties from this contract. If Seller fails to comply with this contract for any other reason, Seller will be in default and Buyer may (a) enforce specific performance, seek such other relief as may be provided by law, or both, or (b) terminate this contract and receive the earnest money, thereby releasing both parties from this contract.

16. MEDIATION: It is the policy of the State of Texas to encourage resolution of disputes through alternative dispute resolution procedures such as mediation. Any dispute between Seller and Buyer related to this contract which is not resolved through informal discussion will be submitted to a mutually acceptable mediation service or provider. The parties to the mediation shall bear

Initialed for identification by Buyer_____ _____ and Seller _____ _____   TREC NO. 25-10

Contract Concerning <u>3013 Rural Lane, Paris, TX</u> _____ Page 7 of 9   4-28-2014
(Address of Property)

the mediation costs equally. This paragraph does not preclude a party from seeking equitable relief from a court of competent jurisdiction.

17.ATTORNEY'S FEES: A Buyer, Seller, Listing Broker, Other Broker, or escrow agent who prevails in any legal proceeding related to this contract is entitled to recover reasonable attorney's fees and all costs of such proceeding.

18.ESCROW:
 A. ESCROW: The escrow agent is not (i) a party to this contract and does not have liability for the performance or nonperformance of any party to this contract, (ii) liable for interest on the earnest money and (iii) liable for the loss of any earnest money caused by the failure of any financial institution in which the earnest money has been deposited unless the financial institution is acting as escrow agent.
 B. EXPENSES: At closing, the earnest money must be applied first to any cash down payment, then to Buyer's Expenses and any excess refunded to Buyer. If no closing occurs, escrow agent may: (i) require a written release of liability of the escrow agent from all parties, (ii) require payment of unpaid expenses incurred on behalf of a party, and (iii) only deduct from the earnest money the amount of unpaid expenses incurred on behalf of the party receiving the earnest money.
 C. DEMAND: Upon termination of this contract, either party or the escrow agent may send a release of earnest money to each party and the parties shall execute counterparts of the release and deliver same to the escrow agent. If either party fails to execute the release, either party may make a written demand to the escrow agent for the earnest money. If only one party makes written demand for the earnest money, escrow agent shall promptly provide a copy of the demand to the other party. If escrow agent does not receive written objection to the demand from the other party within 15 days, escrow agent may disburse the earnest money to the party making demand reduced by the amount of unpaid expenses incurred on behalf of the party receiving the earnest money and escrow agent may pay the same to the creditors. If escrow agent complies with the provisions of this paragraph, each party hereby releases escrow agent from all adverse claims related to the disbursal of the earnest money.
 D. DAMAGES: Any party who wrongfully fails or refuses to sign a release acceptable to the escrow agent within 7 days of receipt of the request will be liable to the other party for liquidated damages in an amount equal to the sum of: (i) three times the amount of the earnest money; (ii) the earnest money; (iii) reasonable attorney's fees; and (iv) all costs of suit.
 E. NOTICES: Escrow agent's notices will be effective when sent in compliance with Paragraph 21. Notice of objection to the demand will be deemed effective upon receipt by escrow agent.

19.REPRESENTATIONS: All covenants, representations and warranties in this contract survive closing. If any representation of Seller in this contract is untrue on the Closing Date, Seller will be in default. Unless expressly prohibited by written agreement, Seller may continue to show the Property and receive, negotiate and accept back up offers.

20.FEDERAL TAX REQUIREMENTS: If Seller is a "foreign person," as defined by applicable law, or if Seller fails to deliver an affidavit to Buyer that Seller is not a "foreign person," then Buyer shall withhold from the sales proceeds an amount sufficient to comply with applicable tax law and deliver the same to the Internal Revenue Service together with appropriate tax forms. Internal Revenue Service regulations require filing written reports if currency in excess of specified amounts is received in the transaction.

21.NOTICES: All notices from one party to the other must be in writing and are effective when mailed to, hand-delivered at, or transmitted by facsimile or electronic transmission as follows:

To Buyer at: | **To Seller at:**

Thomas Perry 1015 Sparkman Ave | Richard Tomas, 3013 Rural Ln, Paris

Allen, TX 75002

Telephone: (   ) N/A | Telephone: (   ) N/A

Facsimile: (   ) N/A | Facsimile: (   ) N/A

E-mail: TomandAnna@ThePerrys.com | E-mail: rtomas@gmail.com

Initialed for identification by Buyer_____ _____ and Seller _____ _____   TREC NO. 25-10

Contract Concerning ___3013 Rural Lane, Paris, TX_____ Page 8 of 9   4-28-2014
(Address of Property)

22.AGREEMENT OF PARTIES: This contract contains the entire agreement of the parties and cannot be changed except by their written agreement. Addenda which are a part of this contract are (check all applicable boxes):

☐ Third Party Financing Addendum for Credit Approval

☐ Seller Financing Addendum

☐ Addendum for Property Subject to Mandatory Membership in a Property Owners Association

☐ Buyer's Temporary Residential Lease

☐ Loan Assumption Addendum

☐ Addendum for Sale of Other Property by Buyer

☐ Addendum for "Back-Up" Contract

☐ Addendum for Coastal Area Property

☒ Environmental Assessment, Threatened or Endangered Species and Wetlands Addendum

☐ Seller's Temporary Residential Lease

☐ Short Sale Addendum

☐ Addendum for Property Located Seaward of the Gulf Intracoastal Waterway

☒ Addendum for Seller's Disclosure of Information on Lead-based Paint and Lead-based Paint Hazards as Required by Federal Law

☐ Addendum for Property in a Propane Gas System Service Area

☒ Other (list): Addendum for Reservation of Oil, Gas & Other

23.TERMINATION OPTION: For nominal consideration, the receipt of which is hereby acknowledged by Seller, and Buyer's agreement to pay Seller $_N/A_____ (Option Fee) within 3 days after the effective date of this contract, Seller grants Buyer the unrestricted right to terminate this contract by giving notice of termination to Seller within __N/A___ days after the effective date of this contract (Option Period). If no dollar amount is stated as the Option Fee or if Buyer fails to pay the Option Fee to Seller within the time prescribed, this paragraph will not be a part of this contract and Buyer shall not have the unrestricted right to terminate this contract. If Buyer gives notice of termination within the time prescribed, the Option Fee will not be refunded; however, any earnest money will be refunded to Buyer. The Option Fee ☐will ☐will not be credited to the Sales Price at closing. **Time is of the essence for this paragraph and strict compliance with the time for performance is required.**

24.CONSULT AN ATTORNEY BEFORE SIGNING: TREC rules prohibit real estate licensees from giving legal advice. READ THIS CONTRACT CAREFULLY.

Buyer's
Attorney is: _N/A_____

_N/A_____

Telephone: (   ) _N/A_____

Facsimile: (   ) _N/A_____

E-mail: _N/A_____

Seller's
Attorney is: _N/A_____

_N/A_____

Telephone: (   ) _N/A_____

Facsimile: (   ) _N/A_____

E-mail: _____N/A_____

**EXECUTED the _____day of _Today's Date_____, 20_XX___ (EFFECTIVE DATE).
(BROKER: FILL IN THE DATE OF FINAL ACCEPTANCE.)**

Buyer Thomas Perry

Buyer Anna Perry

Seller Richard Tomas

Seller N/A

TREC NO. 25-10

Contract Concerning   3013 Rural Lane, Paris, TX   Page 9 of 9   4-28-2014
_____(Address of Property)_____

RATIFICATION OF FEE

Listing Broker has agreed to pay Other Broker N/A   of the total Sales Price when Listing Broker's fee is received. Escrow Agent is authorized and directed to pay Other Broker from Listing Broker's fee at closing.

Other Broker: Listing Broker:

By: _____   By: _____

BROKER INFORMATION AND AGREEMENT FOR PAYMENT OF BROKERS' FEES

N/A	N/A	Your Company	0000000
Other Broker	License No.	Listing or Principal Broker	License No.
N/A	N/A	Your Broker	(000)000-0000
Licensed Supervisor of Associate	Telephone	Licensed Supervisor of Associate	Telephone
N/A		Your Telephone Number	
Associate		Associate	
N/A		Your office Address	
Address		Address	
N/A	N/A	N/A	Allen	TX	75002
City	State	Zip	City	State	Zip
N/A		N/A	N/A		
Telephone		Facsimile	Telephone		Facsimile
N/A			Your e-mail		
E-mail			E-mail		

represents ☐ Buyer only as Buyer's agent
            ☐ Seller as Listing Broker's subagent

represents ☐ Seller only
            ☒ Buyer only
            ☐ Seller and Buyer as an intermediary

Upon closing of the sale by Seller to Buyer of the Property described in the contract to which this fee agreement is attached: (a) ☐ Seller ☐ Buyer will pay Listing/Principal Broker ☐ a cash fee of $ N/A   or ☒ 4.500 % of the total Sales Price; and (b) ☐ Seller ☐ Buyer will pay Other Broker ☐ a cash fee of $ N/A   or ☐ N/A % of the total Sales Price. Seller/Buyer authorizes and directs Escrow Agent to pay the brokers from the proceeds at closing.

Brokers' fees are negotiable. Brokers' fees or the sharing of fees between brokers are not fixed, controlled, recommended, suggested or maintained by the Texas Real Estate Commission.

Seller Richard Tomas   Buyer Thomas Perry

Seller N/A   Buyer Anna Perry

OPTION FEE RECEIPT

Receipt of $ N/A   (Option Fee) in the form of N/A   is acknowledged.

_____   _____
Seller or Listing Broker   Date

CONTRACT AND EARNEST MONEY RECEIPT

Receipt of ☒ Contract and ☒ $ 100,000.00   Earnest Money in the form of a cashiers chk
is acknowledged.
Escrow Agent: Fannin Co. Title & Abstract Co   Date: Within 2 days of eff date

By: _____   ken@Fannintitleandabstract.com
Ken Dunlap, closer   Email Address
1012 Midpoint Dr   Telephone (787) 256-4900
_____
Address
Paris   TX   77023   Facsimile: (787) 256-4902
City   State   Zip

PROMULGATED BY THE TEXAS REAL ESTATE COMMISSION (TREC)   12-05-11

EQUAL HOUSING
OPPORTUNITY

ADDENDUM FOR RESERVATION OF OIL, GAS, AND OTHER MINERALS

ADDENDUM TO CONTRACT CONCERNING THE PROPERTY AT

3013 Rural Lane   Paris
_____
(Street Address and City)

N/A
_____

NOTICE: For use only if Seller reserves all or a portion of the Mineral Estate.

A. "Mineral Estate" means all oil, gas, and other minerals in or under the Property, any royalty under any existing or future lease covering any part of the Property, surface rights (including rights of ingress and egress), production and drilling rights, lease payments, and all related benefits.

B. The Mineral Estate owned by Seller, if any, will be conveyed unless reserved as follows (check one box only):

☐ (1) Seller reserves all of the Mineral Estate owned by Seller.

☒ (2) Seller reserves an undivided __50.000__% interest in the Mineral Estate owned by Seller. *NOTE: If Seller does not own all of the Mineral Estate, Seller reserves only this percentage of Seller's interest.*

C. Seller ☒ waives ☐ does not waive Seller's surface rights (including rights of ingress and egress). *NOTE: Any waiver of surface rights by Seller does not affect any surface rights that may be held by others.*

D. If B(2) applies, Seller shall, on or before the Closing Date, provide Buyer contact information known to Seller for any existing lessee.

If either party is concerned about the legal rights or impact of the above provisions, that party is advised to consult an attorney BEFORE signing.

TREC rules prohibit real estate licensees from giving legal advice.

Buyer Thomas Perry
_____

Seller Richard Tomas
_____

Buyer Anna Perry
_____

Seller N/A
_____

TREC NO. 44-1

APPROVED BY THE TEXAS REAL ESTATE COMMISSION   10-10-11

ADDENDUM FOR SELLER'S DISCLOSURE OF INFORMATION ON LEAD-BASED PAINT AND LEAD-BASED PAINT HAZARDS AS REQUIRED BY FEDERAL LAW

CONCERNING THE PROPERTY AT ___3013 Rural Lane___   ___Paris___
(Street Address and City)

A. LEAD WARNING STATEMENT: "Every purchaser of any interest in residential real property on which a residential dwelling was built prior to 1978 is notified that such property may present exposure to lead from lead-based paint that may place young children at risk of developing lead poisoning. Lead poisoning in young children may produce permanent neurological damage, including learning disabilities, reduced intelligence quotient, behavioral problems, and impaired memory. Lead poisoning also poses a particular risk to pregnant women. The seller of any interest in residential real property is required to provide the buyer with any information on lead-based paint hazards from risk assessments or inspections in the seller's possession and notify the buyer of any known lead-based paint hazards. A risk assessment or inspection for possible lead-paint hazards is recommended prior to purchase."

NOTICE: Inspector must be properly certified as required by federal law.

B. SELLER'S DISCLOSURE:
1. PRESENCE OF LEAD-BASED PAINT AND/OR LEAD-BASED PAINT HAZARDS (check one box only):
   ☐(a) Known lead-based paint and/or lead-based paint hazards are present in the Property (explain): _____
   _____ .
   ☒(b) Seller has no actual knowledge of lead-based paint and/or lead-based paint hazards in the Property.
2. RECORDS AND REPORTS AVAILABLE TO SELLER (check one box only):
   ☐(a) Seller has provided the purchaser with all available records and reports pertaining to lead-based paint and/or lead-based paint hazards in the Property (list documents):_____
   _____ .
   ☒(b) Seller has no reports or records pertaining to lead-based paint and/or lead-based paint hazards in the Property.

C. BUYER'S RIGHTS (check one box only):
   ☒1. Buyer waives the opportunity to conduct a risk assessment or inspection of the Property for the presence of lead-based paint or lead-based paint hazards.
   ☐2. Within ten days after the effective date of this contract, Buyer may have the Property inspected by inspectors selected by Buyer. If lead-based paint or lead-based paint hazards are present, Buyer may terminate this contract by giving Seller written notice within 14 days after the effective date of this contract, and the earnest money will be refunded to Buyer.

D. BUYER'S ACKNOWLEDGMENT (check applicable boxes):
   ☐1. Buyer has received copies of all information listed above.
   ☒2. Buyer has received the pamphlet *Protect Your Family from Lead in Your Home*.

E. BROKERS' ACKNOWLEDGMENT: Brokers have informed Seller of Seller's obligations under 42 U.S.C. 4852d to: (a) provide Buyer with the federally approved pamphlet on lead poisoning prevention; (b) complete this addendum; (c) disclose any known lead-based paint and/or lead-based paint hazards in the Property; (d) deliver all records and reports to Buyer pertaining to lead-based paint and/or lead-based paint hazards in the Property; (e) provide Buyer a period of up to 10 days to have the Property inspected; and (f) retain a completed copy of this addendum for at least 3 years following the sale. Brokers are aware of their responsibility to ensure compliance.

F. CERTIFICATION OF ACCURACY: The following persons have reviewed the information above and certify, to the best of their knowledge, that the information they have provided is true and accurate.

signs

Buyer Thomas Perry _____ Date _____   Seller Richard Tomas _____ Date _____

Buyer Anna Perry _____ Date _____   Seller N/A _____ Date _____

Other Broker N/A _____ Date _____   Listing Broker _____ Date _____
                                                  Your Broker

TREC NO. OP-L

PROMULGATED BY THE TEXAS REAL ESTATE COMMISSION (TREC)   12-05-11

ENVIRONMENTAL ASSESSMENT, THREATENED OR ENDANGERED SPECIES, AND WETLANDS ADDENDUM

TO CONTRACT CONCERNING THE PROPERTY AT

3013 Rural Lane, Paris, TX
(Address of Property)

☒ A. ENVIRONMENTAL ASSESSMENT: Buyer, at Buyer's expense, may obtain an environmental assessment report prepared by an environmental specialist.

☒ B. THREATENED OR ENDANGERED SPECIES: Buyer, at Buyer's expense, may obtain a report from a natural resources professional to determine if there are any threatened or endangered species or their habitats as defined by the Texas Parks and Wildlife Department or the U.S. Fish and Wildlife Service.

☒ C. WETLANDS: Buyer, at Buyer's expense, may obtain a report from an environmental specialist to determine if there are wetlands, as defined by federal or state law or regulation.

Within __20__ days after the effective date of the contract, Buyer may terminate the contract by furnishing Seller a copy of any report noted above that adversely affects the use of the Property and a notice of termination of the contract. Upon termination, the earnest money will be refunded to Buyer.

Buyer Thomas Perry   Seller Richard Tomas

Buyer Anna Perry   Seller N/A

TREC No. 28-2

Transaction: Fleming to Donaldson
(from Chapter 9 of *Texas Promulgated Forms*)

PROMULGATED BY THE TEXAS REAL ESTATE COMMISSION (TREC)
4-28-2014
ONE TO FOUR FAMILY RESIDENTIAL CONTRACT (RESALE)
NOTICE: Not For Use For Condominium Transactions

1. PARTIES: The parties to this contract are _____
(Seller) and _____ (Buyer).
Seller agrees to sell and convey to Buyer and Buyer agrees to buy from Seller the Property defined below.

2. PROPERTY: The land, improvements and accessories are collectively referred to as the "Property".
  A. LAND: Lot _____ Block_____, _____
   Addition, City of _____ , County of _____,
   Texas, known as _____
   (address/zip code), or as described on attached exhibit.
  B. IMPROVEMENTS: The house, garage and all other fixtures and improvements attached to the above-described real property, including without limitation, the following **permanently installed and built-in items,** if any: all equipment and appliances, valances, screens, shutters, awnings, wall-to-wall carpeting, mirrors, ceiling fans, attic fans, mail boxes, television antennas, mounts and brackets for televisions and speakers, heating and air-conditioning units, security and fire detection equipment, wiring, plumbing and lighting fixtures, chandeliers, water softener system, kitchen equipment, garage door openers, cleaning equipment, shrubbery, landscaping, outdoor cooking equipment, and all other property owned by Seller and attached to the above described real property.
  C. ACCESSORIES: The following described related accessories, if any: window air conditioning units, stove, fireplace screens, curtains and rods, blinds, window shades, draperies and rods, door keys, mailbox keys, above ground pool, swimming pool equipment and maintenance accessories, artificial fireplace logs, and controls for: (i) garage doors, (ii) entry gates, and (iii) other improvements and accessories.
  D. EXCLUSIONS: The following improvements and accessories will be retained by Seller and must be removed prior to delivery of possession:_____
   _____.

3. SALES PRICE:
  A. Cash portion of Sales Price payable by Buyer at closing .... $_____
  B. Sum of all financing described below (excluding any loan funding
    fee or mortgage insurance premium) .... $_____
  C. Sales Price (Sum of A and B)... $_____

4. FINANCING (Not for use with reverse mortgage financing): The portion of Sales Price not payable in cash will be paid as follows: (Check applicable boxes below)
❑ A.THIRD PARTY FINANCING: One or more third party mortgage loans in the total amount of $_____ (excluding any loan funding fee or mortgage insurance premium).
  (1) Property Approval: If the Property does not satisfy the lenders' underwriting requirements for the loan(s) (including, but not limited to appraisal, insurability and lender required repairs), Buyer may terminate this contract by giving notice to Seller prior to closing and the earnest money will be refunded to Buyer.
  (2) Credit Approval: (Check one box only)
  ❑   (a) This contract is subject to Buyer being approved for the financing described in the attached Third Party Financing Addendum for Credit Approval.
  ❑   (b) This contract is not subject to Buyer being approved for financing and does not involve FHA or VA financing.
❑ B. ASSUMPTION: The assumption of the unpaid principal balance of one or more promissory notes described in the attached TREC Loan Assumption Addendum.
❑ C. SELLER FINANCING: A promissory note from Buyer to Seller of $_____, secured by vendor's and deed of trust liens, and containing the terms and conditions described in the attached TREC Seller Financing Addendum. If an owner policy of title insurance is furnished, Buyer shall furnish Seller with a mortgagee policy of title insurance.

Initialed for identification by Buyer_____ _____ and Seller _____ _____   TREC NO. 20-12

Contract Concerning _____ Page 2 of 9   4-28-2014
(Address of Property)

5. EARNEST MONEY: Upon execution of this contract by all parties, Buyer shall deposit $_____ as earnest money with _____, as escrow agent, at _____ (address). Buyer shall deposit additional earnest money of $_____ with escrow agent within _____days after the effective date of this contract. If Buyer fails to deposit the earnest money as required by this contract, Buyer will be in default.

6. TITLE POLICY AND SURVEY:

A. TITLE POLICY: Seller shall furnish to Buyer at ❑ Seller's ❑ Buyer's expense an owner policy of title insurance (Title Policy) issued by _____ (Title Company) in the amount of the Sales Price, dated at or after closing, insuring Buyer against loss under the provisions of the Title Policy, subject to the promulgated exclusions (including existing building and zoning ordinances) and the following exceptions:

(1) Restrictive covenants common to the platted subdivision in which the Property is located.

(2) The standard printed exception for standby fees, taxes and assessments.

(3) Liens created as part of the financing described in Paragraph 4.

(4) Utility easements created by the dedication deed or plat of the subdivision in which the Property is located.

(5) Reservations or exceptions otherwise permitted by this contract or as may be approved by Buyer in writing.

(6) The standard printed exception as to marital rights.

(7) The standard printed exception as to waters, tidelands, beaches, streams, and related matters.

(8) The standard printed exception as to discrepancies, conflicts, shortages in area or boundary lines, encroachments or protrusions, or overlapping improvements: ❑(i) will not be amended or deleted from the title policy; ❑(ii) will be amended to read, "shortages in area" at the expense of ❑Buyer ❑Seller.

B. COMMITMENT: Within 20 days after the Title Company receives a copy of this contract, Seller shall furnish to Buyer a commitment for title insurance (Commitment) and, at Buyer's expense, legible copies of restrictive covenants and documents evidencing exceptions in the Commitment (Exception Documents) other than the standard printed exceptions. Seller authorizes the Title Company to deliver the Commitment and Exception Documents to Buyer at Buyer's address shown in Paragraph 21. If the Commitment and Exception Documents are not delivered to Buyer within the specified time, the time for delivery will be automatically extended up to 15 days or 3 days before the Closing Date, whichever is earlier. If, due to factors beyond Seller's control, the Commitment and Exception Documents are not delivered within the time required, Buyer may terminate this contract and the earnest money will be refunded to Buyer.

C. SURVEY: The survey must be made by a registered professional land surveyor acceptable to the Title Company and Buyer's lender(s). (Check one box only)

❑(1) Within _____ days after the effective date of this contract, Seller shall furnish to Buyer and Title Company Seller's existing survey of the Property and a Residential Real Property Affidavit promulgated by the Texas Department of Insurance (T-47 Affidavit). **If Seller fails to furnish the existing survey or affidavit within the time prescribed, Buyer shall obtain a new survey at Seller's expense no later than 3 days prior to Closing Date.** If the existing survey or affidavit is not acceptable to Title Company or Buyer's lender(s), Buyer shall obtain a new survey at ❑Seller's ❑Buyer's expense no later than 3 days prior to Closing Date.

❑(2) Within _____ days after the effective date of this contract, Buyer shall obtain a new survey at Buyer's expense. Buyer is deemed to receive the survey on the date of actual receipt or the date specified in this paragraph, whichever is earlier.

❑(3) Within _____ days after the effective date of this contract, Seller, at Seller's expense shall furnish a new survey to Buyer.

D. OBJECTIONS: Buyer may object in writing to defects, exceptions, or encumbrances to title: disclosed on the survey other than items 6A(1) through (7) above; disclosed in the Commitment other than items 6A(1) through (8) above; or which prohibit the following use or activity: _____
_____.

Buyer must object the earlier of (i) the Closing Date or (ii) _____ days after Buyer receives the Commitment, Exception Documents, and the survey. Buyer's failure to object within the time allowed will constitute a waiver of Buyer's right to object; except that the requirements in Schedule C of the Commitment are not waived by Buyer. Provided Seller is not obligated to incur any expense, Seller shall cure the timely objections of Buyer or any third party lender

Initialed for identification by Buyer_____ _____ and Seller _____ _____   TREC NO. 20-12

within 15 days after Seller receives the objections and the Closing Date will be extended as necessary. If objections are not cured within such 15 day period, this contract will terminate and the earnest money will be refunded to Buyer unless Buyer waives the objections.

E. TITLE NOTICES:
   (1) ABSTRACT OR TITLE POLICY: Broker advises Buyer to have an abstract of title covering the Property examined by an attorney of Buyer's selection, or Buyer should be furnished with or obtain a Title Policy. If a Title Policy is furnished, the Commitment should be promptly reviewed by an attorney of Buyer's choice due to the time limitations on Buyer's right to object.
   (2) MEMBERSHIP IN PROPERTY OWNERS ASSOCIATION(S): The Property ❑is ❑is not subject to mandatory membership in a property owners association(s). If the Property is subject to mandatory membership in a property owners association(s), Seller notifies Buyer under §5.012, Texas Property Code, that, as a purchaser of property in the residential community identified in Paragraph 2A in which the Property is located, you are obligated to be a member of the property owners association(s). Restrictive covenants governing the use and occupancy of the Property and all dedicatory instruments governing the establishment, maintenance, or operation of this residential community have been or will be recorded in the Real Property Records of the county in which the Property is located. Copies of the restrictive covenants and dedicatory instruments may be obtained from the county clerk. **You are obligated to pay assessments to the property owners association(s). The amount of the assessments is subject to change. Your failure to pay the assessments could result in enforcement of the association's lien on and the foreclosure of the Property.**
   Section 207.003, Property Code, entitles an owner to receive copies of any document that governs the establishment, maintenance, or operation of a subdivision, including, but not limited to, restrictions, bylaws, rules and regulations, and a resale certificate from a property owners' association. A resale certificate contains information including, but not limited to, statements specifying the amount and frequency of regular assessments and the style and cause number of lawsuits to which the property owners' association is a party, other than lawsuits relating to unpaid ad valorem taxes of an individual member of the association. These documents must be made available to you by the property owners' association or the association's agent on your request.
   If Buyer is concerned about these matters, the TREC promulgated Addendum for Property Subject to Mandatory Membership in a Property Owners Association(s) should be used.
   (3) STATUTORY TAX DISTRICTS: If the Property is situated in a utility or other statutorily created district providing water, sewer, drainage, or flood control facilities and services, Chapter 49, Texas Water Code, requires Seller to deliver and Buyer to sign the statutory notice relating to the tax rate, bonded indebtedness, or standby fee of the district prior to final execution of this contract.
   (4) TIDE WATERS: If the Property abuts the tidally influenced waters of the state, §33.135, Texas Natural Resources Code, requires a notice regarding coastal area property to be included in the contract. An addendum containing the notice promulgated by TREC or required by the parties must be used.
   (5) ANNEXATION: If the Property is located outside the limits of a municipality, Seller notifies Buyer under §5.011, Texas Property Code, that the Property may now or later be included in the extraterritorial jurisdiction of a municipality and may now or later be subject to annexation by the municipality. Each municipality maintains a map that depicts its boundaries and extraterritorial jurisdiction. To determine if the Property is located within a municipality's extraterritorial jurisdiction or is likely to be located within a municipality's extraterritorial jurisdiction, contact all municipalities located in the general proximity of the Property for further information.
   (6) PROPERTY LOCATED IN A CERTIFICATED SERVICE AREA OF A UTILITY SERVICE PROVIDER: Notice required by §13.257, Water Code: The real property, described in Paragraph 2, that you are about to purchase may be located in a certificated water or sewer service area, which is authorized by law to provide water or sewer service to the properties in the certificated area. If your property is located in a certificated area there may be special costs or charges that you will be required to pay before you can receive water or sewer service. There may be a period required to construct lines or other facilities necessary to provide water or sewer service to your property. You are advised to determine if the property is in a certificated area and contact the utility service provider to determine the cost that you will be required to pay and the period, if any, that is required to provide water or sewer service to your property. The undersigned Buyer hereby acknowledges receipt of the foregoing notice at or before the execution of a binding contract for the purchase of the real property described in Paragraph 2 or at closing of purchase of the real property.

Contract Concerning _____ Page 4 of 9   4-28-2014
(Address of Property)

(7) PUBLIC IMPROVEMENT DISTRICTS: If the Property is in a public improvement district, §5.014, Property Code, requires Seller to notify Buyer as follows: As a purchaser of this parcel of real property you are obligated to pay an assessment to a municipality or county for an improvement project undertaken by a public improvement district under Chapter 372, Local Government Code. The assessment may be due annually or in periodic installments. More information concerning the amount of the assessment and the due dates of that assessment may be obtained from the municipality or county levying the assessment. The amount of the assessments is subject to change. Your failure to pay the assessments could result in a lien on and the foreclosure of your property.

(8) TRANSFER FEES: If the Property is subject to a private transfer fee obligation, §5.205, Property Code, requires Seller to notify Buyer as follows: The private transfer fee obligation may be governed by Chapter 5, Subchapter G of the Texas Property Code.

(9) PROPANE GAS SYSTEM SERVICE AREA: If the Property is located in a propane gas system service area owned by a distribution system retailer, Seller must give Buyer written notice as required by §141.010, Texas Utilities Code. An addendum containing the notice approved by TREC or required by the parties should be used.

7. PROPERTY CONDITION:

A. ACCESS, INSPECTIONS AND UTILITIES: Seller shall permit Buyer and Buyer's agents access to the Property at reasonable times. Buyer may have the Property inspected by inspectors selected by Buyer and licensed by TREC or otherwise permitted by law to make inspections. Seller at Seller's expense shall immediately cause existing utilities to be turned on and shall keep the utilities on during the time this contract is in effect.

B. SELLER'S DISCLOSURE NOTICE PURSUANT TO §5.008, TEXAS PROPERTY CODE (Notice):
(Check one box only)

❑ (1) Buyer has received the Notice.

❑ (2) Buyer has not received the Notice. Within _____ days after the effective date of this contract, Seller shall deliver the Notice to Buyer. If Buyer does not receive the Notice, Buyer may terminate this contract at any time prior to the closing and the earnest money will be refunded to Buyer. If Seller delivers the Notice, Buyer may terminate this contract for any reason within 7 days after Buyer receives the Notice or prior to the closing, whichever first occurs, and the earnest money will be refunded to Buyer.

❑ (3)The Seller is not required to furnish the notice under the Texas Property Code.

C. SELLER'S DISCLOSURE OF LEAD-BASED PAINT AND LEAD-BASED PAINT HAZARDS is required by Federal law for a residential dwelling constructed prior to 1978.

D. ACCEPTANCE OF PROPERTY CONDITION: "As Is" means the present condition of the Property with any and all defects and without warranty except for the warranties of title and the warranties in this contract. Buyer's agreement to accept the Property As Is under Paragraph 7D(1) or (2) does not preclude Buyer from inspecting the Property under Paragraph 7A, from negotiating repairs or treatments in a subsequent amendment, or from terminating this contract during the Option Period, if any.
(Check one box only)

❑ (1) Buyer accepts the Property As Is.

❑ (2) Buyer accepts the Property As Is provided Seller, at Seller's expense, shall complete the following specific repairs and treatments: _____
_____.
(Do not insert general phrases, such as "subject to inspections" that do not identify specific repairs and treatments.)

E. LENDER REQUIRED REPAIRS AND TREATMENTS: Unless otherwise agreed in writing, neither party is obligated to pay for lender required repairs, which includes treatment for wood destroying insects. If the parties do not agree to pay for the lender required repairs or treatments, this contract will terminate and the earnest money will be refunded to Buyer. If the cost of lender required repairs and treatments exceeds 5% of the Sales Price, Buyer may terminate this contract and the earnest money will be refunded to Buyer.

F. COMPLETION OF REPAIRS AND TREATMENTS: Unless otherwise agreed in writing: (i) Seller shall complete all agreed repairs and treatments prior to the Closing Date; and (ii) all required permits must be obtained, and repairs and treatments must be performed by persons who are licensed to provide such repairs or treatments or, if no license is required by law, are commercially engaged in the trade of providing such repairs or treatments.   At Buyer's election, any transferable warranties received by Seller with respect to the repairs and treatments will be transferred to Buyer at Buyer's expense. If Seller fails to complete any agreed repairs and treatments prior to the Closing Date, Buyer may exercise remedies under Paragraph 15 or extend the Closing Date up to 5 days if necessary for Seller to complete the repairs and treatments.

G. ENVIRONMENTAL MATTERS: Buyer is advised that the presence of wetlands, toxic substances, including asbestos and wastes or other environmental hazards, or the presence of a threatened or endangered species or its habitat may affect Buyer's intended use of the

Initialed for identification by Buyer_____ _____ and Seller _____ _____   TREC NO. 20-12

Property. If Buyer is concerned about these matters, an addendum promulgated by TREC or required by the parties should be used.

H. RESIDENTIAL SERVICE CONTRACTS: Buyer may purchase a residential service contract from a residential service company licensed by TREC. If Buyer purchases a residential service contract, Seller shall reimburse Buyer at closing for the cost of the residential service contract in an amount not exceeding $_____. Buyer should review any residential service contract for the scope of coverage, exclusions and limitations. **The purchase of a residential service contract is optional. Similar coverage may be purchased from various companies authorized to do business in Texas.**

8. BROKERS' FEES: All obligations of the parties for payment of brokers' fees are contained in separate written agreements.

9. CLOSING:

A. The closing of the sale will be on or before _____, 20_____, or within 7 days after objections made under Paragraph 6D have been cured or waived, whichever date is later (Closing Date). If either party fails to close the sale by the Closing Date, the non-defaulting party may exercise the remedies contained in Paragraph 15.

B. At closing:

(1) Seller shall execute and deliver a general warranty deed conveying title to the Property to Buyer and showing no additional exceptions to those permitted in Paragraph 6 and furnish tax statements or certificates showing no delinquent taxes on the Property.

(2) Buyer shall pay the Sales Price in good funds acceptable to the escrow agent.

(3) Seller and Buyer shall execute and deliver any notices, statements, certificates, affidavits, releases, loan documents and other documents reasonably required for the closing of the sale and the issuance of the Title Policy.

(4) There will be no liens, assessments, or security interests against the Property which will not be satisfied out of the sales proceeds unless securing the payment of any loans assumed by Buyer and assumed loans will not be in default.

(5) If the Property is subject to a residential lease, Seller shall transfer security deposits (as defined under §92.102, Property Code), if any, to Buyer. In such an event, Buyer shall deliver to the tenant a signed statement acknowledging that the Buyer has received the security deposit and is responsible for the return of the security deposit, and specifying the exact dollar amount of the security deposit.

10. POSSESSION:

A Buyer's Possession: Seller shall deliver to Buyer possession of the Property in its present or required condition, ordinary wear and tear excepted: ❑upon closing and funding ❑according to a temporary residential lease form promulgated by TREC or other written lease required by the parties. Any possession by Buyer prior to closing or by Seller after closing which is not authorized by a written lease will establish a tenancy at sufferance relationship between the parties. **Consult your insurance agent prior to change of ownership and possession because insurance coverage may be limited or terminated. The absence of a written lease or appropriate insurance coverage may expose the parties to economic loss.**

B. Leases:

(1) After the Effective Date, Seller may not execute any lease (including but not limited to mineral leases) or convey any interest in the Property without Buyer's written consent.

(2) If the Property is subject to any lease to which Seller is a party, Seller shall deliver to Buyer copies of the lease(s) and any move-in condition form signed by the tenant within 7 days after the Effective Date of the contract.

11. SPECIAL PROVISIONS: (Insert only factual statements and business details applicable to the sale. TREC rules prohibit licensees from adding factual statements or business details for which a contract addendum, lease or other form has been promulgated by TREC for mandatory use.)

12. SETTLEMENT AND OTHER EXPENSES:

A. The following expenses must be paid at or prior to closing:

(1) Expenses payable by Seller (Seller's Expenses):

(a) Releases of existing liens, including prepayment penalties and recording fees; release of Seller's loan liability; tax statements or certificates; preparation of deed; one-half of escrow fee; and other expenses payable by Seller under this contract.

(b) Seller shall also pay an amount not to exceed $_____ to be applied in the following order: Buyer's Expenses which Buyer is prohibited from paying by FHA, VA, Texas Veterans Land Board or other governmental loan programs, and then to other Buyer's Expenses as allowed by the lender.

(2) Expenses payable by Buyer (Buyer's Expenses): Appraisal fees; loan application fees; adjusted origination charges; credit reports; preparation of loan documents; interest on the notes from date of disbursement to one month prior to dates of first monthly payments; recording fees; copies of easements and restrictions; loan title policy with endorsements required by lender; loan-related inspection fees; photos; amortization schedules; one-half of escrow fee; all prepaid items, including required premiums for flood and hazard insurance, reserve deposits for insurance, ad valorem taxes and special governmental assessments; final compliance inspection; courier fee; repair inspection; underwriting fee; wire transfer fee; expenses incident to any loan; Private Mortgage Insurance Premium (PMI), VA Loan Funding Fee, or FHA Mortgage Insurance Premium (MIP) as required by the lender; and other expenses payable by Buyer under this contract.

B. If any expense exceeds an amount expressly stated in this contract for such expense to be paid by a party, that party may terminate this contract unless the other party agrees to pay such excess. Buyer may not pay charges and fees expressly prohibited by FHA, VA, Texas Veterans Land Board or other governmental loan program regulations.

13. **PRORATIONS:** Taxes for the current year, interest, maintenance fees, assessments, dues and rents will be prorated through the Closing Date. The tax proration may be calculated taking into consideration any change in exemptions that will affect the current year's taxes. If taxes for the current year vary from the amount prorated at closing, the parties shall adjust the prorations when tax statements for the current year are available. If taxes are not paid at or prior to closing, Buyer shall pay taxes for the current year.

14. **CASUALTY LOSS:** If any part of the Property is damaged or destroyed by fire or other casualty after the effective date of this contract, Seller shall restore the Property to its previous condition as soon as reasonably possible, but in any event by the Closing Date. If Seller fails to do so due to factors beyond Seller's control, Buyer may (a) terminate this contract and the earnest money will be refunded to Buyer (b) extend the time for performance up to 15 days and the Closing Date will be extended as necessary or (c) accept the Property in its damaged condition with an assignment of insurance proceeds and receive credit from Seller at closing in the amount of the deductible under the insurance policy. Seller's obligations under this paragraph are independent of any other obligations of Seller under this contract.

15. **DEFAULT:** If Buyer fails to comply with this contract, Buyer will be in default, and Seller may (a) enforce specific performance, seek such other relief as may be provided by law, or both, or (b) terminate this contract and receive the earnest money as liquidated damages, thereby releasing both parties from this contract. If Seller fails to comply with this contract, Seller will be in default and Buyer may (a) enforce specific performance, seek such other relief as may be provided by law, or both, or (b) terminate this contract and receive the earnest money, thereby releasing both parties from this contract.

16. **MEDIATION:** It is the policy of the State of Texas to encourage resolution of disputes through alternative dispute resolution procedures such as mediation. Any dispute between Seller and Buyer related to this contract which is not resolved through informal discussion will be submitted to a mutually acceptable mediation service or provider. The parties to the mediation shall bear the mediation costs equally. This paragraph does not preclude a party from seeking equitable relief from a court of competent jurisdiction.

17. **ATTORNEY'S FEES:** A Buyer, Seller, Listing Broker, Other Broker, or escrow agent who prevails in any legal proceeding related to this contract is entitled to recover reasonable attorney's fees and all costs of such proceeding.

18. **ESCROW:**
A. ESCROW: The escrow agent is not (i) a party to this contract and does not have liability for the performance or nonperformance of any party to this contract, (ii) liable for interest on the earnest money and (iii) liable for the loss of any earnest money caused by the failure of any financial institution in which the earnest money has been deposited unless the financial institution is acting as escrow agent.

B. EXPENSES: At closing, the earnest money must be applied first to any cash down payment, then to Buyer's Expenses and any excess refunded to Buyer. If no closing occurs, escrow agent may: (i) require a written release of liability of the escrow agent from all parties, (ii) require payment of unpaid expenses incurred on behalf of a party, and (iii) only deduct from the earnest money the amount of unpaid expenses incurred on behalf of the party receiving the earnest money.

C. DEMAND: Upon termination of this contract, either party or the escrow agent may send a release of earnest money to each party and the parties shall execute counterparts of the release and deliver same to the escrow agent. If either party fails to execute the release, either party may make a written demand to the escrow agent for the earnest money. If only one party makes written demand for the earnest money, escrow agent shall promptly provide a copy of the demand to the other party. If escrow agent does not receive written objection to the demand from the other party within 15 days, escrow agent may disburse the earnest money to the party making demand reduced by the amount of unpaid expenses incurred on behalf of the party receiving the earnest money and escrow agent may pay the same to the creditors. If escrow agent complies with the provisions of this paragraph, each party hereby releases escrow agent from all adverse claims related to the disbursal of the earnest money.

   D. DAMAGES: Any party who wrongfully fails or refuses to sign a release acceptable to the escrow agent within 7 days of receipt of the request will be liable to the other party for liquidated damages in an amount equal to the sum of: (i) three times the amount of the earnest money; (ii) the earnest money; (iii) reasonable attorney's fees; and (iv) all costs of suit.

   E. NOTICES: Escrow agent's notices will be effective when sent in compliance with Paragraph 21. Notice of objection to the demand will be deemed effective upon receipt by escrow agent.

19. **REPRESENTATIONS:** All covenants, representations and warranties in this contract survive closing. If any representation of Seller in this contract is untrue on the Closing Date, Seller will be in default. Unless expressly prohibited by written agreement, Seller may continue to show the Property and receive, negotiate and accept back up offers.

20. **FEDERAL TAX REQUIREMENTS:** If Seller is a "foreign person," as defined by applicable law, or if Seller fails to deliver an affidavit to Buyer that Seller is not a "foreign person," then Buyer shall withhold from the sales proceeds an amount sufficient to comply with applicable tax law and deliver the same to the Internal Revenue Service together with appropriate tax forms. Internal Revenue Service regulations require filing written reports if currency in excess of specified amounts is received in the transaction.

21. **NOTICES:** All notices from one party to the other must be in writing and are effective when mailed to, hand-delivered at, or transmitted by facsimile or electronic transmission as follows:

To Buyer at: _____	**To Seller at:** _____
_____	_____
Telephone: ( ) _____	Telephone: ( ) _____
Facsimile: ( ) _____	Facsimile: ( ) _____
E-mail: _____	E-mail: _____

22. **AGREEMENT OF PARTIES:** This contract contains the entire agreement of the parties and cannot be changed except by their written agreement. Addenda which are a part of this contract are (Check all applicable boxes):

❑ Third Party Financing Addendum for Credit Approval

❑ Seller Financing Addendum

❑ Addendum for Property Subject to Mandatory Membership in a Property Owners Association

❑ Buyer's Temporary Residential Lease

❑ Loan Assumption Addendum

❑ Addendum for Sale of Other Property by Buyer

❑ Addendum for Reservation of Oil, Gas and Other Minerals

❑ Addendum for "Back-Up" Contract

❑ Addendum for Coastal Area Property

❑ Environmental Assessment, Threatened or Endangered Species and Wetlands Addendum

❑ Seller's Temporary Residential Lease

❑ Short Sale Addendum

❑ Addendum for Property Located Seaward of the Gulf Intracoastal Waterway

❑ Addendum for Seller's Disclosure of Information on Lead-based Paint and Lead-based Paint Hazards as Required by Federal Law

❑ Addendum for Property in a Propane Gas System Service Area

❑ Other (list): _____
_____
_____

Initialed for identification by Buyer_____ _____ and Seller _____ _____   TREC NO. 20-12

Contract Concerning _____ Page 8 of 9   4-28-2014
(Address of Property)

23. TERMINATION OPTION: For nominal consideration, the receipt of which is hereby acknowledged by Seller, and Buyer's agreement to pay Seller $_____ (Option Fee) within 3 days after the effective date of this contract, Seller grants Buyer the unrestricted right to terminate this contract by giving notice of termination to Seller within _____ days after the effective date of this contract (Option Period). If no dollar amount is stated as the Option Fee or if Buyer fails to pay the Option Fee to Seller within the time prescribed, this paragraph will not be a part of this contract and Buyer shall not have the unrestricted right to terminate this contract. If Buyer gives notice of termination within the time prescribed, the Option Fee will not be refunded; however, any earnest money will be refunded to Buyer. The Option Fee ❏will ❏will not be credited to the Sales Price at closing. **Time is of the essence for this paragraph and strict compliance with the time for performance is required.**

24. CONSULT AN ATTORNEY BEFORE SIGNING: TREC rules prohibit real estate licensees from giving legal advice. READ THIS CONTRACT CAREFULLY.

Buyer's
Attorney is: _____

Seller's
Attorney is: _____

_____

_____

Telephone: (_____)_____

Telephone: (_____)_____

Facsimile: (_____)_____

Facsimile: (_____)_____

E-mail: _____

E-mail: _____

EXECUTED the _____day of _____, 20_____ (EFFECTIVE DATE).
(BROKER: FILL IN THE DATE OF FINAL ACCEPTANCE.)

_____
Buyer

_____
Seller

_____
Buyer

_____
Seller

TREC NO. 20-12

Contract Concerning _____Page 9 of 9   4-28-2014
(Address of Property)

BROKER INFORMATION
(Print name(s) only. Do not sign)

Other Broker Firm	License No.		Listing Broker Firm	License No.

represents ☐ Buyer only as Buyer's agent
☐ Seller as Listing Broker's subagent

represents ☐ Seller and Buyer as an intermediary
☐ Seller only as Seller's agent

Name of Associate's Licensed Supervisor   Telephone

Name of Associate's Licensed Supervisor   Telephone

Associate's Name   Telephone

Listing Associate's Name   Telephone

Other Broker's Address   Facsimile

Listing Broker's Office Address   Facsimile

City   State   Zip

City   State   Zip

Associate's Email Address

Listing Associate's Email Address

Selling Associate's Name   Telephone

Name of Selling Associate's Licensed Supervisor   Telephone

Selling Associate's Office Address   Facsimile

City   State   Zip

Selling Associate's Email Address

Listing Broker has agreed to pay Other Broker_____of the total sales price when the Listing Broker's fee is received. Escrow agent is authorized and directed to pay other Broker from Listing Broker's fee at closing.

OPTION FEE RECEIPT

Receipt of $_____ (Option Fee) in the form of _____ is acknowledged.

_____   _____
Seller or Listing Broker   Date

CONTRACT AND EARNEST MONEY RECEIPT

Receipt of ☐Contract and ☐$_____Earnest Money in the form of _____
is acknowledged.

Escrow Agent: _____   Date: _____

By: _____   _____
                                                                                  Email Address

_____   Telephone (____)_____
Address

_____   Facsimile: (____) _____
City   State   Zip

TREC NO. 20-12

APPROVED BY THE TEXAS REAL ESTATE COMMISSION   10-10-11

ADDENDUM FOR SELLER'S DISCLOSURE OF INFORMATION ON LEAD-BASED PAINT AND LEAD-BASED PAINT HAZARDS AS REQUIRED BY FEDERAL LAW

CONCERNING THE PROPERTY AT _____

(Street Address and City)

A. LEAD WARNING STATEMENT: "Every purchaser of any interest in residential real property on which a residential dwelling was built prior to 1978 is notified that such property may present exposure to lead from lead-based paint that may place young children at risk of developing lead poisoning. Lead poisoning in young children may produce permanent neurological damage, including learning disabilities, reduced intelligence quotient, behavioral problems, and impaired memory. Lead poisoning also poses a particular risk to pregnant women. The seller of any interest in residential real property is required to provide the buyer with any information on lead-based paint hazards from risk assessments or inspections in the seller's possession and notify the buyer of any known lead-based paint hazards. A risk assessment or inspection for possible lead-paint hazards is recommended prior to purchase."

NOTICE: Inspector must be properly certified as required by federal law.

B. SELLER'S DISCLOSURE:
1. PRESENCE OF LEAD-BASED PAINT AND/OR LEAD-BASED PAINT HAZARDS (check one box only):
☐(a) Known lead-based paint and/or lead-based paint hazards are present in the Property (explain): _____
_____ .
☐(b) Seller has no actual knowledge of lead-based paint and/or lead-based paint hazards in the Property.
2. RECORDS AND REPORTS AVAILABLE TO SELLER (check one box only):
☐(a) Seller has provided the purchaser with all available records and reports pertaining to lead-based paint and/or lead-based paint hazards in the Property (list documents):_____
_____ .
☐(b) Seller has no reports or records pertaining to lead-based paint and/or lead-based paint hazards in the Property.

C. BUYER'S RIGHTS (check one box only):
☐1. Buyer waives the opportunity to conduct a risk assessment or inspection of the Property for the presence of lead-based paint or lead-based paint hazards.
☐2. Within ten days after the effective date of this contract, Buyer may have the Property inspected by inspectors selected by Buyer. If lead-based paint or lead-based paint hazards are present, Buyer may terminate this contract by giving Seller written notice within 14 days after the effective date of this contract, and the earnest money will be refunded to Buyer.

D. BUYER'S ACKNOWLEDGMENT (check applicable boxes):
☐1. Buyer has received copies of all information listed above.
☐2. Buyer has received the pamphlet *Protect Your Family from Lead in Your Home*.

E. BROKERS' ACKNOWLEDGMENT: Brokers have informed Seller of Seller's obligations under 42 U.S.C. 4852d to: (a) provide Buyer with the federally approved pamphlet on lead poisoning prevention; (b) complete this addendum; (c) disclose any known lead-based paint and/or lead-based paint hazards in the Property; (d) deliver all records and reports to Buyer pertaining to lead-based paint and/or lead-based paint hazards in the Property; (e) provide Buyer a period of up to 10 days to have the Property inspected; and (f) retain a completed copy of this addendum for at least 3 years following the sale. Brokers are aware of their responsibility to ensure compliance.

F. CERTIFICATION OF ACCURACY: The following persons have reviewed the information above and certify, to the best of their knowledge, that the information they have provided is true and accurate.

_____   _____   _____   _____
Buyer   Date   Seller   Date

_____   _____   _____   _____
Buyer   Date   Seller   Date

_____   _____   _____   _____
Other Broker   Date   Listing Broker   Date

TREC NO. OP-L

2-10-2014

PROMULGATED BY THE TEXAS REAL ESTATE COMMISSION (TREC)

THIRD PARTY FINANCING ADDENDUM FOR CREDIT APPROVAL
(Not for use with Reverse Mortgage Financing)

TO CONTRACT CONCERNING THE PROPERTY AT

_____

(Street Address and City)

Buyer shall apply promptly for all financing described below and make every reasonable effort to obtain credit approval for the financing (Credit Approval). Buyer shall furnish all information and documents required by lender for Credit Approval. Credit Approval will be deemed to have been obtained when (1) the terms of the loan(s) described below are available and (2) lender determines that Buyer has satisfied all of lender's requirements related to Buyer's assets, income and credit history. If Buyer cannot obtain Credit Approval, Buyer may give written notice to Seller within _____ days after the effective date of this contract and this contract will terminate and the earnest money will be refunded to Buyer. **If Buyer does not give such notice within the time required, this contract will no longer be subject to Credit Approval. Time is of the essence for this paragraph and strict compliance with the time for performance is required.**

NOTE: Credit Approval does not include approval of lender's underwriting requirements for the Property, as specified in Paragraph 4.A.(1) of the contract.

Each note must be secured by vendor's and deed of trust liens.

CHECK APPLICABLE BOXES:

☐ A. CONVENTIONAL FINANCING:

    ☐ (1) A first mortgage loan in the principal amount of $ _____ (excluding any financed PMI premium), due in full in _____ year(s), with interest not to exceed _____% per annum for the first _____year(s) of the loan with Adjusted Origination Charges as shown on Buyer's Good Faith Estimate for the loan not to exceed _____% of the loan.

    ☐ (2) A second mortgage loan in the principal amount of $_____(excluding any financed PMI premium), due in full in _____year(s), with interest not to exceed _____% per annum for the first _____year(s) of the loan with Adjusted Origination Charges as shown on Buyer's Good Faith Estimate for the loan not to exceed _____ % of the loan.

☐ B. TEXAS VETERANS LOAN: A loan(s) from the Texas Veterans Land Board of $_____ for a period in the total amount of _____years at the interest rate established by the Texas Veterans Land Board.

☐C. FHA INSURED FINANCING: A Section _____ FHA insured loan of not less than $_____ (excluding any financed MIP), amortizable monthly for not less than _____years, with interest not to exceed _____% per annum for the first _____year(s) of the loan with Adjusted Origination Charges as shown on Buyer's Good Faith Estimate for the loan not to exceed _____ % of the loan. As required by HUD-FHA, if FHA valuation is unknown, _"It is expressly agreed that, notwithstanding any other provision of this contract, the purchaser (Buyer) shall not be obligated to complete the purchase of the Property described herein or to incur any penalty by forfeiture of earnest money deposits or otherwise unless the purchaser (Buyer) has been given in accordance with HUD/FHA or VA requirements a written statement issued by the Federal Housing Commissioner, Department of Veterans Affairs, or a Direct Endorsement Lender setting forth the appraised value of the Property of not less than $_____. The purchaser (Buyer) shall have the privilege and option of proceeding with consummation of the contract without regard to the amount of the appraised valuation. The appraised valuation is arrived at to determine the_

Initialed for identification by Buyer_____ _____   and Seller_____ _____   TREC NO. 40-6

Third Party Financing Condition Addendum Concerning   Page 2 of 2   2-10-2014

_____
(Address of Property)

maximum mortgage the Department of Housing and Urban Development will insure. HUD does not warrant the value or the condition of the Property. The purchaser (Buyer) should satisfy himself/herself that the price and the condition of the Property are acceptable."

❑ D. VA GUARANTEED FINANCING: A VA guaranteed loan of not less than $_____ (excluding any financed Funding Fee), amortizable monthly for not less than_____years, with interest not to exceed_____% per annum for the first _____year(s) of the loan with Adjusted Origination Charges as shown on Buyer's Good Faith Estimate for the loan not to exceed _____% of the loan.

VA NOTICE TO BUYER: *"It is expressly agreed that, notwithstanding any other provisions of this contract, the Buyer shall not incur any penalty by forfeiture of earnest money or otherwise or be obligated to complete the purchase of the Property described herein, if the contract purchase price or cost exceeds the reasonable value of the Property established by the Department of Veterans Affairs. The Buyer shall, however, have the privilege and option of proceeding with the consummation of this contract without regard to the amount of the reasonable value established by the Department of Veterans Affairs."*

If Buyer elects to complete the purchase at an amount in excess of the reasonable value established by VA, Buyer shall pay such excess amount in cash from a source which Buyer agrees to disclose to the VA and which Buyer represents will not be from borrowed funds except as approved by VA. If VA reasonable value of the Property is less than the Sales Price, Seller may reduce the Sales Price to an amount equal to the VA reasonable value and the sale will be closed at the lower Sales Price with proportionate adjustments to the down payment and the loan amount.

❑ E.USDA GUARANTEED FINANCING: A USDA-guaranteed loan of not less than $_____ (excluding any financed Funding Fee), amortizable monthly for not less than_____years, with interest not to exceed ____% per annum for the first ____year(s) of the loan with Adjusted Origination Charges as shown on Buyer's Good Faith Estimate for the loan not to exceed _____% of the loan.

Buyer hereby authorizes any lender to furnish to the Seller or Buyer or their representatives information relating only to the status of Credit Approval of Buyer.

_____   _____
Buyer   Seller

_____   _____
Buyer   Seller

PROMULGATED BY THE TEXAS REAL ESTATE COMMISSION (TREC)
4-28-2014
ONE TO FOUR FAMILY RESIDENTIAL CONTRACT (RESALE)
NOTICE: Not For Use For Condominium Transactions

1. PARTIES: The parties to this contract are <u>Larry Fleming, and wife, Marcia Fleming</u>
(Seller) and <u>Troy Donaldson, and wife, Donna Donaldson</u> (Buyer).
Seller agrees to sell and convey to Buyer and Buyer agrees to buy from Seller the Property defined
below.

2. PROPERTY: The land, improvements and accessories are collectively referred to as the "Property".
   A. LAND: Lot <u>20</u> Block <u>17</u>, <u>Meadows subdivision</u>
   Addition, City of <u>Houston</u>, County of <u>Harris</u>,
   Texas, known as <u>3430 Old Master Dr, Houston, TX</u>
   (address/zip code), or as described on attached exhibit.
   B. IMPROVEMENTS: The house, garage and all other fixtures and improvements attached to the
   above-described real property, including without limitation, the following **permanently installed
   and built-in items,** if any: all equipment and appliances, valances, screens, shutters, awnings,
   wall-to-wall carpeting, mirrors, ceiling fans, attic fans, mail boxes, television antennas, mounts
   and brackets for televisions and speakers, heating and air-conditioning units, security and fire
   detection equipment, wiring, plumbing and lighting fixtures, chandeliers, water softener system,
   kitchen equipment, garage door openers, cleaning equipment, shrubbery, landscaping, outdoor
   cooking equipment, and all other property owned by Seller and attached to the above described
   real property.
   C. ACCESSORIES: The following described related accessories, if any: window air conditioning units,
   stove, fireplace screens, curtains and rods, blinds, window shades, draperies and rods, door keys,
   mailbox keys, above ground pool, swimming pool equipment and maintenance accessories,
   artificial fireplace logs, and controls for: (i) garage doors, (ii) entry gates, and (iii) other
   improvements and accessories.
   D. EXCLUSIONS: The following improvements and accessories will be retained by Seller and must
   be removed prior to delivery of possession: <u>N/A</u>
   <u> </u>.

3. SALES PRICE:
   A. Cash portion of Sales Price payable by Buyer at closing .... $ <u>32,500.00</u>
   B. Sum of all financing described below (excluding any loan funding
       fee or mortgage insurance premium) .... $ <u>292,500.00</u>
   C. Sales Price (Sum of A and B).. $ <u>325,000.00</u>

4. FINANCING (Not for use with reverse mortgage financing): The portion of Sales Price not
   payable in cash will be paid as follows: (Check applicable boxes below)
   ☒ A.THIRD PARTY FINANCING: One or more third party mortgage loans in the total amount of
      $<u>292,500.00</u> (excluding any loan funding fee or mortgage insurance premium).
       (1) Property Approval: If the Property does not satisfy the lenders' underwriting requirements for
          the loan(s) (including, but not limited to appraisal, insurability and lender required repairs),
          Buyer may terminate this contract by giving notice to Seller prior to closing and the earnest
          money will be refunded to Buyer.
       (2) Credit Approval: (Check one box only)
         ☒ (a) This contract is subject to Buyer being approved for the financing described in the attached
            Third Party Financing Addendum for Credit Approval.
         ☐ (b) This contract is not subject to Buyer being approved for financing and does not involve FHA
            or VA financing.
   ☐ B. ASSUMPTION: The assumption of the unpaid principal balance of one or more promissory notes
      described in the attached TREC Loan Assumption Addendum.
   ☐ C. SELLER FINANCING: A promissory note from Buyer to Seller of $ <u>N/A</u>, secured by
      vendor's and deed of trust liens, and containing the terms and conditions described in the attached
      TREC Seller Financing Addendum. If an owner policy of title insurance is furnished, Buyer shall
      furnish Seller with a mortgagee policy of title insurance.

Initialed for identification by Buyer_____ _____ and Seller _____ _____   TREC NO. 20-12

Contract Concerning __3430 Old Master Dr, Houston, TX_____Page 2 of 9   4-28-2014
(Address of Property)

5. **EARNEST MONEY:** Upon execution of this contract by all parties, Buyer shall deposit $ _3,500.00_ as earnest money with __ABC Title Company__, as escrow agent, at __1219 Goldrich Dr, Houston, TX__ (address). Buyer shall deposit additional earnest money of $__N/A__ with escrow agent within _N/A_ days after the effective date of this contract. If Buyer fails to deposit the earnest money as required by this contract, Buyer will be in default.

6. **TITLE POLICY AND SURVEY:**
   A. TITLE POLICY: Seller shall furnish to Buyer at ☒ Seller's ☐ Buyer's expense an owner policy of title insurance (Title Policy) issued by __ABC Title Company__ (Title Company) in the amount of the Sales Price, dated at or after closing, insuring Buyer against loss under the provisions of the Title Policy, subject to the promulgated exclusions (including existing building and zoning ordinances) and the following exceptions:
      (1) Restrictive covenants common to the platted subdivision in which the Property is located.
      (2) The standard printed exception for standby fees, taxes and assessments.
      (3) Liens created as part of the financing described in Paragraph 4.
      (4) Utility easements created by the dedication deed or plat of the subdivision in which the Property is located.
      (5) Reservations or exceptions otherwise permitted by this contract or as may be approved by Buyer in writing.
      (6) The standard printed exception as to marital rights.
      (7) The standard printed exception as to waters, tidelands, beaches, streams, and related matters.
      (8) The standard printed exception as to discrepancies, conflicts, shortages in area or boundary lines, encroachments or protrusions, or overlapping improvements: ☒(i) will not be amended or deleted from the title policy; ☐(ii) will be amended to read, "shortages in area" at the expense of ☐Buyer ☐Seller.
   B. COMMITMENT: Within 20 days after the Title Company receives a copy of this contract, Seller shall furnish to Buyer a commitment for title insurance (Commitment) and, at Buyer's expense, legible copies of restrictive covenants and documents evidencing exceptions in the Commitment (Exception Documents) other than the standard printed exceptions. Seller authorizes the Title Company to deliver the Commitment and Exception Documents to Buyer at Buyer's address shown in Paragraph 21. If the Commitment and Exception Documents are not delivered to Buyer within the specified time, the time for delivery will be automatically extended up to 15 days or 3 days before the Closing Date, whichever is earlier. If, due to factors beyond Seller's control, the Commitment and Exception Documents are not delivered within the time required, Buyer may terminate this contract and the earnest money will be refunded to Buyer.
   C. SURVEY: The survey must be made by a registered professional land surveyor acceptable to the Title Company and Buyer's lender(s). (Check one box only)
   ☐(1) Within _n/a_ days after the effective date of this contract, Seller shall furnish to Buyer and Title Company Seller's existing survey of the Property and a Residential Real Property Affidavit promulgated by the Texas Department of Insurance (T-47 Affidavit). **If Seller fails to furnish the existing survey or affidavit within the time prescribed, Buyer shall obtain a new survey at Seller's expense no later than 3 days prior to Closing Date.** If the existing survey or affidavit is not acceptable to Title Company or Buyer's lender(s), Buyer shall obtain a new survey at ☐Seller's ☐Buyer's expense no later than 3 days prior to Closing Date.
   ☒(2) Within _10_ days after the effective date of this contract, Buyer shall obtain a new survey at Buyer's expense. Buyer is deemed to receive the survey on the date of actual receipt or the date specified in this paragraph, whichever is earlier.
   ☐(3) Within _n/a_ days after the effective date of this contract, Seller, at Seller's expense shall furnish a new survey to Buyer.
   D. OBJECTIONS: Buyer may object in writing to defects, exceptions, or encumbrances to title: disclosed on the survey other than items 6A(1) through (7) above; disclosed in the Commitment other than items 6A(1) through (8) above; or which prohibit the following use or activity: __The ability to add a swimming pool in the back yard and to park their RV in their driveway.__.
   Buyer must object the earlier of (i) the Closing Date or (ii) _____ days after Buyer receives the Commitment, Exception Documents, and the survey. Buyer's failure to object within the time allowed will constitute a waiver of Buyer's right to object; except that the requirements in Schedule C of the Commitment are not waived by Buyer. Provided Seller is not obligated to incur any expense, Seller shall cure the timely objections of Buyer or any third party lender

Initialed for identification by Buyer_____ _____ and Seller _____ _____   TREC NO. 20-12

Contract Concerning ___3430 Old Master Dr, Houston, TX_____Page 3 of 9   4-28-2014
(Address of Property)

within 15 days after Seller receives the objections and the Closing Date will be extended as necessary. If objections are not cured within such 15 day period, this contract will terminate and the earnest money will be refunded to Buyer unless Buyer waives the objections.
E. TITLE NOTICES:
   (1) ABSTRACT OR TITLE POLICY: Broker advises Buyer to have an abstract of title covering the Property examined by an attorney of Buyer's selection, or Buyer should be furnished with or obtain a Title Policy. If a Title Policy is furnished, the Commitment should be promptly reviewed by an attorney of Buyer's choice due to the time limitations on Buyer's right to object.
   (2) MEMBERSHIP IN PROPERTY OWNERS ASSOCIATION(S): The Property ☐is ☒is not subject to mandatory membership in a property owners association(s). If the Property is subject to mandatory membership in a property owners association(s), Seller notifies Buyer under §5.012, Texas Property Code, that, as a purchaser of property in the residential community identified in Paragraph 2A in which the Property is located, you are obligated to be a member of the property owners association(s). Restrictive covenants governing the use and occupancy of the Property and all dedicatory instruments governing the establishment, maintenance, or operation of this residential community have been or will be recorded in the Real Property Records of the county in which the Property is located. Copies of the restrictive covenants and dedicatory instruments may be obtained from the county clerk. **You are obligated to pay assessments to the property owners association(s). The amount of the assessments is subject to change. Your failure to pay the assessments could result in enforcement of the association's lien on and the foreclosure of the Property.**
   Section 207.003, Property Code, entitles an owner to receive copies of any document that governs the establishment, maintenance, or operation of a subdivision, including, but not limited to, restrictions, bylaws, rules and regulations, and a resale certificate from a property owners' association. A resale certificate contains information including, but not limited to, statements specifying the amount and frequency of regular assessments and the style and cause number of lawsuits to which the property owners' association is a party, other than lawsuits relating to unpaid ad valorem taxes of an individual member of the association. These documents must be made available to you by the property owners' association or the association's agent on your request.
   If Buyer is concerned about these matters, the TREC promulgated Addendum for Property Subject to Mandatory Membership in a Property Owners Association(s) should be used.
   (3) STATUTORY TAX DISTRICTS: If the Property is situated in a utility or other statutorily created district providing water, sewer, drainage, or flood control facilities and services, Chapter 49, Texas Water Code, requires Seller to deliver and Buyer to sign the statutory notice relating to the tax rate, bonded indebtedness, or standby fee of the district prior to final execution of this contract.
   (4) TIDE WATERS: If the Property abuts the tidally influenced waters of the state, §33.135, Texas Natural Resources Code, requires a notice regarding coastal area property to be included in the contract. An addendum containing the notice promulgated by TREC or required by the parties must be used.
   (5) ANNEXATION: If the Property is located outside the limits of a municipality, Seller notifies Buyer under §5.011, Texas Property Code, that the Property may now or later be included in the extraterritorial jurisdiction of a municipality and may now or later be subject to annexation by the municipality. Each municipality maintains a map that depicts its boundaries and extraterritorial jurisdiction. To determine if the Property is located within a municipality's extraterritorial jurisdiction or is likely to be located within a municipality's extraterritorial jurisdiction, contact all municipalities located in the general proximity of the Property for further information.
   (6) PROPERTY LOCATED IN A CERTIFICATED SERVICE AREA OF A UTILITY SERVICE PROVIDER: Notice required by §13.257, Water Code: The real property, described in Paragraph 2, that you are about to purchase may be located in a certificated water or sewer service area, which is authorized by law to provide water or sewer service to the properties in the certificated area. If your property is located in a certificated area there may be special costs or charges that you will be required to pay before you can receive water or sewer service. There may be a period required to construct lines or other facilities necessary to provide water or sewer service to your property. You are advised to determine if the property is in a certificated area and contact the utility service provider to determine the cost that you will be required to pay and the period, if any, that is required to provide water or sewer service to your property. The undersigned Buyer hereby acknowledges receipt of the foregoing notice at or before the execution of a binding contract for the purchase of the real property described in Paragraph 2 or at closing of purchase of the real property.

Initialed for identification by Buyer_____ _____ and Seller _____ _____   TREC NO. 20-12

Contract Concerning ___3430 Old Master Dr, Houston, TX_____ Page 4 of 9   4-28-2014
(Address of Property)

(7) PUBLIC IMPROVEMENT DISTRICTS: If the Property is in a public improvement district, §5.014, Property Code, requires Seller to notify Buyer as follows: As a purchaser of this parcel of real property you are obligated to pay an assessment to a municipality or county for an improvement project undertaken by a public improvement district under Chapter 372, Local Government Code. The assessment may be due annually or in periodic installments. More information concerning the amount of the assessment and the due dates of that assessment may be obtained from the municipality or county levying the assessment. The amount of the assessments is subject to change. Your failure to pay the assessments could result in a lien on and the foreclosure of your property.

(8) TRANSFER FEES: If the Property is subject to a private transfer fee obligation, §5.205, Property Code, requires Seller to notify Buyer as follows: The private transfer fee obligation may be governed by Chapter 5, Subchapter G of the Texas Property Code.

(9) PROPANE GAS SYSTEM SERVICE AREA: If the Property is located in a propane gas system service area owned by a distribution system retailer, Seller must give Buyer written notice as required by §141.010, Texas Utilities Code. An addendum containing the notice approved by TREC or required by the parties should be used.

7. PROPERTY CONDITION:

A. ACCESS, INSPECTIONS AND UTILITIES: Seller shall permit Buyer and Buyer's agents access to the Property at reasonable times. Buyer may have the Property inspected by inspectors selected by Buyer and licensed by TREC or otherwise permitted by law to make inspections. Seller at Seller's expense shall immediately cause existing utilities to be turned on and shall keep the utilities on during the time this contract is in effect.

B. SELLER'S DISCLOSURE NOTICE PURSUANT TO §5.008, TEXAS PROPERTY CODE (Notice): (Check one box only)

☒ (1) Buyer has received the Notice.

☐ (2) Buyer has not received the Notice. Within _____ days after the effective date of this contract, Seller shall deliver the Notice to Buyer. If Buyer does not receive the Notice, Buyer may terminate this contract at any time prior to the closing and the earnest money will be refunded to Buyer. If Seller delivers the Notice, Buyer may terminate this contract for any reason within 7 days after Buyer receives the Notice or prior to the closing, whichever first occurs, and the earnest money will be refunded to Buyer.

☐ (3) The Seller is not required to furnish the notice under the Texas Property Code.

C. SELLER'S DISCLOSURE OF LEAD-BASED PAINT AND LEAD-BASED PAINT HAZARDS is required by Federal law for a residential dwelling constructed prior to 1978.

D. ACCEPTANCE OF PROPERTY CONDITION: "As Is" means the present condition of the Property with any and all defects and without warranty except for the warranties of title and the warranties in this contract. Buyer's agreement to accept the Property As Is under Paragraph 7D(1) or (2) does not preclude Buyer from inspecting the Property under Paragraph 7A, from negotiating repairs or treatments in a subsequent amendment, or from terminating this contract during the Option Period, if any. (Check one box only)

☐ (1) Buyer accepts the Property As Is.

☒ (2) Buyer accepts the Property As Is provided Seller, at Seller's expense, shall complete the following specific repairs and treatments: ___Replace the four fogged windows in the kitchen._____.

(Do not insert general phrases, such as "subject to inspections" that do not identify specific repairs and treatments.)

E. LENDER REQUIRED REPAIRS AND TREATMENTS: Unless otherwise agreed in writing, neither party is obligated to pay for lender required repairs, which includes treatment for wood destroying insects. If the parties do not agree to pay for the lender required repairs or treatments, this contract will terminate and the earnest money will be refunded to Buyer. If the cost of lender required repairs and treatments exceeds 5% of the Sales Price, Buyer may terminate this contract and the earnest money will be refunded to Buyer.

F. COMPLETION OF REPAIRS AND TREATMENTS: Unless otherwise agreed in writing: (i) Seller shall complete all agreed repairs and treatments prior to the Closing Date; and (ii) all required permits must be obtained, and repairs and treatments must be performed by persons who are licensed to provide such repairs or treatments or, if no license is required by law, are commercially engaged in the trade of providing such repairs or treatments.   At Buyer's election, any transferable warranties received by Seller with respect to the repairs and treatments will be transferred to Buyer at Buyer's expense. If Seller fails to complete any agreed repairs and treatments prior to the Closing Date, Buyer may exercise remedies under Paragraph 15 or extend the Closing Date up to 5 days if necessary for Seller to complete the repairs and treatments.

G. ENVIRONMENTAL MATTERS: Buyer is advised that the presence of wetlands, toxic substances, including asbestos and wastes or other environmental hazards, or the presence of a threatened or endangered species or its habitat may affect Buyer's intended use of the

Initialed for identification by Buyer_____ _____ and Seller _____ _____   TREC NO. 20-12

Contract Concerning ___3430 Old Master Dr, Houston, TX_____ Page 5 of 9   4-28-2014
(Address of Property)

Property. If Buyer is concerned about these matters, an addendum promulgated by TREC or required by the parties should be used.

H. RESIDENTIAL SERVICE CONTRACTS: Buyer may purchase a residential service contract from a residential service company licensed by TREC. If Buyer purchases a residential service contract, Seller shall reimburse Buyer at closing for the cost of the residential service contract in an amount not exceeding $ _425.00_____. Buyer should review any residential service contract for the scope of coverage, exclusions and limitations. **The purchase of a residential service contract is optional. Similar coverage may be purchased from various companies authorized to do business in Texas.**

8. **BROKERS' FEES:** All obligations of the parties for payment of brokers' fees are contained in separate written agreements.

9. **CLOSING:**
   A. The closing of the sale will be on or before _(end of next month)_, 20____, or within 7 days after objections made under Paragraph 6D have been cured or waived, whichever date is later (Closing Date). If either party fails to close the sale by the Closing Date, the non-defaulting party may exercise the remedies contained in Paragraph 15.
   B. At closing:
   (1) Seller shall execute and deliver a general warranty deed conveying title to the Property to Buyer and showing no additional exceptions to those permitted in Paragraph 6 and furnish tax statements or certificates showing no delinquent taxes on the Property.
   (2) Buyer shall pay the Sales Price in good funds acceptable to the escrow agent.
   (3) Seller and Buyer shall execute and deliver any notices, statements, certificates, affidavits, releases, loan documents and other documents reasonably required for the closing of the sale and the issuance of the Title Policy.
   (4) There will be no liens, assessments, or security interests against the Property which will not be satisfied out of the sales proceeds unless securing the payment of any loans assumed by Buyer and assumed loans will not be in default.
   (5) If the Property is subject to a residential lease, Seller shall transfer security deposits (as defined under §92.102, Property Code), if any, to Buyer. In such an event, Buyer shall deliver to the tenant a signed statement acknowledging that the Buyer has received the security deposit and is responsible for the return of the security deposit, and specifying the exact dollar amount of the security deposit.

10. **POSSESSION:**
    A Buyer's Possession: Seller shall deliver to Buyer possession of the Property in its present or required condition, ordinary wear and tear excepted: ☒upon closing and funding ❏according to a temporary residential lease form promulgated by TREC or other written lease required by the parties. Any possession by Buyer prior to closing or by Seller after closing which is not authorized by a written lease will establish a tenancy at sufferance relationship between the parties. **Consult your insurance agent prior to change of ownership and possession because insurance coverage may be limited or terminated. The absence of a written lease or appropriate insurance coverage may expose the parties to economic loss.**
    B. Leases:
       (1) After the Effective Date, Seller may not execute any lease (including but not limited to mineral leases) or convey any interest in the Property without Buyer's written consent.
       (2) If the Property is subject to any lease to which Seller is a party, Seller shall deliver to Buyer copies of the lease(s) and any move-in condition form signed by the tenant within 7 days after the Effective Date of the contract.

11. **SPECIAL PROVISIONS:** (Insert only factual statements and business details applicable to the sale. TREC rules prohibit licensees from adding factual statements or business details for which a contract addendum, lease or other form has been promulgated by TREC for mandatory use.) The interest on the adjustable rate mortgage described in the Third Party Financing Addendum cannot change more than once a year and cannot increase more than 2% per year or 5% over the life of the loan.

12. **SETTLEMENT AND OTHER EXPENSES:**
    A. The following expenses must be paid at or prior to closing:
       (1) Expenses payable by Seller (Seller's Expenses):
          (a) Releases of existing liens, including prepayment penalties and recording fees; release of Seller's loan liability; tax statements or certificates; preparation of deed; one-half of escrow fee; and other expenses payable by Seller under this contract.
          (b) Seller shall also pay an amount not to exceed $ _N/A_____ to be applied in the

Initialed for identification by Buyer_____ _____ and Seller _____ _____   TREC NO. 20-12

Contract Concerning <u>3430 Old Master Dr, Houston, TX</u> _____ Page 6 of 9 4-28-2014
(Address of Property)

following order: Buyer's Expenses which Buyer is prohibited from paying by FHA, VA, Texas Veterans Land Board or other governmental loan programs, and then to other Buyer's Expenses as allowed by the lender.

(2) Expenses payable by Buyer (Buyer's Expenses): Appraisal fees; loan application fees; adjusted origination charges; credit reports; preparation of loan documents; interest on the notes from date of disbursement to one month prior to dates of first monthly payments; recording fees; copies of easements and restrictions; loan title policy with endorsements required by lender; loan-related inspection fees; photos; amortization schedules; one-half of escrow fee; all prepaid items, including required premiums for flood and hazard insurance, reserve deposits for insurance, ad valorem taxes and special governmental assessments; final compliance inspection; courier fee; repair inspection; underwriting fee; wire transfer fee; expenses incident to any loan; Private Mortgage Insurance Premium (PMI), VA Loan Funding Fee, or FHA Mortgage Insurance Premium (MIP) as required by the lender; and other expenses payable by Buyer under this contract.

B. If any expense exceeds an amount expressly stated in this contract for such expense to be paid by a party, that party may terminate this contract unless the other party agrees to pay such excess. Buyer may not pay charges and fees expressly prohibited by FHA, VA, Texas Veterans Land Board or other governmental loan program regulations.

13. **PRORATIONS:** Taxes for the current year, interest, maintenance fees, assessments, dues and rents will be prorated through the Closing Date. The tax proration may be calculated taking into consideration any change in exemptions that will affect the current year's taxes. If taxes for the current year vary from the amount prorated at closing, the parties shall adjust the prorations when tax statements for the current year are available. If taxes are not paid at or prior to closing, Buyer shall pay taxes for the current year.

14. **CASUALTY LOSS:** If any part of the Property is damaged or destroyed by fire or other casualty after the effective date of this contract, Seller shall restore the Property to its previous condition as soon as reasonably possible, but in any event by the Closing Date. If Seller fails to do so due to factors beyond Seller's control, Buyer may (a) terminate this contract and the earnest money will be refunded to Buyer (b) extend the time for performance up to 15 days and the Closing Date will be extended as necessary or (c) accept the Property in its damaged condition with an assignment of insurance proceeds and receive credit from Seller at closing in the amount of the deductible under the insurance policy. Seller's obligations under this paragraph are independent of any other obligations of Seller under this contract.

15. **DEFAULT:** If Buyer fails to comply with this contract, Buyer will be in default, and Seller may (a) enforce specific performance, seek such other relief as may be provided by law, or both, or (b) terminate this contract and receive the earnest money as liquidated damages, thereby releasing both parties from this contract. If Seller fails to comply with this contract, Seller will be in default and Buyer may (a) enforce specific performance, seek such other relief as may be provided by law, or both, or (b) terminate this contract and receive the earnest money, thereby releasing both parties from this contract.

16. **MEDIATION:** It is the policy of the State of Texas to encourage resolution of disputes through alternative dispute resolution procedures such as mediation. Any dispute between Seller and Buyer related to this contract which is not resolved through informal discussion will be submitted to a mutually acceptable mediation service or provider. The parties to the mediation shall bear the mediation costs equally. This paragraph does not preclude a party from seeking equitable relief from a court of competent jurisdiction.

17. **ATTORNEY'S FEES:** A Buyer, Seller, Listing Broker, Other Broker, or escrow agent who prevails in any legal proceeding related to this contract is entitled to recover reasonable attorney's fees and all costs of such proceeding.

18. **ESCROW:**
A. ESCROW: The escrow agent is not (i) a party to this contract and does not have liability for the performance or nonperformance of any party to this contract, (ii) liable for interest on the earnest money and (iii) liable for the loss of any earnest money caused by the failure of any financial institution in which the earnest money has been deposited unless the financial institution is acting as escrow agent.
B. EXPENSES: At closing, the earnest money must be applied first to any cash down payment, then to Buyer's Expenses and any excess refunded to Buyer. If no closing occurs, escrow agent may: (i) require a written release of liability of the escrow agent from all parties, (ii) require payment of unpaid expenses incurred on behalf of a party, and (iii) only deduct from the earnest money the amount of unpaid expenses incurred on behalf of the party receiving the earnest money.
C. DEMAND: Upon termination of this contract, either party or the escrow agent may send a release of earnest money to each party and the parties shall execute counterparts of

Initialed for identification by Buyer_____ _____ and Seller _____ _____ TREC NO. 20-12

Contract Concerning 3430 Old Master Dr, Houston, TX   Page 7 of 9   4-28-2014
(Address of Property)

the release and deliver same to the escrow agent. If either party fails to execute the release, either party may make a written demand to the escrow agent for the earnest money. If only one party makes written demand for the earnest money, escrow agent shall promptly provide a copy of the demand to the other party. If escrow agent does not receive written objection to the demand from the other party within 15 days, escrow agent may disburse the earnest money to the party making demand reduced by the amount of unpaid expenses incurred on behalf of the party receiving the earnest money and escrow agent may pay the same to the creditors. If escrow agent complies with the provisions of this paragraph, each party hereby releases escrow agent from all adverse claims related to the disbursal of the earnest money.

    D. DAMAGES: Any party who wrongfully fails or refuses to sign a release acceptable to the escrow agent within 7 days of receipt of the request will be liable to the other party for liquidated damages in an amount equal to the sum of: (i) three times the amount of the earnest money; (ii) the earnest money; (iii) reasonable attorney's fees; and (iv) all costs of suit.

    E. NOTICES: Escrow agent's notices will be effective when sent in compliance with Paragraph 21. Notice of objection to the demand will be deemed effective upon receipt by escrow agent.

19. REPRESENTATIONS: All covenants, representations and warranties in this contract survive closing. If any representation of Seller in this contract is untrue on the Closing Date, Seller will be in default. Unless expressly prohibited by written agreement, Seller may continue to show the Property and receive, negotiate and accept back up offers.

20. FEDERAL TAX REQUIREMENTS: If Seller is a "foreign person," as defined by applicable law, or if Seller fails to deliver an affidavit to Buyer that Seller is not a "foreign person," then Buyer shall withhold from the sales proceeds an amount sufficient to comply with applicable tax law and deliver the same to the Internal Revenue Service together with appropriate tax forms. Internal Revenue Service regulations require filing written reports if currency in excess of specified amounts is received in the transaction.

21. NOTICES: All notices from one party to the other must be in writing and are effective when mailed to, hand-delivered at, or transmitted by facsimile or electronic transmission as follows:

To Buyer at: c/o Your name	**To Seller at:** c/o Tom Price
I sell More Properties	Wonderful Properties
Telephone: ( )Your tele numb	Telephone: (713)276-4799
Facsimile: ( )Your fax numbe	Facsimile: (713) 298-2245
E-mail: you@yahoo.com	E-mail: tomprice@gmail.com

22. AGREEMENT OF PARTIES: This contract contains the entire agreement of the parties and cannot be changed except by their written agreement. Addenda which are a part of this contract are (Check all applicable boxes):

☒ Third Party Financing Addendum for Credit Approval

☐ Seller Financing Addendum

☐ Addendum for Property Subject to Mandatory Membership in a Property Owners Association

☐ Buyer's Temporary Residential Lease

☐ Loan Assumption Addendum

☐ Addendum for Sale of Other Property by Buyer

☐ Addendum for Reservation of Oil, Gas and Other Minerals

☐ Addendum for "Back-Up" Contract

☐ Addendum for Coastal Area Property

☐ Environmental Assessment, Threatened or Endangered Species and Wetlands Addendum

☐ Seller's Temporary Residential Lease

☐ Short Sale Addendum

☐ Addendum for Property Located Seaward of the Gulf Intracoastal Waterway

☒ Addendum for Seller's Disclosure of Information on Lead-based Paint and Lead-based Paint Hazards as Required by Federal Law

☐ Addendum for Property in a Propane Gas System Service Area

☐ Other (list): _____

_____

_____

Initialed for identification by Buyer_____ _____ and Seller _____ _____   TREC NO. 20-12

Contract Concerning 3430 Old Master Dr, Houston, TX _____ Page 8 of 9   4-28-2014
                          (Address of Property)

23. TERMINATION OPTION: For nominal consideration, the receipt of which is hereby acknowledged by Seller, and Buyer's agreement to pay Seller $1,500.00_____ (Option Fee) within 3 days after the effective date of this contract, Seller grants Buyer the unrestricted right to terminate this contract by giving notice of termination to Seller within 15_____ days after the effective date of this contract (Option Period). If no dollar amount is stated as the Option Fee or if Buyer fails to pay the Option Fee to Seller within the time prescribed, this paragraph will not be a part of this contract and Buyer shall not have the unrestricted right to terminate this contract. If Buyer gives notice of termination within the time prescribed, the Option Fee will not be refunded; however, any earnest money will be refunded to Buyer. The Option Fee ☒will ☐will not be credited to the Sales Price at closing. **Time is of the essence for this paragraph and strict compliance with the time for performance is required.**

24. CONSULT AN ATTORNEY BEFORE SIGNING: TREC rules prohibit real estate licensees from giving legal advice. READ THIS CONTRACT CAREFULLY.

Buyer's
Attorney is: N/A _____

Seller's
Attorney is: N/A _____

_____

_____

Telephone: (   ) _____

Telephone: (   ) _____

Facsimile: (   ) _____

Facsimile: (   ) _____

E-mail: _____

E-mail: _____

EXECUTED the _____ day of today's date _____, **20____ (EFFECTIVE DATE).**
(BROKER: FILL IN THE DATE OF FINAL ACCEPTANCE.)

Buyer Troy Donaldson

Seller Larry Fleming

Buyer and wife, Donna Donaldson

Seller and wife, Marcia Fleming

TREC NO. 20-12

Contract Concerning _3430 Old Master Dr, Houston_____ Page 9 of 9   4-28-2014
                              (Address of Property)

BROKER INFORMATION
(Print name(s) only. Do not sign)

I sell More Properties 00000000		_Wonderful Properties_ 00000000	
Other Broker Firm License No.		Listing Broker Firm License No.	

represents ☐ Buyer only as Buyer's agent   represents ☐ Seller and Buyer as an intermediary
            ☐ Seller as Listing Broker's subagent   ☒ Seller only as Seller's agent

_Samantha Smith_____   _George Jenkins_____ _(713)325-4798_
Name of Associate's Licensed Supervisor   Telephone   Name of Associate's Licensed Supervisor   Telephone

Your Names   _your telephone no_   _Tom Price_   _(713)276-4799_
Associate's Name   Telephone   Listing Associate's Name   Telephone

2033 Winston Ave,   _your fax_   _1213 Sellmore St_
Other Broker's Address   Facsimile   Listing Broker's Office Address   Facsimile

Corsicanna   _TX_   _76694_   _Houston_   _TX_   _77056_
City   State   Zip   City   State   Zip

_you@yahoo.com_____   _tomprice@gmail.com_____
Associate's Email Address   Listing Associate's Email Address

                                           _N/A_____
                                           Selling Associate's Name   Telephone

                                           _____
                                           Name of Selling Associate's Licensed Supervisor   Telephone

                                           _____
                                           Selling Associate's Office Address   Facsimile

                                           _____
                                           City   State   Zip

                                           _____
                                           Selling Associate's Email Address

Listing Broker has agreed to pay Other Broker_____ _4%_____ of the total sales price when the Listing Broker's
fee is received. Escrow agent is authorized and directed to pay other Broker from Listing Broker's fee at closing.

OPTION FEE RECEIPT

Receipt of $_1,500.00_____ (Option Fee) in the form of _check no 1210_____ is acknowledged.

_____   _within 3 days of executed date_____
Seller or Listing Broker   Date
Tom price, Wonderful Properties

CONTRACT AND EARNEST MONEY RECEIPT

Receipt of ☒Contract and ☒$_3,500.00_ Earnest Money in the form of _cashiers check_____
is acknowledged.

Escrow Agent: _ABC Title Company_____   Date: _2nd working day closing_

By:_Larry Spence_____   _Larryspence@abctitle.com_____
                                  Email Address
_1219 Goodrich St_____   Telephone _(713)278-4901_
Address

Houston   _TX_   _77057_   Facsimile: _(713)_ _278-4900_
City   State   Zip

TREC NO. 20-12

APPROVED BY THE TEXAS REAL ESTATE COMMISSION   10-10-11

EQUAL HOUSING
OPPORTUNITY

ADDENDUM FOR SELLER'S DISCLOSURE OF INFORMATION ON LEAD-BASED PAINT AND LEAD-BASED PAINT HAZARDS AS REQUIRED BY FEDERAL LAW

CONCERNING THE PROPERTY AT <u>3430 Old Master Dr, Houston TX</u>
(Street Address and City)

A. LEAD WARNING STATEMENT: "Every purchaser of any interest in residential real property on which a residential dwelling was built prior to 1978 is notified that such property may present exposure to lead from lead-based paint that may place young children at risk of developing lead poisoning. Lead poisoning in young children may produce permanent neurological damage, including learning disabilities, reduced intelligence quotient, behavioral problems, and impaired memory. Lead poisoning also poses a particular risk to pregnant women. The seller of any interest in residential real property is required to provide the buyer with any information on lead-based paint hazards from risk assessments or inspections in the seller's possession and notify the buyer of any known lead-based paint hazards. A risk assessment or inspection for possible lead-paint hazards is recommended prior to purchase."
  NOTICE: Inspector must be properly certified as required by federal law.
B. SELLER'S DISCLOSURE:
  1. PRESENCE OF LEAD-BASED PAINT AND/OR LEAD-BASED PAINT HAZARDS (check one box only):
  ☐(a) Known lead-based paint and/or lead-based paint hazards are present in the Property (explain): _____
  _____ .
  ☒(b) Seller has no actual knowledge of lead-based paint and/or lead-based paint hazards in the Property.
  2. RECORDS AND REPORTS AVAILABLE TO SELLER (check one box only):
  ☐(a) Seller has provided the purchaser with all available records and reports pertaining to lead-based paint and/or lead-based paint hazards in the Property (list documents):_____
  _____ .
  ☒(b) Seller has no reports or records pertaining to lead-based paint and/or lead-based paint hazards in the Property.
C. BUYER'S RIGHTS (check one box only)**:**
  ☐1. Buyer waives the opportunity to conduct a risk assessment or inspection of the Property for the presence of lead-based paint or lead-based paint hazards.
  ☒2. Within ten days after the effective date of this contract, Buyer may have the Property inspected by inspectors selected by Buyer. If lead-based paint or lead-based paint hazards are present, Buyer may terminate this contract by giving Seller written notice within 14 days after the effective date of this contract, and the earnest money will be refunded to Buyer.
D. BUYER'S ACKNOWLEDGMENT (check applicable boxes)**:**
  ☐1. Buyer has received copies of all information listed above.
  ☒2. Buyer has received the pamphlet *Protect Your Family from Lead in Your Home*.
E. BROKERS' ACKNOWLEDGMENT: Brokers have informed Seller of Seller's obligations under 42 U.S.C. 4852d to: (a) provide Buyer with the federally approved pamphlet on lead poisoning prevention; (b) complete this addendum; (c) disclose any known lead-based paint and/or lead-based paint hazards in the Property; (d) deliver all records and reports to Buyer pertaining to lead-based paint and/or lead-based paint hazards in the Property; (e) provide Buyer a period of up to 10 days to have the Property inspected; and (f) retain a completed copy of this addendum for at least 3 years following the sale. Brokers are aware of their responsibility to ensure compliance.
F. CERTIFICATION OF ACCURACY: The following persons have reviewed the information above and certify, to the best of their knowledge, that the information they have provided is true and accurate.

_____   _____
Buyer Troy Donaldson   Date   Seller Larry Fleming   Date

_____   _____
Buyer   Date   Seller   Date
and wife, Donna Donaldson   and wife, Marcia Fleming

_____   _____
Other Broker   Date   Listing Broker   Date

TREC NO. OP-L

2-10-2014

PROMULGATED BY THE TEXAS REAL ESTATE COMMISSION (TREC)

THIRD PARTY FINANCING ADDENDUM FOR CREDIT APPROVAL
(Not for use with Reverse Mortgage Financing)

TO CONTRACT CONCERNING THE PROPERTY AT

3430 Old Master Dr, Houston, TX
_____
(Street Address and City)

Buyer shall apply promptly for all financing described below and make every reasonable effort to obtain credit approval for the financing (Credit Approval). Buyer shall furnish all information and documents required by lender for Credit Approval. Credit Approval will be deemed to have been obtained when (1) the terms of the loan(s) described below are available and (2) lender determines that Buyer has satisfied all of lender's requirements related to Buyer's assets, income and credit history. If Buyer cannot obtain Credit Approval, Buyer may give written notice to Seller within 20___ days after the effective date of this contract and this contract will terminate and the earnest money will be refunded to Buyer. **If Buyer does not give such notice within the time required, this contract will no longer be subject to Credit Approval. Time is of the essence for this paragraph and strict compliance with the time for performance is required.**

NOTE: Credit Approval does not include approval of lender's underwriting requirements for the Property, as specified in Paragraph 4.A.(1) of the contract.

Each note must be secured by vendor's and deed of trust liens.

CHECK APPLICABLE BOXES:

☒ A. CONVENTIONAL FINANCING:

   ☒ (1) A first mortgage loan in the principal amount of $ 292,500.00_____ (excluding any financed PMI premium), due in full in 30_____ year(s), with interest not to exceed 5.00____% per annum for the first 1_____year(s) of the loan with Adjusted Origination Charges as shown on Buyer's Good Faith Estimate for the loan not to exceed 1.000_____% of the loan.

   ☐ (2) A second mortgage loan in the principal amount of $_____(excluding any financed PMI premium), due in full in _____year(s), with interest not to exceed _____% per annum for the first _____year(s) of the loan with Adjusted Origination Charges as shown on Buyer's Good Faith Estimate for the loan not to exceed _____ % of the loan.

☐ B. TEXAS VETERANS LOAN: A loan(s) from the Texas Veterans Land Board of $_____ for a period in the total amount of _____years at the interest rate established by the Texas Veterans Land Board.

☐ C. FHA INSURED FINANCING: A Section _____ FHA insured loan of not less than $_____ (excluding any financed MIP), amortizable monthly for not less than _____years, with interest not to exceed _____% per annum for the first _____year(s) of the loan with Adjusted Origination Charges as shown on Buyer's Good Faith Estimate for the loan not to exceed _____ % of the loan. As required by HUD-FHA, if FHA valuation is unknown, *"It is expressly agreed that, notwithstanding any other provision of this contract, the purchaser (Buyer) shall not be obligated to complete the purchase of the Property described herein or to incur any penalty by forfeiture of earnest money deposits or otherwise unless the purchaser (Buyer) has been given in accordance with HUD/FHA or VA requirements a written statement issued by the Federal Housing Commissioner, Department of Veterans Affairs, or a Direct Endorsement Lender setting forth the appraised value of the Property of not less than $_____. The purchaser (Buyer) shall have the privilege and option of proceeding with consummation of the contract without regard to the amount of the appraised valuation. The appraised valuation is arrived at to determine the*

Third Party Financing Condition Addendum Concerning   Page 2 of 2   2-10-2014

3430 Old Master Dr, Houston, TX
_____
(Address of Property)

maximum mortgage the Department of Housing and Urban Development will insure. HUD does not warrant the value or the condition of the Property. The purchaser (Buyer) should satisfy himself/herself that the price and the condition of the Property are acceptable."

❏ D. VA GUARANTEED FINANCING: A VA guaranteed loan of not less than $_____ (excluding any financed Funding Fee), amortizable monthly for not less than_____years, with interest not to exceed_____% per annum for the first _____year(s) of the loan with Adjusted Origination Charges as shown on Buyer's Good Faith Estimate for the loan not to exceed _____% of the loan.

VA NOTICE TO BUYER: *"It is expressly agreed that, notwithstanding any other provisions of this contract, the Buyer shall not incur any penalty by forfeiture of earnest money or otherwise or be obligated to complete the purchase of the Property described herein, if the contract purchase price or cost exceeds the reasonable value of the Property established by the Department of Veterans Affairs. The Buyer shall, however, have the privilege and option of proceeding with the consummation of this contract without regard to the amount of the reasonable value established by the Department of Veterans Affairs."*

If Buyer elects to complete the purchase at an amount in excess of the reasonable value established by VA, Buyer shall pay such excess amount in cash from a source which Buyer agrees to disclose to the VA and which Buyer represents will not be from borrowed funds except as approved by VA. If VA reasonable value of the Property is less than the Sales Price, Seller may reduce the Sales Price to an amount equal to the VA reasonable value and the sale will be closed at the lower Sales Price with proportionate adjustments to the down payment and the loan amount.

❏ E.USDA GUARANTEED FINANCING: A USDA-guaranteed loan of not less than $_____ (excluding any financed Funding Fee), amortizable monthly for not less than_____years, with interest not to exceed ____% per annum for the first ____year(s) of the loan with Adjusted Origination Charges as shown on Buyer's Good Faith Estimate for the loan not to exceed _____% of the loan.

Buyer hereby authorizes any lender to furnish to the Seller or Buyer or their representatives information relating only to the status of Credit Approval of Buyer.

_____   _____
Buyer Troy Donaldson   Seller Larry Fleming

_____   _____
Buyer   Seller
 and wife, Donna Donaldson   and wife, Marcia Fleming

TREC NO. 40-6

Transaction: Johnson to Swanson
(from Chapter 9 of *Texas Promulgated Forms*)

4-28-2014

PROMULGATED BY THE TEXAS REAL ESTATE COMMISSION (TREC)
ONE TO FOUR FAMILY RESIDENTIAL CONTRACT (RESALE)
NOTICE: Not For Use For Condominium Transactions

1. PARTIES: The parties to this contract are _____
(Seller) and _____(Buyer).
Seller agrees to sell and convey to Buyer and Buyer agrees to buy from Seller the Property defined below.

2. PROPERTY: The land, improvements and accessories are collectively referred to as the "Property".
  A. LAND: Lot _____ Block_____, _____
    Addition, City of _____ , County of _____,
    Texas, known as _____
    (address/zip code), or as described on attached exhibit.
  B. IMPROVEMENTS: The house, garage and all other fixtures and improvements attached to the above-described real property, including without limitation, the following **permanently installed and built-in items,** if any: all equipment and appliances, valances, screens, shutters, awnings, wall-to-wall carpeting, mirrors, ceiling fans, attic fans, mail boxes, television antennas, mounts and brackets for televisions and speakers, heating and air-conditioning units, security and fire detection equipment, wiring, plumbing and lighting fixtures, chandeliers, water softener system, kitchen equipment, garage door openers, cleaning equipment, shrubbery, landscaping, outdoor cooking equipment, and all other property owned by Seller and attached to the above described real property.
  C. ACCESSORIES: The following described related accessories, if any: window air conditioning units, stove, fireplace screens, curtains and rods, blinds, window shades, draperies and rods, door keys, mailbox keys, above ground pool, swimming pool equipment and maintenance accessories, artificial fireplace logs, and controls for: (i) garage doors, (ii) entry gates, and (iii) other improvements and accessories.
  D. EXCLUSIONS: The following improvements and accessories will be retained by Seller and must be removed prior to delivery of possession:_____
    _____.

3. SALES PRICE:
  A. Cash portion of Sales Price payable by Buyer at closing .... $_____
  B. Sum of all financing described below (excluding any loan funding
     fee or mortgage insurance premium) .... $_____
  C. Sales Price (Sum of A and B)... $_____

4. FINANCING (Not for use with reverse mortgage financing): The portion of Sales Price not payable in cash will be paid as follows: (Check applicable boxes below)
❑ A. THIRD PARTY FINANCING: One or more third party mortgage loans in the total amount of $_____ (excluding any loan funding fee or mortgage insurance premium).
  (1) Property Approval: If the Property does not satisfy the lenders' underwriting requirements for the loan(s) (including, but not limited to appraisal, insurability and lender required repairs), Buyer may terminate this contract by giving notice to Seller prior to closing and the earnest money will be refunded to Buyer.
  (2) Credit Approval: (Check one box only)
  ❑   (a) This contract is subject to Buyer being approved for the financing described in the attached Third Party Financing Addendum for Credit Approval.
  ❑   (b) This contract is not subject to Buyer being approved for financing and does not involve FHA or VA financing.
❑ B. ASSUMPTION: The assumption of the unpaid principal balance of one or more promissory notes described in the attached TREC Loan Assumption Addendum.
❑ C. SELLER FINANCING: A promissory note from Buyer to Seller of $_____, secured by vendor's and deed of trust liens, and containing the terms and conditions described in the attached TREC Seller Financing Addendum. If an owner policy of title insurance is furnished, Buyer shall furnish Seller with a mortgagee policy of title insurance.

Initialed for identification by Buyer_____ _____ and Seller _____ _____   TREC NO. 20-12

Contract Concerning _____Page 2 of 9   4-28-2014
(Address of Property)

5. **EARNEST MONEY:** Upon execution of this contract by all parties, Buyer shall deposit $_____ as earnest money with _____, as escrow agent, at _____ (address). Buyer shall deposit additional earnest money of $_____ with escrow agent within _____days after the effective date of this contract. If Buyer fails to deposit the earnest money as required by this contract, Buyer will be in default.

6. **TITLE POLICY AND SURVEY:**
   A. TITLE POLICY: Seller shall furnish to Buyer at ❑ Seller's ❑ Buyer's expense an owner policy of title insurance (Title Policy) issued by _____ (Title Company) in the amount of the Sales Price, dated at or after closing, insuring Buyer against loss under the provisions of the Title Policy, subject to the promulgated exclusions (including existing building and zoning ordinances) and the following exceptions:
   (1) Restrictive covenants common to the platted subdivision in which the Property is located.
   (2) The standard printed exception for standby fees, taxes and assessments.
   (3) Liens created as part of the financing described in Paragraph 4.
   (4) Utility easements created by the dedication deed or plat of the subdivision in which the Property is located.
   (5) Reservations or exceptions otherwise permitted by this contract or as may be approved by Buyer in writing.
   (6) The standard printed exception as to marital rights.
   (7) The standard printed exception as to waters, tidelands, beaches, streams, and related matters.
   (8) The standard printed exception as to discrepancies, conflicts, shortages in area or boundary lines, encroachments or protrusions, or overlapping improvements: ❑(i) will not be amended or deleted from the title policy; ❑(ii) will be amended to read, "shortages in area" at the expense of ❑Buyer ❑Seller.
   B. COMMITMENT: Within 20 days after the Title Company receives a copy of this contract, Seller shall furnish to Buyer a commitment for title insurance (Commitment) and, at Buyer's expense, legible copies of restrictive covenants and documents evidencing exceptions in the Commitment (Exception Documents) other than the standard printed exceptions. Seller authorizes the Title Company to deliver the Commitment and Exception Documents to Buyer at Buyer's address shown in Paragraph 21. If the Commitment and Exception Documents are not delivered to Buyer within the specified time, the time for delivery will be automatically extended up to 15 days or 3 days before the Closing Date, whichever is earlier. If, due to factors beyond Seller's control, the Commitment and Exception Documents are not delivered within the time required, Buyer may terminate this contract and the earnest money will be refunded to Buyer.
   C. SURVEY: The survey must be made by a registered professional land surveyor acceptable to the Title Company and Buyer's lender(s). (Check one box only)
   ❑(1) Within _____ days after the effective date of this contract, Seller shall furnish to Buyer and Title Company Seller's existing survey of the Property and a Residential Real Property Affidavit promulgated by the Texas Department of Insurance (T-47 Affidavit). **If Seller fails to furnish the existing survey or affidavit within the time prescribed, Buyer shall obtain a new survey at Seller's expense no later than 3 days prior to Closing Date.** If the existing survey or affidavit is not acceptable to Title Company or Buyer's lender(s), Buyer shall obtain a new survey at ❑Seller's ❑Buyer's expense no later than 3 days prior to Closing Date.
   ❑(2) Within _____ days after the effective date of this contract, Buyer shall obtain a new survey at Buyer's expense. Buyer is deemed to receive the survey on the date of actual receipt or the date specified in this paragraph, whichever is earlier.
   ❑(3) Within _____ days after the effective date of this contract, Seller, at Seller's expense shall furnish a new survey to Buyer.
   D. OBJECTIONS: Buyer may object in writing to defects, exceptions, or encumbrances to title: disclosed on the survey other than items 6A(1) through (7) above; disclosed in the Commitment other than items 6A(1) through (8) above; or which prohibit the following use or activity: _____
   _____.
   Buyer must object the earlier of (i) the Closing Date or (ii) _____ days after Buyer receives the Commitment, Exception Documents, and the survey. Buyer's failure to object within the time allowed will constitute a waiver of Buyer's right to object; except that the requirements in Schedule C of the Commitment are not waived by Buyer. Provided Seller is not obligated to incur any expense, Seller shall cure the timely objections of Buyer or any third party lender

Initialed for identification by Buyer_____ _____ and Seller _____ _____   TREC NO. 20-12

Contract Concerning _____Page 3 of 9   4-28-2014
(Address of Property)

within 15 days after Seller receives the objections and the Closing Date will be extended as necessary. If objections are not cured within such 15 day period, this contract will terminate and the earnest money will be refunded to Buyer unless Buyer waives the objections.

E. TITLE NOTICES:

(1) ABSTRACT OR TITLE POLICY: Broker advises Buyer to have an abstract of title covering the Property examined by an attorney of Buyer's selection, or Buyer should be furnished with or obtain a Title Policy. If a Title Policy is furnished, the Commitment should be promptly reviewed by an attorney of Buyer's choice due to the time limitations on Buyer's right to object.

(2) MEMBERSHIP IN PROPERTY OWNERS ASSOCIATION(S): The Property ❑is ❑is not subject to mandatory membership in a property owners association(s). If the Property is subject to mandatory membership in a property owners association(s), Seller notifies Buyer under §5.012, Texas Property Code, that, as a purchaser of property in the residential community identified in Paragraph 2A in which the Property is located, you are obligated to be a member of the property owners association(s). Restrictive covenants governing the use and occupancy of the Property and all dedicatory instruments governing the establishment, maintenance, or operation of this residential community have been or will be recorded in the Real Property Records of the county in which the Property is located. Copies of the restrictive covenants and dedicatory instruments may be obtained from the county clerk. **You are obligated to pay assessments to the property owners association(s). The amount of the assessments is subject to change. Your failure to pay the assessments could result in enforcement of the association's lien on and the foreclosure of the Property.** Section 207.003, Property Code, entitles an owner to receive copies of any document that governs the establishment, maintenance, or operation of a subdivision, including, but not limited to, restrictions, bylaws, rules and regulations, and a resale certificate from a property owners' association. A resale certificate contains information including, but not limited to, statements specifying the amount and frequency of regular assessments and the style and cause number of lawsuits to which the property owners' association is a party, other than lawsuits relating to unpaid ad valorem taxes of an individual member of the association. These documents must be made available to you by the property owners' association or the association's agent on your request. **If Buyer is concerned about these matters, the TREC promulgated Addendum for Property Subject to Mandatory Membership in a Property Owners Association(s) should be used.**

(3) STATUTORY TAX DISTRICTS: If the Property is situated in a utility or other statutorily created district providing water, sewer, drainage, or flood control facilities and services, Chapter 49, Texas Water Code, requires Seller to deliver and Buyer to sign the statutory notice relating to the tax rate, bonded indebtedness, or standby fee of the district prior to final execution of this contract.

(4) TIDE WATERS: If the Property abuts the tidally influenced waters of the state, §33.135, Texas Natural Resources Code, requires a notice regarding coastal area property to be included in the contract. An addendum containing the notice promulgated by TREC or required by the parties must be used.

(5) ANNEXATION: If the Property is located outside the limits of a municipality, Seller notifies Buyer under §5.011, Texas Property Code, that the Property may now or later be included in the extraterritorial jurisdiction of a municipality and may now or later be subject to annexation by the municipality. Each municipality maintains a map that depicts its boundaries and extraterritorial jurisdiction. To determine if the Property is located within a municipality's extraterritorial jurisdiction or is likely to be located within a municipality's extraterritorial jurisdiction, contact all municipalities located in the general proximity of the Property for further information.

(6) PROPERTY LOCATED IN A CERTIFICATED SERVICE AREA OF A UTILITY SERVICE PROVIDER: Notice required by §13.257, Water Code: The real property, described in Paragraph 2, that you are about to purchase may be located in a certificated water or sewer service area, which is authorized by law to provide water or sewer service to the properties in the certificated area. If your property is located in a certificated area there may be special costs or charges that you will be required to pay before you can receive water or sewer service. There may be a period required to construct lines or other facilities necessary to provide water or sewer service to your property. You are advised to determine if the property is in a certificated area and contact the utility service provider to determine the cost that you will be required to pay and the period, if any, that is required to provide water or sewer service to your property. The undersigned Buyer hereby acknowledges receipt of the foregoing notice at or before the execution of a binding contract for the purchase of the real property described in Paragraph 2 or at closing of purchase of the real property.

Initialed for identification by Buyer_____ _____ and Seller _____ _____   TREC NO. 20-12

(7) PUBLIC IMPROVEMENT DISTRICTS: If the Property is in a public improvement district, §5.014, Property Code, requires Seller to notify Buyer as follows: As a purchaser of this parcel of real property you are obligated to pay an assessment to a municipality or county for an improvement project undertaken by a public improvement district under Chapter 372, Local Government Code. The assessment may be due annually or in periodic installments. More information concerning the amount of the assessment and the due dates of that assessment may be obtained from the municipality or county levying the assessment. The amount of the assessments is subject to change. Your failure to pay the assessments could result in a lien on and the foreclosure of your property.

(8) TRANSFER FEES: If the Property is subject to a private transfer fee obligation, §5.205, Property Code, requires Seller to notify Buyer as follows: The private transfer fee obligation may be governed by Chapter 5, Subchapter G of the Texas Property Code.

(9) PROPANE GAS SYSTEM SERVICE AREA: If the Property is located in a propane gas system service area owned by a distribution system retailer, Seller must give Buyer written notice as required by §141.010, Texas Utilities Code. An addendum containing the notice approved by TREC or required by the parties should be used.

7. PROPERTY CONDITION:

A. ACCESS, INSPECTIONS AND UTILITIES: Seller shall permit Buyer and Buyer's agents access to the Property at reasonable times. Buyer may have the Property inspected by inspectors selected by Buyer and licensed by TREC or otherwise permitted by law to make inspections. Seller at Seller's expense shall immediately cause existing utilities to be turned on and shall keep the utilities on during the time this contract is in effect.

B. SELLER'S DISCLOSURE NOTICE PURSUANT TO §5.008, TEXAS PROPERTY CODE (Notice): (Check one box only)

❑ (1) Buyer has received the Notice.

❑ (2) Buyer has not received the Notice. Within _____ days after the effective date of this contract, Seller shall deliver the Notice to Buyer. If Buyer does not receive the Notice, Buyer may terminate this contract at any time prior to the closing and the earnest money will be refunded to Buyer. If Seller delivers the Notice, Buyer may terminate this contract for any reason within 7 days after Buyer receives the Notice or prior to the closing, whichever first occurs, and the earnest money will be refunded to Buyer.

❑ (3)The Seller is not required to furnish the notice under the Texas Property Code.

C. SELLER'S DISCLOSURE OF LEAD-BASED PAINT AND LEAD-BASED PAINT HAZARDS is required by Federal law for a residential dwelling constructed prior to 1978.

D. ACCEPTANCE OF PROPERTY CONDITION: "As Is" means the present condition of the Property with any and all defects and without warranty except for the warranties of title and the warranties in this contract. Buyer's agreement to accept the Property As Is under Paragraph 7D(1) or (2) does not preclude Buyer from inspecting the Property under Paragraph 7A, from negotiating repairs or treatments in a subsequent amendment, or from terminating this contract during the Option Period, if any.
(Check one box only)

❑ (1) Buyer accepts the Property As Is.

❑ (2) Buyer accepts the Property As Is provided Seller, at Seller's expense, shall complete the following specific repairs and treatments: _____
_____.
(Do not insert general phrases, such as "subject to inspections" that do not identify specific repairs and treatments.)

E. LENDER REQUIRED REPAIRS AND TREATMENTS: Unless otherwise agreed in writing, neither party is obligated to pay for lender required repairs, which includes treatment for wood destroying insects. If the parties do not agree to pay for the lender required repairs or treatments, this contract will terminate and the earnest money will be refunded to Buyer. If the cost of lender required repairs and treatments exceeds 5% of the Sales Price, Buyer may terminate this contract and the earnest money will be refunded to Buyer.

F. COMPLETION OF REPAIRS AND TREATMENTS: Unless otherwise agreed in writing: (i) Seller shall complete all agreed repairs and treatments prior to the Closing Date; and (ii) all required permits must be obtained, and repairs and treatments must be performed by persons who are licensed to provide such repairs or treatments or, if no license is required by law, are commercially engaged in the trade of providing such repairs or treatments.   At Buyer's election, any transferable warranties received by Seller with respect to the repairs and treatments will be transferred to Buyer at Buyer's expense. If Seller fails to complete any agreed repairs and treatments prior to the Closing Date, Buyer may exercise remedies under Paragraph 15 or extend the Closing Date up to 5 days if necessary for Seller to complete the repairs and treatments.

G. ENVIRONMENTAL MATTERS: Buyer is advised that the presence of wetlands, toxic substances, including asbestos and wastes or other environmental hazards, or the presence of a threatened or endangered species or its habitat may affect Buyer's intended use of the

Contract Concerning _____Page 5 of 9   4-28-2014
(Address of Property)

Property. If Buyer is concerned about these matters, an addendum promulgated by TREC or required by the parties should be used.

  H. RESIDENTIAL SERVICE CONTRACTS: Buyer may purchase a residential service contract from a residential service company licensed by TREC. If Buyer purchases a residential service contract, Seller shall reimburse Buyer at closing for the cost of the residential service contract in an amount not exceeding $_____. Buyer should review any residential service contract for the scope of coverage, exclusions and limitations. **The purchase of a residential service contract is optional. Similar coverage may be purchased from various companies authorized to do business in Texas.**

8. BROKERS' FEES: All obligations of the parties for payment of brokers' fees are contained in separate written agreements.

9. CLOSING:

  A. The closing of the sale will be on or before _____, 20_____, or within 7 days after objections made under Paragraph 6D have been cured or waived, whichever date is later (Closing Date). If either party fails to close the sale by the Closing Date, the non-defaulting party may exercise the remedies contained in Paragraph 15.

  B. At closing:

    (1) Seller shall execute and deliver a general warranty deed conveying title to the Property to Buyer and showing no additional exceptions to those permitted in Paragraph 6 and furnish tax statements or certificates showing no delinquent taxes on the Property.

    (2) Buyer shall pay the Sales Price in good funds acceptable to the escrow agent.

    (3) Seller and Buyer shall execute and deliver any notices, statements, certificates, affidavits, releases, loan documents and other documents reasonably required for the closing of the sale and the issuance of the Title Policy.

    (4) There will be no liens, assessments, or security interests against the Property which will not be satisfied out of the sales proceeds unless securing the payment of any loans assumed by Buyer and assumed loans will not be in default.

    (5) If the Property is subject to a residential lease, Seller shall transfer security deposits (as defined under §92.102, Property Code), if any, to Buyer. In such an event, Buyer shall deliver to the tenant a signed statement acknowledging that the Buyer has received the security deposit and is responsible for the return of the security deposit, and specifying the exact dollar amount of the security deposit.

10. POSSESSION:

  A Buyer's Possession: Seller shall deliver to Buyer possession of the Property in its present or required condition, ordinary wear and tear excepted: ❑upon closing and funding ❑according to a temporary residential lease form promulgated by TREC or other written lease required by the parties. Any possession by Buyer prior to closing or by Seller after closing which is not authorized by a written lease will establish a tenancy at sufferance relationship between the parties. **Consult your insurance agent prior to change of ownership and possession because insurance coverage may be limited or terminated. The absence of a written lease or appropriate insurance coverage may expose the parties to economic loss.**

  B. Leases:

    (1) After the Effective Date, Seller may not execute any lease (including but not limited to mineral leases) or convey any interest in the Property without Buyer's written consent.

    (2) If the Property is subject to any lease to which Seller is a party, Seller shall deliver to Buyer copies of the lease(s) and any move-in condition form signed by the tenant within 7 days after the Effective Date of the contract.

11. SPECIAL PROVISIONS: (Insert only factual statements and business details applicable to the sale. TREC rules prohibit licensees from adding factual statements or business details for which a contract addendum, lease or other form has been promulgated by TREC for mandatory use.)

12. SETTLEMENT AND OTHER EXPENSES:

  A. The following expenses must be paid at or prior to closing:

    (1) Expenses payable by Seller (Seller's Expenses):

      (a) Releases of existing liens, including prepayment penalties and recording fees; release of Seller's loan liability; tax statements or certificates; preparation of deed; one-half of escrow fee; and other expenses payable by Seller under this contract.

      (b) Seller shall also pay an amount not to exceed $_____ to be applied in the

Initialed for identification by Buyer_____ _____ and Seller _____ _____   TREC NO. 20-12

       following order: Buyer's Expenses which Buyer is prohibited from paying by FHA, VA, Texas Veterans Land Board or other governmental loan programs, and then to other Buyer's Expenses as allowed by the lender.

    (2) Expenses payable by Buyer (Buyer's Expenses): Appraisal fees; loan application fees; adjusted origination charges; credit reports; preparation of loan documents; interest on the notes from date of disbursement to one month prior to dates of first monthly payments; recording fees; copies of easements and restrictions; loan title policy with endorsements required by lender; loan-related inspection fees; photos; amortization schedules; one-half of escrow fee; all prepaid items, including required premiums for flood and hazard insurance, reserve deposits for insurance, ad valorem taxes and special governmental assessments; final compliance inspection; courier fee; repair inspection; underwriting fee; wire transfer fee; expenses incident to any loan; Private Mortgage Insurance Premium (PMI), VA Loan Funding Fee, or FHA Mortgage Insurance Premium (MIP) as required by the lender; and other expenses payable by Buyer under this contract.

  B. If any expense exceeds an amount expressly stated in this contract for such expense to be paid by a party, that party may terminate this contract unless the other party agrees to pay such excess. Buyer may not pay charges and fees expressly prohibited by FHA, VA, Texas Veterans Land Board or other governmental loan program regulations.

13. PRORATIONS: Taxes for the current year, interest, maintenance fees, assessments, dues and rents will be prorated through the Closing Date. The tax proration may be calculated taking into consideration any change in exemptions that will affect the current year's taxes. If taxes for the current year vary from the amount prorated at closing, the parties shall adjust the prorations when tax statements for the current year are available. If taxes are not paid at or prior to closing, Buyer shall pay taxes for the current year.

14. CASUALTY LOSS: If any part of the Property is damaged or destroyed by fire or other casualty after the effective date of this contract, Seller shall restore the Property to its previous condition as soon as reasonably possible, but in any event by the Closing Date. If Seller fails to do so due to factors beyond Seller's control, Buyer may (a) terminate this contract and the earnest money will be refunded to Buyer (b) extend the time for performance up to 15 days and the Closing Date will be extended as necessary or (c) accept the Property in its damaged condition with an assignment of insurance proceeds and receive credit from Seller at closing in the amount of the deductible under the insurance policy. Seller's obligations under this paragraph are independent of any other obligations of Seller under this contract.

15. DEFAULT: If Buyer fails to comply with this contract, Buyer will be in default, and Seller may (a) enforce specific performance, seek such other relief as may be provided by law, or both, or (b) terminate this contract and receive the earnest money as liquidated damages, thereby releasing both parties from this contract. If Seller fails to comply with this contract, Seller will be in default and Buyer may (a) enforce specific performance, seek such other relief as may be provided by law, or both, or (b) terminate this contract and receive the earnest money, thereby releasing both parties from this contract.

16. MEDIATION: It is the policy of the State of Texas to encourage resolution of disputes through alternative dispute resolution procedures such as mediation. Any dispute between Seller and Buyer related to this contract which is not resolved through informal discussion will be submitted to a mutually acceptable mediation service or provider. The parties to the mediation shall bear the mediation costs equally. This paragraph does not preclude a party from seeking equitable relief from a court of competent jurisdiction.

17. ATTORNEY'S FEES: A Buyer, Seller, Listing Broker, Other Broker, or escrow agent who prevails in any legal proceeding related to this contract is entitled to recover reasonable attorney's fees and all costs of such proceeding.

18. ESCROW:

  A. ESCROW: The escrow agent is not (i) a party to this contract and does not have liability for the performance or nonperformance of any party to this contract, (ii) liable for interest on the earnest money and (iii) liable for the loss of any earnest money caused by the failure of any financial institution in which the earnest money has been deposited unless the financial institution is acting as escrow agent.

  B. EXPENSES: At closing, the earnest money must be applied first to any cash down payment, then to Buyer's Expenses and any excess refunded to Buyer. If no closing occurs, escrow agent may: (i) require a written release of liability of the escrow agent from all parties, (ii) require payment of unpaid expenses incurred on behalf of a party, and (iii) only deduct from the earnest money the amount of unpaid expenses incurred on behalf of the party receiving the earnest money.

  C. DEMAND: Upon termination of this contract, either party or the escrow agent may send a release of earnest money to each party and the parties shall execute counterparts of the release and deliver same to the escrow agent. If either party fails to execute the release, either party may make a written demand to the escrow agent for the earnest money. If only one party makes written demand for the earnest money, escrow agent shall promptly provide a copy of the demand to the other party. If escrow agent does not receive written objection to the demand from the other party within 15 days, escrow agent may disburse the earnest money to the party making demand reduced by the amount of unpaid expenses incurred on behalf of the party receiving the earnest money and escrow agent may pay the same to the creditors. If escrow agent complies with the provisions of this paragraph, each party hereby releases escrow agent from all adverse claims related to the disbursal of the earnest money.

    D. DAMAGES: Any party who wrongfully fails or refuses to sign a release acceptable to the escrow agent within 7 days of receipt of the request will be liable to the other party for liquidated damages in an amount equal to the sum of: (i) three times the amount of the earnest money; (ii) the earnest money; (iii) reasonable attorney's fees; and (iv) all costs of suit.

    E. NOTICES: Escrow agent's notices will be effective when sent in compliance with Paragraph 21. Notice of objection to the demand will be deemed effective upon receipt by escrow agent.

19. **REPRESENTATIONS:** All covenants, representations and warranties in this contract survive closing. If any representation of Seller in this contract is untrue on the Closing Date, Seller will be in default. Unless expressly prohibited by written agreement, Seller may continue to show the Property and receive, negotiate and accept back up offers.

20. **FEDERAL TAX REQUIREMENTS:** If Seller is a "foreign person," as defined by applicable law, or if Seller fails to deliver an affidavit to Buyer that Seller is not a "foreign person," then Buyer shall withhold from the sales proceeds an amount sufficient to comply with applicable tax law and deliver the same to the Internal Revenue Service together with appropriate tax forms. Internal Revenue Service regulations require filing written reports if currency in excess of specified amounts is received in the transaction.

21. **NOTICES:** All notices from one party to the other must be in writing and are effective when mailed to, hand-delivered at, or transmitted by facsimile or electronic transmission as follows:

To Buyer at: _____   **To Seller at:** _____

_____   _____

Telephone: (   ) _____   Telephone: (   ) _____

Facsimile: (   ) _____   Facsimile: (   ) _____

E-mail: _____   E-mail: _____

22. **AGREEMENT OF PARTIES:** This contract contains the entire agreement of the parties and cannot be changed except by their written agreement. Addenda which are a part of this contract are (Check all applicable boxes):

❑ Third Party Financing Addendum for Credit Approval

❑ Seller Financing Addendum

❑ Addendum for Property Subject to Mandatory Membership in a Property Owners Association

❑ Buyer's Temporary Residential Lease

❑ Loan Assumption Addendum

❑ Addendum for Sale of Other Property by Buyer

❑ Addendum for Reservation of Oil, Gas and Other Minerals

❑ Addendum for "Back-Up" Contract

❑ Addendum for Coastal Area Property

❑ Environmental Assessment, Threatened or Endangered Species and Wetlands Addendum

❑ Seller's Temporary Residential Lease

❑ Short Sale Addendum

❑ Addendum for Property Located Seaward of the Gulf Intracoastal Waterway

❑ Addendum for Seller's Disclosure of Information on Lead-based Paint and Lead-based Paint Hazards as Required by Federal Law

❑ Addendum for Property in a Propane Gas System Service Area

❑ Other (list): _____

_____

_____

Contract Concerning _____ Page 8 of 9   4-28-2014
(Address of Property)

23. TERMINATION OPTION: For nominal consideration, the receipt of which is hereby acknowledged by Seller, and Buyer's agreement to pay Seller $_____ (Option Fee) within 3 days after the effective date of this contract, Seller grants Buyer the unrestricted right to terminate this contract by giving notice of termination to Seller within _____ days after the effective date of this contract (Option Period). If no dollar amount is stated as the Option Fee or if Buyer fails to pay the Option Fee to Seller within the time prescribed, this paragraph will not be a part of this contract and Buyer shall not have the unrestricted right to terminate this contract. If Buyer gives notice of termination within the time prescribed, the Option Fee will not be refunded; however, any earnest money will be refunded to Buyer. The Option Fee ☐will ☐will not be credited to the Sales Price at closing. **Time is of the essence for this paragraph and strict compliance with the time for performance is required.**

24. CONSULT AN ATTORNEY BEFORE SIGNING: TREC rules prohibit real estate licensees from giving legal advice. READ THIS CONTRACT CAREFULLY.

Buyer's
Attorney is: _____

Seller's
Attorney is: _____

_____

_____

Telephone: (____) _____

Telephone: (____) _____

Facsimile: (____) _____

Facsimile: (____) _____

E-mail: _____

E-mail: _____

**EXECUTED the _____day of _____, 20____ (EFFECTIVE DATE).
(BROKER: FILL IN THE DATE OF FINAL ACCEPTANCE.)**

_____
Buyer

_____
Seller

_____
Buyer

_____
Seller

TREC NO. 20-12

Contract Concerning _____Page 9 of 9   4-28-2014
(Address of Property)

BROKER INFORMATION
(Print name(s) only. Do not sign)

| Other Broker Firm   License No. | Listing Broker Firm   License No. |

represents ☐ Buyer only as Buyer's agent
☐ Seller as Listing Broker's subagent

represents ☐ Seller and Buyer as an intermediary
☐ Seller only as Seller's agent

Name of Associate's Licensed Supervisor   Telephone

Name of Associate's Licensed Supervisor   Telephone

Associate's Name   Telephone

Listing Associate's Name   Telephone

Other Broker's Address   Facsimile

Listing Broker's Office Address   Facsimile

City   State   Zip

City   State   Zip

Associate's Email Address

Listing Associate's Email Address

Selling Associate's Name   Telephone

Name of Selling Associate's Licensed Supervisor   Telephone

Selling Associate's Office Address   Facsimile

City   State   Zip

Selling Associate's Email Address

Listing Broker has agreed to pay Other Broker_____of the total sales price when the Listing Broker's fee is received. Escrow agent is authorized and directed to pay other Broker from Listing Broker's fee at closing.

OPTION FEE RECEIPT

Receipt of $_____ (Option Fee) in the form of _____ is acknowledged.

_____   _____
Seller or Listing Broker   Date

CONTRACT AND EARNEST MONEY RECEIPT

Receipt of ☐Contract and ☐$_____Earnest Money in the form of _____
is acknowledged.

Escrow Agent: _____   Date: _____

By: _____   _____
                                                 Email Address

_____   Telephone (____)_____
Address

City   State   Zip   Facsimile: (____) _____

PROMULGATED BY THE TEXAS REAL ESTATE COMMISSION (TREC)   12-05-11

ENVIRONMENTAL ASSESSMENT, THREATENED OR ENDANGERED SPECIES, AND WETLANDS ADDENDUM

TO CONTRACT CONCERNING THE PROPERTY AT

_____

(Address of Property)

❑ A. ENVIRONMENTAL ASSESSMENT: Buyer, at Buyer's expense, may obtain an environmental assessment report prepared by an environmental specialist.

❑ B. THREATENED OR ENDANGERED SPECIES: Buyer, at Buyer's expense, may obtain a report from a natural resources professional to determine if there are any threatened or endangered species or their habitats as defined by the Texas Parks and Wildlife Department or the U.S. Fish and Wildlife Service.

❑ C. WETLANDS: Buyer, at Buyer's expense, may obtain a report from an environmental specialist to determine if there are wetlands, as defined by federal or state law or regulation.

Within _____ days after the effective date of the contract, Buyer may terminate the contract by furnishing Seller a copy of any report noted above that adversely affects the use of the Property and a notice of termination of the contract. Upon termination, the earnest money will be refunded to Buyer.

_____   _____
Buyer   Seller

_____   _____
Buyer   Seller

TREC No. 28-2

PROMULGATED BY THE TEXAS REAL ESTATE COMMISSION (TREC)   12-05-11

SELLER FINANCING ADDENDUM
TO CONTRACT CONCERNING THE PROPERTY AT

_____
(Address of Property)

A. CREDIT DOCUMENTATION. To establish Buyer's creditworthiness, Buyer shall deliver to Seller within_____days after the effective date of this contract, ❏ credit report ❏ verification of employment, including salary ❏ verification of funds on deposit in financial institutions ❏ current financial statement and ❏ _____
_____. Buyer hereby authorizes any credit reporting agency to furnish copies of Buyer's credit reports to Seller at Buyer's sole expense.

B. CREDIT APPROVAL.   If the credit documentation described in Paragraph A is not delivered within the specified time, Seller may terminate this contract by notice to Buyer within 7 days after expiration of the time for delivery, and the earnest money will be paid to Seller. If the credit documentation is timely delivered, and Seller determines in Seller's sole discretion that Buyer's credit is unacceptable, Seller may terminate this contract by notice to Buyer within 7 days after expiration of the time for delivery and the earnest money will be refunded to Buyer. If Seller does not terminate this contract, Seller will be deemed to have approved Buyer's creditworthiness.

C. PROMISSORY NOTE. The promissory note (Note) described in Paragraph 4 of this contract payable by Buyer to the order of Seller will bear interest at the rate of _____% per annum and be payable at the place designated by Seller. Buyer may prepay the Note in whole or in part at any time without penalty. Any prepayments are to be applied to the payment of the installments of principal last maturing and interest will immediately cease on the prepaid principal. The Note will contain a provision for payment of a late fee of 5% of any installment not paid within 10 days of the due date. Matured unpaid amounts will bear interest at the rate of 1½% per month or at the highest lawful rate, whichever is less. The Note will be payable as follows:

❏ (1) In one payment due _____ after the date of the Note
     with interest payable ❏ at maturity ❏ monthly ❏ quarterly. (check one box only)

❏ (2) In monthly installments of $ _____ ❏ including interest ❏ plus interest (check
     one box only) beginning _____ after the date of the Note and continuing
     monthly thereafter for_____ months when the balance of the Note will be due and
     payable.

❏ (3) Interest only in monthly installments for the first _____ month(s) and thereafter in
     installments of $_____ ❏ including interest ❏ plus interest (check one box
     only) beginning _____ after the date of the Note and continuing monthly
     thereafter for _____ months when the balance of the Note will be due and payable.

D. DEED OF TRUST. The deed of trust securing the Note will provide for the following:

(1) PROPERTY TRANSFERS: (check one box only)

❏ (a) Consent Not Required: The Property may be sold, conveyed or leased without the
       consent of Seller, provided any subsequent buyer assumes the Note.

❏ (b) Consent Required: If all or any part of the Property is sold, conveyed, leased for a
       period longer than 3 years, leased with an option to purchase, or otherwise sold
       (including any contract for deed), without Seller's prior written consent, which consent
       may be withheld in Seller's sole discretion, Seller may declare the balance of the Note
       to be immediately due and payable. The creation of a subordinate lien, any conveyance

Initialed for identification by Buyer_____ and Seller_____   TREC NO. 26-6

_____
(Address of Property)

under threat or order of condemnation, any deed solely between buyers, or the passage of title by reason of the death of a buyer or by operation of law will not entitle Seller to exercise the remedies provided in this paragraph.

NOTE: *Under (a) or (b), Buyer's liability to pay the Note will continue unless Buyer obtains a release of liability from Seller.*

(2) TAX AND INSURANCE ESCROW: (check one box only)

   ❑ (a) Escrow Not Required: Buyer shall furnish Seller, before each year's ad valorem taxes become delinquent, evidence that all ad valorem taxes on the Property have been paid. Buyer shall annually furnish Seller evidence of paid-up casualty insurance naming Seller as a mortgagee loss payee.

   ❑ (b) Escrow Required: With each installment Buyer shall deposit in escrow with Seller a pro rata part of the estimated annual ad valorem taxes and casualty insurance premiums for the Property. Buyer shall pay any deficiency within 30 days after notice from Seller. Buyer's failure to pay the deficiency will be a default under the deed of trust. Buyer is not required to deposit any escrow payments for taxes and insurance that are deposited with a superior lienholder. The casualty insurance must name Seller as a mortgagee loss payee.

(3) PRIOR LIENS: Any default under any lien superior to the lien securing the Note will be a default under the deed of trust securing the Note.

_____   _____
Buyer   Seller

_____   _____
Buyer   Seller

TREC NO. 26-6

4-28-2014

PROMULGATED BY THE TEXAS REAL ESTATE COMMISSION (TREC)
ONE TO FOUR FAMILY RESIDENTIAL CONTRACT (RESALE)
NOTICE: Not For Use For Condominium Transactions

1. PARTIES: The parties to this contract are <u>Samuel A. Johnson, a single man</u>
(Seller) and <u>Tim J. Swanson and wife, Sarah J Swanson</u> (Buyer).
Seller agrees to sell and convey to Buyer and Buyer agrees to buy from Seller the Property defined below.

2. PROPERTY: The land, improvements and accessories are collectively referred to as the "Property".
   A. LAND: Lot <u>6</u> Block <u>8</u>, <u>Terrace Addition</u>
   Addition, City of <u> </u>, County of <u>McLennon</u>,
   Texas, known as <u>15630 Paradise Ave, Waco, TX</u>
   (address/zip code), or as described on attached exhibit.
   B. IMPROVEMENTS: The house, garage and all other fixtures and improvements attached to the above-described real property, including without limitation, the following **permanently installed and built-in items,** if any: all equipment and appliances, valances, screens, shutters, awnings, wall-to-wall carpeting, mirrors, ceiling fans, attic fans, mail boxes, television antennas, mounts and brackets for televisions and speakers, heating and air-conditioning units, security and fire detection equipment, wiring, plumbing and lighting fixtures, chandeliers, water softener system, kitchen equipment, garage door openers, cleaning equipment, shrubbery, landscaping, outdoor cooking equipment, and all other property owned by Seller and attached to the above described real property.
   C. ACCESSORIES: The following described related accessories, if any: window air conditioning units, stove, fireplace screens, curtains and rods, blinds, window shades, draperies and rods, door keys, mailbox keys, above ground pool, swimming pool equipment and maintenance accessories, artificial fireplace logs, and controls for: (i) garage doors, (ii) entry gates, and (iii) other improvements and accessories.
   D. EXCLUSIONS: The following improvements and accessories will be retained by Seller and must be removed prior to delivery of possession:<u> </u>
   <u> </u>.

3. SALES PRICE:
   A. Cash portion of Sales Price payable by Buyer at closing .... $<u>48,500.00</u>
   B. Sum of all financing described below (excluding any loan funding
      fee or mortgage insurance premium) .... $<u>25,000.00</u>
   C. Sales Price (Sum of A and B)... $<u>73,500.00</u>

4. FINANCING (Not for use with reverse mortgage financing): The portion of Sales Price not payable in cash will be paid as follows: (Check applicable boxes below)
☐ A.THIRD PARTY FINANCING: One or more third party mortgage loans in the total amount of $<u> </u> (excluding any loan funding fee or mortgage insurance premium).
  (1) Property Approval: If the Property does not satisfy the lenders' underwriting requirements for the loan(s) (including, but not limited to appraisal, insurability and lender required repairs), Buyer may terminate this contract by giving notice to Seller prior to closing and the earnest money will be refunded to Buyer.
  (2) Credit Approval: (Check one box only)
  ☐ (a) This contract is subject to Buyer being approved for the financing described in the attached Third Party Financing Addendum for Credit Approval.
  ☐ (b) This contract is not subject to Buyer being approved for financing and does not involve FHA or VA financing.
☐ B. ASSUMPTION: The assumption of the unpaid principal balance of one or more promissory notes described in the attached TREC Loan Assumption Addendum.
☒ C. SELLER FINANCING: A promissory note from Buyer to Seller of $<u>25,000.00</u>, secured by vendor's and deed of trust liens, and containing the terms and conditions described in the attached TREC Seller Financing Addendum. If an owner policy of title insurance is furnished, Buyer shall furnish Seller with a mortgagee policy of title insurance.

Initialed for identification by Buyer<u> </u> <u> </u> and Seller <u> </u> <u> </u>   TREC NO. 20-12

Contract Concerning ___15630 Paradise Ave, Waco, TX_____ Page 2 of 9   4-28-2014
(Address of Property)

5. **EARNEST MONEY:** Upon execution of this contract by all parties, Buyer shall deposit $ _2,000.00____ as earnest money with ___Secure Title Company_____, as escrow agent, at ____1010 Westway, Waco, TX 76710_____ (address). Buyer shall deposit additional earnest money of $_____N/A_____ with escrow agent within N/A days after the effective date of this contract. If Buyer fails to deposit the earnest money as required by this contract, Buyer will be in default.

6. **TITLE POLICY AND SURVEY:**
   A. TITLE POLICY: Seller shall furnish to Buyer at ☒ Seller's ☐ Buyer's expense an owner policy of title insurance (Title Policy) issued by _Secure Title Company_____ (Title Company) in the amount of the Sales Price, dated at or after closing, insuring Buyer against loss under the provisions of the Title Policy, subject to the promulgated exclusions (including existing building and zoning ordinances) and the following exceptions:
      (1) Restrictive covenants common to the platted subdivision in which the Property is located.
      (2) The standard printed exception for standby fees, taxes and assessments.
      (3) Liens created as part of the financing described in Paragraph 4.
      (4) Utility easements created by the dedication deed or plat of the subdivision in which the Property is located.
      (5) Reservations or exceptions otherwise permitted by this contract or as may be approved by Buyer in writing.
      (6) The standard printed exception as to marital rights.
      (7) The standard printed exception as to waters, tidelands, beaches, streams, and related matters.
      (8) The standard printed exception as to discrepancies, conflicts, shortages in area or boundary lines, encroachments or protrusions, or overlapping improvements: ☐(i) will not be amended or deleted from the title policy; ☒(ii) will be amended to read, "shortages in area" at the expense of ☒Buyer ☐Seller.
   B. COMMITMENT: Within 20 days after the Title Company receives a copy of this contract, Seller shall furnish to Buyer a commitment for title insurance (Commitment) and, at Buyer's expense, legible copies of restrictive covenants and documents evidencing exceptions in the Commitment (Exception Documents) other than the standard printed exceptions. Seller authorizes the Title Company to deliver the Commitment and Exception Documents to Buyer at Buyer's address shown in Paragraph 21. If the Commitment and Exception Documents are not delivered to Buyer within the specified time, the time for delivery will be automatically extended up to 15 days or 3 days before the Closing Date, whichever is earlier. If, due to factors beyond Seller's control, the Commitment and Exception Documents are not delivered within the time required, Buyer may terminate this contract and the earnest money will be refunded to Buyer.
   C. SURVEY: The survey must be made by a registered professional land surveyor acceptable to the Title Company and Buyer's lender(s). (Check one box only)
   ☐(1) Within _____ days after the effective date of this contract, Seller shall furnish to Buyer and Title Company Seller's existing survey of the Property and a Residential Real Property Affidavit promulgated by the Texas Department of Insurance (T-47 Affidavit). **If Seller fails to furnish the existing survey or affidavit within the time prescribed, Buyer shall obtain a new survey at Seller's expense no later than 3 days prior to Closing Date.** If the existing survey or affidavit is not acceptable to Title Company or Buyer's lender(s), Buyer shall obtain a new survey at ☐Seller's ☐Buyer's expense no later than 3 days prior to Closing Date.
   ☐(2) Within _____ days after the effective date of this contract, Buyer shall obtain a new survey at Buyer's expense. Buyer is deemed to receive the survey on the date of actual receipt or the date specified in this paragraph, whichever is earlier.
   ☒(3) Within _10____ days after the effective date of this contract, Seller, at Seller's expense shall furnish a new survey to Buyer.
   D. OBJECTIONS: Buyer may object in writing to defects, exceptions, or encumbrances to title: disclosed on the survey other than items 6A(1) through (7) above; disclosed in the Commitment other than items 6A(1) through (8) above; or which prohibit the following use or activity: _Cable TV Services are available_____
   _____.
   Buyer must object the earlier of (i) the Closing Date or (ii) _10___ days after Buyer receives the Commitment, Exception Documents, and the survey. Buyer's failure to object within the time allowed will constitute a waiver of Buyer's right to object; except that the requirements in Schedule C of the Commitment are not waived by Buyer. Provided Seller is not obligated to incur any expense, Seller shall cure the timely objections of Buyer or any third party lender

Initialed for identification by Buyer_____ _____ and Seller _____ _____   TREC NO. 20-12

Contract Concerning _____15630 Paradise Ave, Waco, TX_____ Page 3 of 9　4-28-2014
(Address of Property)

within 15 days after Seller receives the objections and the Closing Date will be extended as necessary. If objections are not cured within such 15 day period, this contract will terminate and the earnest money will be refunded to Buyer unless Buyer waives the objections.

E.　TITLE NOTICES:
(1)　ABSTRACT OR TITLE POLICY: Broker advises Buyer to have an abstract of title covering the Property examined by an attorney of Buyer's selection, or Buyer should be furnished with or obtain a Title Policy. If a Title Policy is furnished, the Commitment should be promptly reviewed by an attorney of Buyer's choice due to the time limitations on Buyer's right to object.

(2)　MEMBERSHIP IN PROPERTY OWNERS ASSOCIATION(S): The Property ☐is ☒is not subject to mandatory membership in a property owners association(s). If the Property is subject to mandatory membership in a property owners association(s), Seller notifies Buyer under §5.012, Texas Property Code, that, as a purchaser of property in the residential community identified in Paragraph 2A in which the Property is located, you are obligated to be a member of the property owners association(s). Restrictive covenants governing the use and occupancy of the Property and all dedicatory instruments governing the establishment, maintenance, or operation of this residential community have been or will be recorded in the Real Property Records of the county in which the Property is located. Copies of the restrictive covenants and dedicatory instruments may be obtained from the county clerk. **You are obligated to pay assessments to the property owners association(s). The amount of the assessments is subject to change. Your failure to pay the assessments could result in enforcement of the association's lien on and the foreclosure of the Property.**
Section 207.003, Property Code, entitles an owner to receive copies of any document that governs the establishment, maintenance, or operation of a subdivision, including, but not limited to, restrictions, bylaws, rules and regulations, and a resale certificate from a property owners' association. A resale certificate contains information including, but not limited to, statements specifying the amount and frequency of regular assessments and the style and cause number of lawsuits to which the property owners' association is a party, other than lawsuits relating to unpaid ad valorem taxes of an individual member of the association. These documents must be made available to you by the property owners' association or the association's agent on your request.
If Buyer is concerned about these matters, the TREC promulgated Addendum for Property Subject to Mandatory Membership in a Property Owners Association(s) should be used.

(3)　STATUTORY TAX DISTRICTS: If the Property is situated in a utility or other statutorily created district providing water, sewer, drainage, or flood control facilities and services, Chapter 49, Texas Water Code, requires Seller to deliver and Buyer to sign the statutory notice relating to the tax rate, bonded indebtedness, or standby fee of the district prior to final execution of this contract.

(4)　TIDE WATERS: If the Property abuts the tidally influenced waters of the state, §33.135, Texas Natural Resources Code, requires a notice regarding coastal area property to be included in the contract. An addendum containing the notice promulgated by TREC or required by the parties must be used.

(5)　ANNEXATION: If the Property is located outside the limits of a municipality, Seller notifies Buyer under §5.011, Texas Property Code, that the Property may now or later be included in the extraterritorial jurisdiction of a municipality and may now or later be subject to annexation by the municipality. Each municipality maintains a map that depicts its boundaries and extraterritorial jurisdiction. To determine if the Property is located within a municipality's extraterritorial jurisdiction or is likely to be located within a municipality's extraterritorial jurisdiction, contact all municipalities located in the general proximity of the Property for further information.

(6)　PROPERTY LOCATED IN A CERTIFICATED SERVICE AREA OF A UTILITY SERVICE PROVIDER: Notice required by §13.257, Water Code: The real property, described in Paragraph 2, that you are about to purchase may be located in a certificated water or sewer service area, which is authorized by law to provide water or sewer service to the properties in the certificated area. If your property is located in a certificated area there may be special costs or charges that you will be required to pay before you can receive water or sewer service. There may be a period required to construct lines or other facilities necessary to provide water or sewer service to your property. You are advised to determine if the property is in a certificated area and contact the utility service provider to determine the cost that you will be required to pay and the period, if any, that is required to provide water or sewer service to your property. The undersigned Buyer hereby acknowledges receipt of the foregoing notice at or before the execution of a binding contract for the purchase of the real property described in Paragraph 2 or at closing of purchase of the real property.

Initialed for identification by Buyer_____ _____ and Seller _____ _____　　TREC NO. 20-12

Contract Concerning ___15630 Paradise Ave, Waco, TX_____ Page 4 of 9   4-28-2014
(Address of Property)

(7) PUBLIC IMPROVEMENT DISTRICTS: If the Property is in a public improvement district, §5.014, Property Code, requires Seller to notify Buyer as follows: As a purchaser of this parcel of real property you are obligated to pay an assessment to a municipality or county for an improvement project undertaken by a public improvement district under Chapter 372, Local Government Code. The assessment may be due annually or in periodic installments. More information concerning the amount of the assessment and the due dates of that assessment may be obtained from the municipality or county levying the assessment. The amount of the assessments is subject to change. Your failure to pay the assessments could result in a lien on and the foreclosure of your property.

(8) TRANSFER FEES: If the Property is subject to a private transfer fee obligation, §5.205, Property Code, requires Seller to notify Buyer as follows: The private transfer fee obligation may be governed by Chapter 5, Subchapter G of the Texas Property Code.

(9) PROPANE GAS SYSTEM SERVICE AREA: If the Property is located in a propane gas system service area owned by a distribution system retailer, Seller must give Buyer written notice as required by §141.010, Texas Utilities Code. An addendum containing the notice approved by TREC or required by the parties should be used.

7. PROPERTY CONDITION:
A. ACCESS, INSPECTIONS AND UTILITIES: Seller shall permit Buyer and Buyer's agents access to the Property at reasonable times. Buyer may have the Property inspected by inspectors selected by Buyer and licensed by TREC or otherwise permitted by law to make inspections. Seller at Seller's expense shall immediately cause existing utilities to be turned on and shall keep the utilities on during the time this contract is in effect.

B. SELLER'S DISCLOSURE NOTICE PURSUANT TO §5.008, TEXAS PROPERTY CODE (Notice): (Check one box only)
☒ (1) Buyer has received the Notice.
☐ (2) Buyer has not received the Notice. Within _____ days after the effective date of this contract, Seller shall deliver the Notice to Buyer. If Buyer does not receive the Notice, Buyer may terminate this contract at any time prior to the closing and the earnest money will be refunded to Buyer. If Seller delivers the Notice, Buyer may terminate this contract for any reason within 7 days after Buyer receives the Notice or prior to the closing, whichever first occurs, and the earnest money will be refunded to Buyer.
☐ (3)The Seller is not required to furnish the notice under the Texas Property Code.

C. SELLER'S DISCLOSURE OF LEAD-BASED PAINT AND LEAD-BASED PAINT HAZARDS is required by Federal law for a residential dwelling constructed prior to 1978.

D. ACCEPTANCE OF PROPERTY CONDITION: "As Is" means the present condition of the Property with any and all defects and without warranty except for the warranties of title and the warranties in this contract. Buyer's agreement to accept the Property As Is under Paragraph 7D(1) or (2) does not preclude Buyer from inspecting the Property under Paragraph 7A, from negotiating repairs or treatments in a subsequent amendment, or from terminating this contract during the Option Period, if any.
(Check one box only)
☒ (1) Buyer accepts the Property As Is.
☐ (2) Buyer accepts the Property As Is provided Seller, at Seller's expense, shall complete the following specific repairs and treatments: _____
_____.
(Do not insert general phrases, such as "subject to inspections" that do not identify specific repairs and treatments.)

E. LENDER REQUIRED REPAIRS AND TREATMENTS: Unless otherwise agreed in writing, neither party is obligated to pay for lender required repairs, which includes treatment for wood destroying insects. If the parties do not agree to pay for the lender required repairs or treatments, this contract will terminate and the earnest money will be refunded to Buyer. If the cost of lender required repairs and treatments exceeds 5% of the Sales Price, Buyer may terminate this contract and the earnest money will be refunded to Buyer.

F. COMPLETION OF REPAIRS AND TREATMENTS: Unless otherwise agreed in writing: (i) Seller shall complete all agreed repairs and treatments prior to the Closing Date; and (ii) all required permits must be obtained, and repairs and treatments must be performed by persons who are licensed to provide such repairs or treatments or, if no license is required by law, are commercially engaged in the trade of providing such repairs or treatments. At Buyer's election, any transferable warranties received by Seller with respect to the repairs and treatments will be transferred to Buyer at Buyer's expense. If Seller fails to complete any agreed repairs and treatments prior to the Closing Date, Buyer may exercise remedies under Paragraph 15 or extend the Closing Date up to 5 days if necessary for Seller to complete the repairs and treatments.

G. ENVIRONMENTAL MATTERS: Buyer is advised that the presence of wetlands, toxic substances, including asbestos and wastes or other environmental hazards, or the presence of a threatened or endangered species or its habitat may affect Buyer's intended use of the

Initialed for identification by Buyer_____ _____ and Seller _____ _____   TREC NO. 20-12

Contract Concerning ___15630 Paradise Ave, Waco, TX_____ Page 5 of 9   4-28-2014
(Address of Property)

Property. If Buyer is concerned about these matters, an addendum promulgated by TREC or required by the parties should be used.

H. RESIDENTIAL SERVICE CONTRACTS: Buyer may purchase a residential service contract from a residential service company licensed by TREC. If Buyer purchases a residential service contract, Seller shall reimburse Buyer at closing for the cost of the residential service contract in an amount not exceeding $ N/A_____. Buyer should review any residential service contract for the scope of coverage, exclusions and limitations. **The purchase of a residential service contract is optional. Similar coverage may be purchased from various companies authorized to do business in Texas.**

8. **BROKERS' FEES:** All obligations of the parties for payment of brokers' fees are contained in separate written agreements.

9. **CLOSING:**
   A. The closing of the sale will be on or before ___WITHIN 15 DAYS_____, 20XX__, or within 7 days after objections made under Paragraph 6D have been cured or waived, whichever date is later (Closing Date). If either party fails to close the sale by the Closing Date, the non-defaulting party may exercise the remedies contained in Paragraph 15.
   B. At closing:
      (1) Seller shall execute and deliver a general warranty deed conveying title to the Property to Buyer and showing no additional exceptions to those permitted in Paragraph 6 and furnish tax statements or certificates showing no delinquent taxes on the Property.
      (2) Buyer shall pay the Sales Price in good funds acceptable to the escrow agent.
      (3) Seller and Buyer shall execute and deliver any notices, statements, certificates, affidavits, releases, loan documents and other documents reasonably required for the closing of the sale and the issuance of the Title Policy.
      (4) There will be no liens, assessments, or security interests against the Property which will not be satisfied out of the sales proceeds unless securing the payment of any loans assumed by Buyer and assumed loans will not be in default.
      (5)If the Property is subject to a residential lease, Seller shall transfer security deposits (as defined under §92.102, Property Code), if any, to Buyer. In such an event, Buyer shall deliver to the tenant a signed statement acknowledging that the Buyer has received the security deposit and is responsible for the return of the security deposit, and specifying the exact dollar amount of the security deposit.

10. **POSSESSION:**
   A Buyer's Possession: Seller shall deliver to Buyer possession of the Property in its present or required condition, ordinary wear and tear excepted: ☒upon closing and funding ❑according to a temporary residential lease form promulgated by TREC or other written lease required by the parties. Any possession by Buyer prior to closing or by Seller after closing which is not authorized by a written lease will establish a tenancy at sufferance relationship between the parties. **Consult your insurance agent prior to change of ownership and possession because insurance coverage may be limited or terminated. The absence of a written lease or appropriate insurance coverage may expose the parties to economic loss.**
   B. Leases:
      (1)After the Effective Date, Seller may not execute any lease (including but not limited to mineral leases) or convey any interest in the Property without Buyer's written consent.
      (2) If the Property is subject to any lease to which Seller is a party, Seller shall deliver to Buyer copies of the lease(s) and any move-in condition form signed by the tenant within 7 days after the Effective Date of the contract.

11. **SPECIAL PROVISIONS:** (Insert only factual statements and business details applicable to the sale. TREC rules prohibit licensees from adding factual statements or business details for which a contract addendum, lease or other form has been promulgated by TREC for mandatory use.)

12. **SETTLEMENT AND OTHER EXPENSES:**
   A. The following expenses must be paid at or prior to closing:
      (1) Expenses payable by Seller (Seller's Expenses):
         (a) Releases of existing liens, including prepayment penalties and recording fees; release of Seller's loan liability; tax statements or certificates; preparation of deed; one-half of escrow fee; and other expenses payable by Seller under this contract.
         (b) Seller shall also pay an amount not to exceed $ N/A_____ to be applied in the

Initialed for identification by Buyer_____ _____ and Seller _____ _____   TREC NO. 20-12

Contract Concerning ___15630 Paradise Ave, Waco, TX_____ Page 6 of 9   4-28-2014
(Address of Property)

following order: Buyer's Expenses which Buyer is prohibited from paying by FHA, VA, Texas Veterans Land Board or other governmental loan programs, and then to other Buyer's Expenses as allowed by the lender.

(2) Expenses payable by Buyer (Buyer's Expenses): Appraisal fees; loan application fees; adjusted origination charges; credit reports; preparation of loan documents; interest on the notes from date of disbursement to one month prior to dates of first monthly payments; recording fees; copies of easements and restrictions; loan title policy with endorsements required by lender; loan-related inspection fees; photos; amortization schedules; one-half of escrow fee; all prepaid items, including required premiums for flood and hazard insurance, reserve deposits for insurance, ad valorem taxes and special governmental assessments; final compliance inspection; courier fee; repair inspection; underwriting fee; wire transfer fee; expenses incident to any loan; Private Mortgage Insurance Premium (PMI), VA Loan Funding Fee, or FHA Mortgage Insurance Premium (MIP) as required by the lender; and other expenses payable by Buyer under this contract.

B. If any expense exceeds an amount expressly stated in this contract for such expense to be paid by a party, that party may terminate this contract unless the other party agrees to pay such excess. Buyer may not pay charges and fees expressly prohibited by FHA, VA, Texas Veterans Land Board or other governmental loan program regulations.

13. **PRORATIONS:** Taxes for the current year, interest, maintenance fees, assessments, dues and rents will be prorated through the Closing Date. The tax proration may be calculated taking into consideration any change in exemptions that will affect the current year's taxes. If taxes for the current year vary from the amount prorated at closing, the parties shall adjust the prorations when tax statements for the current year are available. If taxes are not paid at or prior to closing, Buyer shall pay taxes for the current year.

14. **CASUALTY LOSS:** If any part of the Property is damaged or destroyed by fire or other casualty after the effective date of this contract, Seller shall restore the Property to its previous condition as soon as reasonably possible, but in any event by the Closing Date. If Seller fails to do so due to factors beyond Seller's control, Buyer may (a) terminate this contract and the earnest money will be refunded to Buyer (b) extend the time for performance up to 15 days and the Closing Date will be extended as necessary or (c) accept the Property in its damaged condition with an assignment of insurance proceeds and receive credit from Seller at closing in the amount of the deductible under the insurance policy. Seller's obligations under this paragraph are independent of any other obligations of Seller under this contract.

15. **DEFAULT:** If Buyer fails to comply with this contract, Buyer will be in default, and Seller may (a) enforce specific performance, seek such other relief as may be provided by law, or both, or (b) terminate this contract and receive the earnest money as liquidated damages, thereby releasing both parties from this contract. If Seller fails to comply with this contract, Seller will be in default and Buyer may (a) enforce specific performance, seek such other relief as may be provided by law, or both, or (b) terminate this contract and receive the earnest money, thereby releasing both parties from this contract.

16. **MEDIATION:** It is the policy of the State of Texas to encourage resolution of disputes through alternative dispute resolution procedures such as mediation. Any dispute between Seller and Buyer related to this contract which is not resolved through informal discussion will be submitted to a mutually acceptable mediation service or provider. The parties to the mediation shall bear the mediation costs equally. This paragraph does not preclude a party from seeking equitable relief from a court of competent jurisdiction.

17. **ATTORNEY'S FEES:** A Buyer, Seller, Listing Broker, Other Broker, or escrow agent who prevails in any legal proceeding related to this contract is entitled to recover reasonable attorney's fees and all costs of such proceeding.

18. **ESCROW:**

A. ESCROW: The escrow agent is not (i) a party to this contract and does not have liability for the performance or nonperformance of any party to this contract, (ii) liable for interest on the earnest money and (iii) liable for the loss of any earnest money caused by the failure of any financial institution in which the earnest money has been deposited unless the financial institution is acting as escrow agent.

B. EXPENSES: At closing, the earnest money must be applied first to any cash down payment, then to Buyer's Expenses and any excess refunded to Buyer. If no closing occurs, escrow agent may: (i) require a written release of liability of the escrow agent from all parties, (ii) require payment of unpaid expenses incurred on behalf of a party, and (iii) only deduct from the earnest money the amount of unpaid expenses incurred on behalf of the party receiving the earnest money.

C. DEMAND: Upon termination of this contract, either party or the escrow agent may send a release of earnest money to each party and the parties shall execute counterparts of

Initialed for identification by Buyer_____ _____ and Seller _____ _____   TREC NO. 20-12

Contract Concerning __15630 Paradise Ave, Waco, TX_____ Page 7 of 9   4-28-2014
(Address of Property)

the release and deliver same to the escrow agent. If either party fails to execute the release, either party may make a written demand to the escrow agent for the earnest money. If only one party makes written demand for the earnest money, escrow agent shall promptly provide a copy of the demand to the other party. If escrow agent does not receive written objection to the demand from the other party within 15 days, escrow agent may disburse the earnest money to the party making demand reduced by the amount of unpaid expenses incurred on behalf of the party receiving the earnest money and escrow agent may pay the same to the creditors. If escrow agent complies with the provisions of this paragraph, each party hereby releases escrow agent from all adverse claims related to the disbursal of the earnest money.

   D. DAMAGES: Any party who wrongfully fails or refuses to sign a release acceptable to the escrow agent within 7 days of receipt of the request will be liable to the other party for liquidated damages in an amount equal to the sum of: (i) three times the amount of the earnest money; (ii) the earnest money; (iii) reasonable attorney's fees; and (iv) all costs of suit.

   E. NOTICES: Escrow agent's notices will be effective when sent in compliance with Paragraph 21. Notice of objection to the demand will be deemed effective upon receipt by escrow agent.

19. REPRESENTATIONS: All covenants, representations and warranties in this contract survive closing. If any representation of Seller in this contract is untrue on the Closing Date, Seller will be in default. Unless expressly prohibited by written agreement, Seller may continue to show the Property and receive, negotiate and accept back up offers.

20. FEDERAL TAX REQUIREMENTS: If Seller is a "foreign person," as defined by applicable law, or if Seller fails to deliver an affidavit to Buyer that Seller is not a "foreign person," then Buyer shall withhold from the sales proceeds an amount sufficient to comply with applicable tax law and deliver the same to the Internal Revenue Service together with appropriate tax forms. Internal Revenue Service regulations require filing written reports if currency in excess of specified amounts is received in the transaction.

21. NOTICES: All notices from one party to the other must be in writing and are effective when mailed to, hand-delivered at, or transmitted by facsimile or electronic transmission as follows:

To Buyer at: Tim J Swanson   **To Seller at:** Samuel A Johnson
1450 Crestridge Ave, Dallas TX   15630 Paradise Ave, Waco, TX
Telephone: (214) 590-1410   Telephone: (817) 283-1498
Facsimile: ( )   Facsimile: ( )
E-mail: Timswanson@amazon.com   E-mail: samaj2312@yahoo.com

22. AGREEMENT OF PARTIES: This contract contains the entire agreement of the parties and cannot be changed except by their written agreement. Addenda which are a part of this contract are (Check all applicable boxes):

- ☐ Third Party Financing Addendum for Credit Approval
- ☒ Seller Financing Addendum
- ☐ Addendum for Property Subject to Mandatory Membership in a Property Owners Association
- ☐ Buyer's Temporary Residential Lease
- ☐ Loan Assumption Addendum
- ☐ Addendum for Sale of Other Property by Buyer
- ☐ Addendum for Reservation of Oil, Gas and Other Minerals
- ☐ Addendum for "Back-Up" Contract
- ☐ Addendum for Coastal Area Property

- ☒ Environmental Assessment, Threatened or Endangered Species and Wetlands Addendum
- ☐ Seller's Temporary Residential Lease
- ☐ Short Sale Addendum
- ☐ Addendum for Property Located Seaward of the Gulf Intracoastal Waterway
- ☐ Addendum for Seller's Disclosure of Information on Lead-based Paint and Lead-based Paint Hazards as Required by Federal Law
- ☐ Addendum for Property in a Propane Gas System Service Area
- ☐ Other (list): _____

Initialed for identification by Buyer_____ _____ and Seller _____ _____   TREC NO. 20-12

Contract Concerning __15630 Paradise Ave, Waco, TX_____ Page 8 of 9   4-28-2014
(Address of Property)

23. **TERMINATION OPTION:** For nominal consideration, the receipt of which is hereby acknowledged by Seller, and Buyer's agreement to pay Seller $__150.00_____ (Option Fee) within 3 days after the effective date of this contract, Seller grants Buyer the unrestricted right to terminate this contract by giving notice of termination to Seller within __10____ days after the effective date of this contract (Option Period). If no dollar amount is stated as the Option Fee or if Buyer fails to pay the Option Fee to Seller within the time prescribed, this paragraph will not be a part of this contract and Buyer shall not have the unrestricted right to terminate this contract. If Buyer gives notice of termination within the time prescribed, the Option Fee will not be refunded; however, any earnest money will be refunded to Buyer. The Option Fee ☐will ☒will not be credited to the Sales Price at closing. **Time is of the essence for this paragraph and strict compliance with the time for performance is required.**

24. **CONSULT AN ATTORNEY BEFORE SIGNING:** TREC rules prohibit real estate licensees from giving legal advice. READ THIS CONTRACT CAREFULLY.

Buyer's
Attorney is: __N/A_____

Seller's
Attorney is: __N/A_____

_____

_____

Telephone: (___)_____

Telephone: (___)_____

Facsimile: (___)_____

Facsimile: (___)_____

E-mail: _____

E-mail: _____

EXECUTED the _____day of ___Today_____, 20_XX_ (EFFECTIVE DATE).
(BROKER: FILL IN THE DATE OF FINAL ACCEPTANCE.)

_____
Buyer Tim J. Swanson and wife

_____
Seller Samuel A. Johnson, a single man

_____
Buyer Sarah J. Swanson

_____
Seller N/A

TREC NO. 20-12

Contract Concerning ___15630 Paradise Ave, Waco, TX_____ Page 9 of 9   4-28-2014
(Address of Property)

BROKER INFORMATION
(Print name(s) only. Do not sign)

N/A
Other Broker Firm   License No.

represents   ☐ Buyer only as Buyer's agent
             ☐ Seller as Listing Broker's subagent

Name of Associate's Licensed Supervisor   Telephone

Associate's Name   Telephone

Other Broker's Address   Facsimile

City   State   Zip

Associate's Email Address

Smooth Sales Realty   00000000
Listing Broker Firm   License No.

represents   ☐ Seller and Buyer as an intermediary
             ☒ Seller only as Seller's agent

Your Broker
Name of Associate's Licensed Supervisor   Telephone

Your Name
Listing Associate's Name   Telephone

Your office Address
Listing Broker's Office Address   Facsimile

City   State   Zip

Your e-mail
Listing Associate's Email Address

Your name
Selling Associate's Name   Telephone

Your Broker
Name of Selling Associate's Licensed Supervisor   Telephone

Your Broker
Selling Associate's Office Address   Facsimile

Your office address
City   State   Zip

Your e-mail
Selling Associate's Email Address

Listing Broker has agreed to pay Other Broker___N/A_____of the total sales price when the Listing Broker's fee is received. Escrow agent is authorized and directed to pay other Broker from Listing Broker's fee at closing.

OPTION FEE RECEIPT

Receipt of $__150.00_____ (Option Fee) in the form of ___check no. xx_____ is acknowledged.

_____   within 3 days of eff date_____
Seller or Listing Broker   Date
Samuel A. Johnson

CONTRACT AND EARNEST MONEY RECEIPT

Receipt of ☒Contract and ☒$_200.00____Earnest Money in the form of __cashier check_____ is acknowledged.

Escrow Agent: __Secure Title_____   Date:within 2 days of eff date

By: _____   Tina@securetitle.com
  Tina Frost   1010 Westway_____   Email Address   Telephone (817) 694-1010
Address

Waco   TX   76710   Facsimile: (817) 694-1011
City   State   Zip

PROMULGATED BY THE TEXAS REAL ESTATE COMMISSION (TREC)   12-05-11

EQUAL HOUSING
OPPORTUNITY

ENVIRONMENTAL ASSESSMENT, THREATENED OR ENDANGERED SPECIES, AND WETLANDS ADDENDUM

TO CONTRACT CONCERNING THE PROPERTY AT

15630 Paradise Ave, Waco, TX
(Address of Property)

☒ A. ENVIRONMENTAL ASSESSMENT: Buyer, at Buyer's expense, may obtain an environmental assessment report prepared by an environmental specialist.

❑ B. THREATENED OR ENDANGERED SPECIES: Buyer, at Buyer's expense, may obtain a report from a natural resources professional to determine if there are any threatened or endangered species or their habitats as defined by the Texas Parks and Wildlife Department or the U.S. Fish and Wildlife Service.

❑ C. WETLANDS: Buyer, at Buyer's expense, may obtain a report from an environmental specialist to determine if there are wetlands, as defined by federal or state law or regulation.

Within 10 days after the effective date of the contract, Buyer may terminate the contract by furnishing Seller a copy of any report noted above that adversely affects the use of the Property and a notice of termination of the contract. Upon termination, the earnest money will be refunded to Buyer.

Buyer Tim J. Swanson and wife

Seller Samuel A. Johnson, a single man

Buyer Sarah J Swanson

Seller

TREC No. 28-2

SELLER FINANCING ADDENDUM
TO CONTRACT CONCERNING THE PROPERTY AT

15630 Paradise Ave, Waco, TX
(Address of Property)

A. CREDIT DOCUMENTATION. To establish Buyer's creditworthiness, Buyer shall deliver to Seller within_5_days after the effective date of this contract, ☒ credit report ❑ verification of employment, including salary ❑ verification of funds on deposit in financial institutions ❑ current financial statement and ❑ _____
_____. Buyer hereby authorizes any credit reporting agency to furnish copies of Buyer's credit reports to Seller at Buyer's sole expense.

B. CREDIT APPROVAL. If the credit documentation described in Paragraph A is not delivered within the specified time, Seller may terminate this contract by notice to Buyer within 7 days after expiration of the time for delivery, and the earnest money will be paid to Seller. If the credit documentation is timely delivered, and Seller determines in Seller's sole discretion that Buyer's credit is unacceptable, Seller may terminate this contract by notice to Buyer within 7 days after expiration of the time for delivery and the earnest money will be refunded to Buyer. If Seller does not terminate this contract, Seller will be deemed to have approved Buyer's creditworthiness.

C. PROMISSORY NOTE. The promissory note (Note) described in Paragraph 4 of this contract payable by Buyer to the order of Seller will bear interest at the rate of _5.000_% per annum and be payable at the place designated by Seller. Buyer may prepay the Note in whole or in part at any time without penalty. Any prepayments are to be applied to the payment of the installments of principal last maturing and interest will immediately cease on the prepaid principal. The Note will contain a provision for payment of a late fee of 5% of any installment not paid within 10 days of the due date. Matured unpaid amounts will bear interest at the rate of 1½% per month or at the highest lawful rate, whichever is less. The Note will be payable as follows:

☒ (1) In one payment due _5 years_____ after the date of the Note with interest payable ❑ at maturity ☒ monthly ❑ quarterly. (check one box only)

❑ (2) In monthly installments of $ _N/A_____ ❑ including interest ❑plus interest (check one box only) beginning _____ after the date of the Note and continuing monthly thereafter for_____ months when the balance of the Note will be due and payable.

❑ (3) Interest only in monthly installments for the first _N/A_____ month(s) and thereafter in installments of $_N/A_____ ❑ including interest ❑ plus interest (check one box only) beginning _____N/A_____ after the date of the Note and continuing monthly thereafter for ___N/A___ months when the balance of the Note will be due and payable.

D. DEED OF TRUST. The deed of trust securing the Note will provide for the following:

(1) PROPERTY TRANSFERS: (check one box only)

❑ (a) Consent Not Required: The Property may be sold, conveyed or leased without the consent of Seller, provided any subsequent buyer assumes the Note.

☒ (b) Consent Required: If all or any part of the Property is sold, conveyed, leased for a period longer than 3 years, leased with an option to purchase, or otherwise sold (including any contract for deed), without Seller's prior written consent, which consent may be withheld in Seller's sole discretion, Seller may declare the balance of the Note to be immediately due and payable. The creation of a subordinate lien, any conveyance

Initialed for identification by Buyer_____ and Seller_____ TREC NO. 26-6

<u>   15630 Paradise Ave, Waco, TX   </u>

(Address of Property)

under threat or order of condemnation, any deed solely between buyers, or the passage of title by reason of the death of a buyer or by operation of law will not entitle Seller to exercise the remedies provided in this paragraph.

NOTE: *Under (a) or (b), Buyer's liability to pay the Note will continue unless Buyer obtains a release of liability from Seller.*

(2) TAX AND INSURANCE ESCROW: (check one box only)

☒ (a) Escrow Not Required: Buyer shall furnish Seller, before each year's ad valorem taxes become delinquent, evidence that all ad valorem taxes on the Property have been paid. Buyer shall annually furnish Seller evidence of paid-up casualty insurance naming Seller as a mortgagee loss payee.

❑ (b) Escrow Required: With each installment Buyer shall deposit in escrow with Seller a pro rata part of the estimated annual ad valorem taxes and casualty insurance premiums for the Property. Buyer shall pay any deficiency within 30 days after notice from Seller. Buyer's failure to pay the deficiency will be a default under the deed of trust. Buyer is not required to deposit any escrow payments for taxes and insurance that are deposited with a superior lienholder. The casualty insurance must name Seller as a mortgagee loss payee.

(3) PRIOR LIENS: Any default under any lien superior to the lien securing the Note will be a default under the deed of trust securing the Note.

Buyer Tim J. Swanson and wife   Seller Samuel A. Johnson, a single man

Buyer Sarah J. Swanson   Seller

Transaction: Kramer to Sweeney
(from Chapter 9 of *Texas Promulgated Forms*)

PROMULGATED BY THE TEXAS REAL ESTATE COMMISSION (TREC)   4-28-2014
NOTICE: Not For Use Where Seller Owns Fee Simple Title To Land Beneath Unit

RESIDENTIAL CONDOMINIUM CONTRACT (RESALE)

1. PARTIES: The parties to this contract are _____(Seller) and
_____(Buyer). Seller agrees to
sell and convey to Buyer and Buyer agrees to buy from Seller the Property defined below.

2. PROPERTY AND CONDOMINIUM DOCUMENTS:

A. The Condominium Unit, improvements and accessories described below are collectively
referred to as the "Property".
   (1) CONDOMINIUM UNIT: Unit _____, in Building _____,
    of _____, a condominium project, located at
    _____
    (address/zip code), City of _____,County of _____
    Texas, described in the Condominium Declaration and Plat and any amendments thereto
    of record in said County; together with such Unit's undivided interest in the Common
    Elements designated by the Declaration, including those areas reserved as Limited
    Common Elements appurtenant to the Unit and such other rights to use the Common
    Elements which have been specifically assigned to the Unit in any other manner. Parking
    areas assigned to the Unit are:_____.

   (2) IMPROVEMENTS: All fixtures and improvements attached to the above described real
    property including without limitation, the following **permanently installed and built-in
    items**, if any: all equipment and appliances, valances, screens, shutters, awnings, wall-
    to-wall carpeting, mirrors, ceiling fans, attic fans, mail boxes, television antennas,
    mounts and brackets for televisions and speakers, heating and air conditioning units,
    security and fire detection equipment, wiring, plumbing and lighting fixtures, chandeliers,
    shrubbery, landscaping, outdoor cooking equipment, and all other property owned by
    Seller and attached to the above described Condominium Unit.

   (3) ACCESSORIES: The following described related accessories, if any: window air
    conditioning units, stove, fireplace screens, curtains and rods, blinds, window shades,
    draperies and rods, door keys, mailbox keys, above ground pool, swimming pool
    equipment and maintenance accessories, artificial fireplace logs, and controls for:
    (i) garage doors, (ii) entry gates, and (iii) other improvements and accessories.

   (4) EXCLUSIONS: The following improvements and accessories will be retained by Seller and
    must be removed prior to delivery of possession: _____
    _____.

B. The Declaration, Bylaws and any Rules of the Association are called "Documents". (Check one
box only):
❑ (1) Buyer has received a copy of the Documents. Buyer is advised to read the Documents
    before signing the contract.
❑ (2) Buyer has not received a copy of the Documents. Seller shall deliver the Documents to
    Buyer within _____ days after the effective date of the contract. Buyer may cancel the
    contract before the sixth day after Buyer receives the Documents by hand-delivering or
    mailing written notice of cancellation to Seller by certified United States mail, return
    receipt requested. If Buyer cancels the contract pursuant to this paragraph, the contract
    will terminate and the earnest money will be refunded to Buyer.

C. The Resale Certificate from the condominium owners association (the Association) is called
the "Certificate". The Certificate must be in a form promulgated by TREC or required by the
parties. The Certificate must have been prepared no more than 3 months before the date it
is delivered to Buyer and must contain at a minimum the information required by Section
82.157, Texas Property Code.
(Check one box only):
❑ (1) Buyer has received the Certificate.
❑ (2) Buyer has not received the Certificate. Seller shall deliver the Certificate to Buyer within
    _____ days after the effective date of the contract. Buyer may cancel the contract before
    the sixth day after the date Buyer receives the Certificate by hand-delivering or mailing
    written notice of cancellation to Seller by certified United States mail, return receipt
    requested. If Buyer cancels the contract pursuant to this paragraph, the contract will
    terminate and the earnest money will be refunded to Buyer.
❑ (3) Buyer has received Seller's affidavit that Seller requested information from the
    Association concerning its financial condition as required by the Texas Property Code, and
    that the Association did not provide a Certificate or information required in the
    Certificate. Buyer and Seller agree to waive the requirement to furnish the Certificate.

Contract Concerning_____Page 2 of 8   4-28-2014
(Address of Property)

3. SALES PRICE:
   A. Cash portion of Sales Price payable by Buyer at closing ....$_____

   B. Sum of all financing described below (excluding any loan funding
      fee or mortgage insurance premium)..$_____
   C. Sales Price (Sum of A and B) ....$_____

4. FINANCING (Not for use with reverse mortgage financing): The portion of Sales Price not payable in cash will be paid as follows: (Check applicable boxes below)
❏A. THIRD PARTY FINANCING: One or more third party mortgage loans in the total amount of $_____ (excluding any loan funding fee or mortgage insurance premium).
   (1)Property Approval: If the Property does not satisfy the lenders' underwriting requirements for the loan(s), (including, but not limited to appraisal, insurability and lender required repairs), Buyer may terminate this contract by giving notice to Seller prior to closing and the earnest money will be refunded to Buyer.
   (2)Credit Approval: (Check one box only)
      ❏ (a) This contract is subject to Buyer being approved for the financing described in the attached Third Party Financing Addendum for Credit Approval.
      ❏ (b) This contract is not subject to Buyer being approved for financing and does not involve FHA or VA financing.
❏B. ASSUMPTION: The assumption of the unpaid principal balance of one or more promissory notes described in the attached TREC Loan Assumption Addendum.
❏C. SELLER FINANCING: A promissory note from Buyer to Seller of $_____, secured by vendor's and deed of trust liens, and containing the terms and conditions described in the attached TREC Seller Financing Addendum. If an owner policy of title insurance is furnished, Buyer shall furnish Seller with a mortgagee policy of title insurance.

5. EARNEST MONEY: Upon execution of this contract by all parties, Buyer shall deposit $_____ as earnest money with _____, as escrow agent, at _____ (address).   Buyer shall deposit additional earnest money of $_____ with escrow agent within _____ days after the effective date of this contract. If Buyer fails to deposit the earnest money as required by this contract, Buyer will be in default.

6. TITLE POLICY:
   A. TITLE POLICY: Seller shall furnish to Buyer at ❏Seller's ❏Buyer's expense an owner policy of title insurance (Title Policy) issued by _____(Title Company) in the amount of the Sales Price, dated at or after closing, insuring Buyer against loss under the provisions of the Title Policy, subject to the promulgated exclusions (including existing building and zoning ordinances) and the following exceptions:
      (1) Restrictive covenants common to the platted subdivision in which the Property is located.
      (2) The standard printed exception for standby fees, taxes and assessments.
      (3) Liens created as part of the financing described in Paragraph 4.
      (4) Terms and provisions of the Documents including the assessments and platted easements.
      (5) Reservations or exceptions otherwise permitted by this contract or as may be approved by Buyer in writing.
      (6) The standard printed exception as to marital rights.
      (7) The standard printed exception as to waters, tidelands, beaches, streams, and related matters.
      (8) The standard printed exception as to discrepancies, conflicts, shortages in area or boundary lines, encroachments or protrusions, or overlapping improvements.
   B. COMMITMENT: Within 20 days after the Title Company receives a copy of this contract, Seller shall furnish to Buyer a commitment for title insurance (Commitment) and, at Buyer's expense, legible copies of restrictive covenants and documents evidencing exceptions in the Commitment (Exception Documents) other than the standard printed exceptions. Seller authorizes the Title Company to deliver the Commitment and Exception Documents to Buyer at Buyer's address shown in Paragraph 21. If the Commitment and Exception Documents are not delivered to Buyer within the specified time, the time for delivery will be automatically extended up to 15 days or 3 days before the Closing Date, whichever is earlier. If, due to factors beyond Seller's control, the Commitment and Exception Documents are not delivered within the time required, Buyer may terminate this contract and the earnest money will be refunded to Buyer.
   C. OBJECTIONS: Buyer may object in writing to defects, exceptions, or encumbrances to title: disclosed in the Commitment other than items 6A(1) through (8) above; or which prohibit the following use or activity: _____.
   Buyer must object the earlier of (i) the Closing Date or (ii) _____ days after Buyer receives the Commitment and Exception Documents. Buyer's failure to object within the time allowed will constitute a waiver of Buyer's right to object; except that the requirements in

   Schedule C of the Commitment are not waived by Buyer. Provided Seller is not obligated to incur any expense, Seller shall cure the timely objections of Buyer or any third party lender within 15 days after Seller receives the objections and the Closing Date will be extended as necessary. If objections are not cured within such 15 day period, this contract will terminate and the earnest money will be refunded to Buyer unless Buyer waives the objections.

D. TITLE NOTICES:
  (1) ABSTRACT OR TITLE POLICY: Broker advises Buyer to have an abstract of title covering the Property examined by an attorney of Buyer's selection, or Buyer should be furnished with or obtain a Title Policy. If a Title Policy is furnished, the Commitment should be promptly reviewed by an attorney of Buyer's choice due to the time limitations on Buyer's right to object.
  (2) STATUTORY TAX DISTRICTS: If the Property is situated in a utility or other statutorily created district providing water, sewer, drainage, or flood control facilities and services, Chapter 49, Texas Water Code, requires Seller to deliver and Buyer to sign the statutory notice relating to the tax rate, bonded indebtedness, or standby fee of the district prior to final execution of this contract.
  (3) TIDE WATERS: If the Property abuts the tidally influenced waters of the state, §33.135, Texas Natural Resources Code, requires a notice regarding coastal area property to be included in the contract. An addendum containing the notice promulgated by TREC or required by the parties must be used.
  (4) ANNEXATION: If the Property is located outside the limits of a municipality, Seller notifies Buyer under §5.011, Texas Property Code, that the Property may now or later be included in the extraterritorial jurisdiction of a municipality and may now or later be subject to annexation by the municipality. Each municipality maintains a map that depicts its boundaries and extraterritorial jurisdiction. To determine if the Property is located within a municipality's extraterritorial jurisdiction or is likely to be located within a municipality's extraterritorial jurisdiction, contact all municipalities located in the general proximity of the Property for further information.
  (5) PROPERTY LOCATED IN A CERTIFICATED SERVICE AREA OF A UTILITY SERVICE PROVIDER: Notice required by §13.257, Water Code: The real property, described in Paragraph 2, that you are about to purchase may be located in a certificated water or sewer service area, which is authorized by law to provide water or sewer service to the properties in the certificated area. If your property is located in a certificated area there may be special costs or charges that you will be required to pay before you can receive water or sewer service. There may be a period required to construct lines or other facilities necessary to provide water or sewer service to your property. You are advised to determine if the property is in a certificated area and contact the utility service provider to determine the cost that you will be required to pay and the period, if any, that is required to provide water or sewer service to your property. The undersigned Buyer hereby acknowledges receipt of the foregoing notice at or before the execution of a binding contract for the purchase of the real property described in Paragraph 2 or at closing of purchase of the real property.
  (6) TRANSFER FEES: If the Property is subject to a private transfer fee obligation, §5.205, Property Code, requires Seller to notify Buyer as follows: The private transfer fee obligation may be governed by Chapter 5, Subchapter G of the Texas Property Code.
  (7) PROPANE GAS SYSTEM SERVICE AREA: If the Property is located in a propane gas system service area owned by a distribution system retailer, Seller must give Buyer written notice as required by §141.010, Texas Utilities Code. An addendum containing the notice approved by TREC or required by the parties should be used.

7. PROPERTY CONDITION:
  A. ACCESS, INSPECTIONS AND UTILITIES: Seller shall permit Buyer and Buyer's agents access to the Property at reasonable times. Buyer may have the Property inspected by inspectors selected by Buyer and licensed by TREC or otherwise permitted by law to make inspections. Seller at Seller's expense shall immediately cause existing utilities to be turned on and shall keep the utilities on during the time this contract is in effect .
  B. SELLER'S DISCLOSURE NOTICE PURSUANT TO §5.008, TEXAS PROPERTY CODE (Notice): (Check one box only)
  ☐ (1) Buyer has received the Notice.
  ☐ (2) Buyer has not received the Notice. Within _____ days after the effective date of this contract, Seller shall deliver the Notice to Buyer. If Buyer does not receive the Notice, Buyer may terminate this contract at any time prior to the closing and the earnest money will be refunded to Buyer. If Seller delivers the Notice, Buyer may terminate this contract for any reason within 7 days after Buyer receives the Notice or prior to the closing, whichever first occurs, and the earnest money will be refunded to Buyer.
  ☐ (3) The Texas Property Code does not require this Seller to furnish the Notice.
  C. SELLER'S DISCLOSURE OF LEAD-BASED PAINT AND LEAD-BASED PAINT HAZARDS is required by Federal law for a residential dwelling constructed prior to 1978.
  D. ACCEPTANCE OF PROPERTY CONDITION: "As Is" means the present condition of the Property with any and all defects and without warranty except for the warranties of title and the warranties in this contract. Buyer's agreement to accept the Property As Is under Paragraph 7D(1) or (2) does not preclude Buyer from inspecting the Property under Paragraph 7A, from negotiating repairs or treatments in a subsequent amendment, or from terminating this contract during the Option Period, if any.

Contract Concerning_____Page 4 of 8   4-28-2014
(Address of Property)

(Check one box only)
- ❏ (1) Buyer accepts the Property As Is.
- ❏ (2) Buyer accepts the Property As Is provided Seller, at Seller's expense, shall complete the following specific repairs and treatments: _____
  (Do not insert general phrases, such as "subject to inspections," that do not identify specific repairs and treatments.)

E. LENDER REQUIRED REPAIRS AND TREATMENTS: Unless otherwise agreed in writing, neither party is obligated to pay for lender required repairs, which includes treatment for wood destroying insects. If the parties do not agree to pay for the lender required repairs or treatments, this contract will terminate and the earnest money will be refunded to Buyer. If the cost of lender required repairs and treatments exceeds 5% of the Sales Price, Buyer may terminate this contract and the earnest money will be refunded to Buyer.

F. COMPLETION OF REPAIRS AND TREATMENTS: Unless otherwise agreed in writing: (i) Seller shall complete all agreed repairs and treatments prior to the Closing Date; and (ii) all required permits must be obtained, and repairs and treatments must be performed by persons who are licensed to provide such repairs or treatments or, if no license is required by law, are commercially engaged in the trade of providing such repairs or treatments. At Buyer's election, any transferable warranties received by Seller with respect to the repairs and treatments will be transferred to Buyer at Buyer's expense. If Seller fails to complete any agreed repairs and treatments prior to the Closing Date, Buyer may exercise remedies under Paragraph 15 or extend the Closing Date up to 5 days if necessary for Seller to complete repairs and treatments.

G. ENVIRONMENTAL MATTERS: Buyer is advised that the presence of wetlands, toxic substances, including asbestos and wastes or other environmental hazards or the presence of a threatened or endangered species or its habitat may affect Buyer's intended use of the Property. If Buyer is concerned about these matters, an addendum promulgated by TREC or required by the parties should be used.

H. RESIDENTIAL SERVICE CONTRACTS: Buyer may purchase a residential service contract from a residential service company licensed by TREC. If Buyer purchases a residential service contract, Seller shall reimburse Buyer at closing for the cost of the residential service contract in an amount not exceeding $_____. Buyer should review any residential service contract for the scope of coverage, exclusions and limitations. **The purchase of a residential service contract is optional. Similar coverage may be purchased from various companies authorized to do business in Texas.**

8. BROKERS' FEES: All obligations of the parties for payment of brokers' fees are contained in separate written agreements.

9. CLOSING:
A. The closing of the sale will be on or before _____, 20____, or within 7 days after objections to matters disclosed in the Commitment have been cured, whichever date is later (Closing Date). If either party fails to close the sale by the Closing Date, the non-defaulting party may exercise the remedies contained in Paragraph 15.

B. At closing:
   (1) Seller shall execute and deliver a general warranty deed conveying title to the Property to Buyer and showing no additional exceptions to those permitted in Paragraph 6 and furnish tax statements or certificates showing no delinquent taxes on the Property.
   (2) Buyer shall pay the Sales Price in good funds acceptable to the escrow agent.
   (3) Seller and Buyer shall execute and deliver any notices, statements, certificates, affidavits, releases, loan documents and other documents reasonably required for the closing of the sale and the issuance of the Title Policy.
   (4) There will be no liens, assessments, or security interests against the Property which will not be satisfied out of the sales proceeds unless securing the payment of any loans assumed by Buyer and assumed loans will not be in default.
   (5) If the Property is subject to a residential lease, Seller shall transfer security deposits (as defined under §92.102, Property Code), if any, to Buyer. In such an event, Buyer shall deliver to the tenant a signed statement acknowledging that the Buyer has received the security deposit and is responsible for the return of the security deposit, and specifying the exact dollar amount of the security deposit.

10. POSSESSION:
A. Buyers Possession: Seller shall deliver to Buyer possession of the Property in its present or required condition, ordinary wear and tear excepted: ❏ upon closing and funding ❏ according to a temporary residential lease form promulgated by TREC or other written lease required by the parties. Any possession by Buyer prior to closing or by Seller after closing which is not authorized by a written lease will establish a tenancy at sufferance relationship between the parties. **Consult your insurance agent prior to change of ownership and possession because insurance coverage may be limited or terminated. The absence of a written lease or appropriate insurance coverage may expose the parties to economic loss.**

B. Leases:
   (1) After the Effective Date, Seller may not execute any lease (including but not limited to mineral leases) or convey any interest in the Property without Buyer's written consent.

Initialed for identification by Buyer_____ _____ and Seller _____ _____   TREC NO. 30-11

(2) If the Property is subject to any lease to which Seller is a party, Seller shall deliver to Buyer copies of the lease(s) and any move-in condition form signed by the tenant within 7 days after the Effective Date of the contract.

11. SPECIAL PROVISIONS: (Insert only factual statements and business details applicable to the sale. TREC rules prohibit licensees from adding factual statements or business details for which a contract addendum, lease or other form has been promulgated by TREC for mandatory use.)

12. SETTLEMENT AND OTHER EXPENSES:
 A. The following expenses must be paid at or prior to closing:
   (1) Expenses payable by Seller (Seller's Expenses):
      (a) Releases of existing liens, including prepayment penalties and recording fees; lender, FHA, or VA completion requirements; tax statements or certificates; preparation of deed; one-half of escrow fee; and other expenses payable by Seller under this contract.
      (b) Seller shall also pay an amount not to exceed $ _____ to be applied in the following order: Buyer's Expenses which Buyer is prohibited from paying by FHA, VA, Texas Veterans Land Board or other governmental loan programs, and then to other Buyer's Expenses as allowed by the lender.
   (2) Expenses payable by Buyer (Buyer's Expenses): Appraisal fees; loan application fees; adjusted origination charges; credit reports; preparation of loan documents; interest on the notes from date of disbursement to one month prior to dates of first monthly payments; recording fees; copies of easements and restrictions; loan title policy with endorsements required by lender; loan-related inspection fees; photos; amortization schedules; one-half of escrow fee; all prepaid items, including required premiums for flood and hazard insurance, reserve deposits for insurance, ad valorem taxes and special governmental assessments; final compliance inspection; courier fee; repair inspection; underwriting fee; wire transfer fee; expenses incident to any loan; Private Mortgage Insurance Premium (PMI), VA Loan Funding Fee, or FHA Mortgage Insurance Premium (MIP) as required by the lender; and other expenses payable by Buyer under this contract.
   (3) Except as provided by 12(A)(4) below, Buyer shall pay any and all Association fees or other charges resulting from the transfer of the Property not to exceed $___ and Seller shall pay any excess.
   (4) Buyer shall pay any deposits for reserves required at closing by the Association.
 B. If any expense exceeds an amount expressly stated in this contract for such expense to be paid by a party, that party may terminate this contract unless the other party agrees to pay such excess. Buyer may not pay charges and fees expressly prohibited by FHA, VA, Texas Veterans Land Board or other governmental loan program regulations.

13. PRORATIONS: Taxes for the current year, interest, maintenance fees, regular condominium assessments, dues and rents will be prorated through the Closing Date. The tax proration may be calculated taking into consideration any change in exemptions that will affect the current year's taxes. If taxes for the current year vary from the amount prorated at closing, the parties shall adjust the prorations when tax statements for the current year are available. If taxes are not paid at or prior to closing, Buyer shall pay taxes for the current year. Cash reserves from regular condominium assessments for deferred maintenance or capital improvements established by the Association will not be credited to Seller. Any special condominium assessment due and unpaid at closing will be the obligation of Seller.

14. CASUALTY LOSS: If any part of the Unit which Seller is solely obligated to maintain and repair under the terms of the Declaration is damaged or destroyed by fire or other casualty, Seller shall restore the same to its previous condition as soon as reasonably possible, but in any event by the Closing Date. If Seller fails to do so due to factors beyond Seller's control, Buyer may (a) terminate this contract and the earnest money will be refunded to Buyer, (b) extend the time for performance up to 15 days and the Closing Date will be extended as necessary or (c) accept the Property in its damaged condition with an assignment of insurance proceeds and receive credit from Seller at closing in the amount of the deductible under the insurance policy. If any part of the Common Elements or Limited Common Elements appurtenant to the Unit is damaged or destroyed by fire or other casualty loss, Buyer will have 7 days from receipt of notice of such casualty loss within which to notify Seller in writing that the contract will be terminated unless Buyer receives written confirmation from the Association that the damaged condition will be restored to its previous condition within a reasonable time at no cost to Buyer. Unless Buyer gives such notice within such time, Buyer will be deemed to have accepted the Property without confirmation of such restoration. Seller will have 7 days from the date of receipt of Buyer's notice within which to cause to be delivered to Buyer such confirmation. If written confirmation is not delivered to Buyer as required above, Buyer may terminate this contract and the earnest money will be refunded to Buyer. Seller's obligations under this paragraph are independent of any other obligations of Seller under this contract.

Initialed for identification by Buyer_____ _____ and Seller _____ _____   TREC NO. 30-11

Contract Concerning_____Page 6 of 8 4-28-2014
(Address of Property)

15. **DEFAULT:** If Buyer fails to comply with this contract, Buyer will be in default, and Seller may (a) enforce specific performance, seek such other relief as may be provided by law, or both, or (b) terminate this contract and receive the earnest money as liquidated damages, thereby releasing both parties from this contract. If Seller fails to comply with this contract for any other reason, Seller will be in default and Buyer may (a) enforce specific performance, seek such other relief as may be provided by law, or both, or (b) terminate this contract and receive the earnest money, thereby releasing both parties from this contract.

16. **MEDIATION:** It is the policy of the State of Texas to encourage resolution of disputes through alternative dispute resolution procedures such as mediation. Any dispute between Seller and Buyer related to this contract which is not resolved through informal discussion will be submitted to a mutually acceptable mediation service or provider. The parties to the mediation shall bear the mediation costs equally. This paragraph does not preclude a party from seeking equitable relief from a court of competent jurisdiction.

17. **ATTORNEY'S FEES:** A Buyer, Seller, Listing Broker, Other Broker, or escrow agent who prevails in any legal proceeding related to this contract is entitled to recover reasonable attorney's fees and all costs of such proceeding.

18. **ESCROW:**
    A. ESCROW: The escrow agent is not (i) a party to this contract and does not have liability for the performance or nonperformance of any party to this contract, (ii) liable for interest on the earnest money and (iii) liable for the loss of any earnest money caused by the failure of any financial institution in which the earnest money has been deposited unless the financial institution is acting as escrow agent.
    B. EXPENSES: At closing, the earnest money must be applied first to any cash down payment, then to Buyer's Expenses and any excess refunded to Buyer. If no closing occurs, escrow agent may: (i) require a written release of liability of the escrow agent from all parties, (ii) require payment of unpaid expenses incurred on behalf of a party, and (iii) only deduct from the earnest money the amount of unpaid expenses incurred on behalf of the party receiving the earnest money.
    C. DEMAND: Upon termination of this contract, either party or the escrow agent may send a release of earnest money to each party and the parties shall execute counterparts of the release and deliver same to the escrow agent. If either party fails to execute the release, either party may make a written demand to the escrow agent for the earnest money. If only one party makes written demand for the earnest money, escrow agent shall promptly provide a copy of the demand to the other party. If escrow agent does not receive written objection to the demand from the other party within 15 days, escrow agent may disburse the earnest money to the party making demand reduced by the amount of unpaid expenses incurred on behalf of the party receiving the earnest money and escrow agent may pay the same to the creditors. If escrow agent complies with the provisions of this paragraph, each party hereby releases escrow agent from all adverse claims related to the disbursal of the earnest money.
    D. DAMAGES: Any party who wrongfully fails or refuses to sign a release acceptable to the escrow agent within 7 days of receipt of the request will be liable to the other party for liquidated damages in an amount equal to the sum of: (i) three times the amount of the earnest money; (ii) the earnest money; (iii) reasonable attorney's fees; and (iv) all costs of suit.
    E. NOTICES: Escrow agent's notices will be effective when sent in compliance with Paragraph 21. Notice of objection to the demand will be deemed effective upon receipt by escrow agent.

19. **REPRESENTATIONS:** All covenants, representations and warranties in this contract survive closing. If any representation of Seller in this contract is untrue on the Closing Date, Seller will be in default. Unless expressly prohibited by written agreement, Seller may continue to show the Property and receive, negotiate and accept back up offers.

20. **FEDERAL TAX REQUIREMENTS:** If Seller is a "foreign person," as defined by applicable law, or if Seller fails to deliver an affidavit to Buyer that Seller is not a "foreign person," then Buyer shall withhold from the sales proceeds an amount sufficient to comply with applicable tax law and deliver the same to the Internal Revenue Service together with appropriate tax forms. Internal Revenue Service regulations require filing written reports if currency in excess of specified amounts is received in the transaction.

21. **NOTICES:** All notices from one party to the other must be in writing and are effective when mailed to, hand-delivered at, or transmitted by facsimile or electronic transmission as follows:

To Buyer at: **To Seller at:**

_____   _____

_____   _____

Telephone: ( )_____   Telephone: ( )_____

Facsimile: ( )_____   Facsimile: ( )_____

E-mail: _____   E-mail: _____

Initialed for identification by Buyer_____ _____ and Seller _____ _____   TREC NO. 30-11

Contract Concerning_____Page 7 of 8   4-28-2014
(Address of Property)

22. AGREEMENT OF PARTIES: This contract contains the entire agreement of the parties and cannot be changed except by their written agreement. Addenda which are a part of this contract are (check all applicable boxes):

❑ Third Party Financing Addendum for Credit Approval

❑ Loan Assumption Addendum

❑ Buyer's Temporary Residential Lease

❑ Seller's Temporary Residential Lease

❑ Addendum for Sale of Other Property by Buyer

❑ Addendum for "Back-Up" Contract

❑ Seller Financing Addendum

❑ Addendum for Coastal Area Property

❑ Short Sale Addendum

❑ Addendum for Seller's Disclosure of Information on Lead-based Paint and Lead-based Paint Hazards as Required by Federal Law

❑ Environmental Assessment, Threatened or Endangered Species and Wetlands Addendum

❑ Addendum for Property Located Seaward of the Gulf Intracoastal Waterway

❑ Addendum for Release of Liability on Assumption of FHA, VA, or Conventional Loan Restoration of Seller's Entitlement for VA Guaranteed Loan

❑ Addendum for Property in a Propane Gas System Service Area

❑ Other (list): _____
_____
_____

23. TERMINATION OPTION: For nominal consideration, the receipt of which is hereby acknowledged by Seller, and Buyer's agreement to pay Seller $_____ (Option Fee) within 3 days after the effective date of this contract, Seller grants Buyer the unrestricted right to terminate this contract by giving notice of termination to Seller within _____ days after the effective date of this contract (Option Period).   If no dollar amount is stated as the Option Fee or if Buyer fails to pay the Option Fee to Seller within the time prescribed, this paragraph will not be a part of this contract and Buyer shall not have the unrestricted right to terminate this contract. If Buyer gives notice of termination within the time prescribed, the Option Fee will not be refunded; however, any earnest money will be refunded to Buyer. The Option Fee ❑will ❑will not be credited to the Sales Price at closing. **Time is of the essence for this paragraph and strict compliance with the time for performance is required.**

24. CONSULT AN ATTORNEY BEFORE SIGNING: TREC rules prohibit real estate licensees from giving legal advice. READ THIS CONTRACT CAREFULLY.

Buyer's
Attorney is: _____

_____

Telephone: (____)_____

Facsimile: (____)_____

E-mail: _____

Seller's
Attorney is: _____

_____

Telephone: (____)_____

Facsimile: (____)_____

E-mail: _____

EXECUTED the _____day of _____, 20_____ (EFFECTIVE DATE).
(BROKER: FILL IN THE DATE OF FINAL ACCEPTANCE.)

_____   _____
Buyer   Seller

_____   _____
Buyer   Seller

Initialed for identification by Buyer_____ _____ and Seller _____ _____   TREC NO. 30-11

Contract Concerning_____Page 8 of 8   4-28-2014
(Address of Property)

BROKER INFORMATION
(Print name(s) only. Do not sign)

Other Broker Firm _____ License No.

represents   ☐ Buyer only as Buyer's agent
☐ Seller as Listing Broker's subagent

Name of Associate's Licensed Supervisor   Telephone

Associate's Name   Telephone

Other Broker's Address   Facsimile

City   State   Zip

Associate's Email Address

Listing Broker Firm _____ License No.

represents   ☐ Seller and Buyer as an intermediary
☐ Seller only as Seller's agent

Name of Associate's Licensed Supervisor   Telephone

Listing Associate's Name   Telephone

Listing Broker's Office Address   Facsimile

City   State
Zip

Listing Associate's Email Address

Selling Associate's Name   Telephone

Name of Selling Associate's Licensed Supervisor   Telephone

Selling Associate's Office Address   Facsimile

City   State   Zip

Selling Associate's Email Address

Listing Broker has agreed to pay Other Broker_____of the total sales price when the Listing Broker's fee is received. Escrow agent is authorized and directed to pay other Broker from Listing Broker's fee at closing.

OPTION FEE RECEIPT

Receipt of $_____ (Option Fee) in the form of _____ is acknowledged.

Seller or Listing Broker _____   Date _____

CONTRACT AND EARNEST MONEY RECEIPT

Receipt of ☐Contract and ☐$_____ Earnest Money in the form of _____ is acknowledged.
Escrow Agent: _____   Date: _____

By: _____

Email Address

_____
Address

Telephone (_____) _____

_____
City   State   Zip

Facsimile: (_____) _____

TREC NO. 30-11

PROMULGATED BY THE TEXAS REAL ESTATE COMMISSION (TREC)   12-05-11

LOAN ASSUMPTION ADDENDUM
TO CONTRACT CONCERNING THE PROPERTY AT

_____
(Address of Property)

A. CREDIT DOCUMENTATION. To establish Buyer's creditworthiness, Buyer shall deliver to Seller within_____days after the effective date of this contract ❑ credit report ❑ verification of employment, including salary ❑ verification of funds on deposit in financial institutions ❑ current financial statement and ❑_____
_____.
Buyer hereby authorizes any credit reporting agency to furnish copies of Buyer's credit reports to Seller at Buyer's sole expense.

B. CREDIT APPROVAL. If the credit documentation described in Paragraph A is not delivered within the specified time, Seller may terminate this contract by notice to Buyer within 7 days after expiration of the time for delivery, and the earnest money will be paid to Seller. If the credit documentation is timely delivered, and Seller determines in Seller's sole discretion that Buyer's credit is unacceptable, Seller may terminate this contract by notice to Buyer within 7 days after expiration of the time for delivery and the earnest money will be refunded to Buyer. If Seller does not terminate this contract within the time specified, Seller will be deemed to have approved Buyer's creditworthiness.

C. ASSUMPTION. Buyer's assumption of an existing note includes all obligations imposed by the deed of trust securing the note.
❑ (1) The unpaid principal balance of a first lien promissory note payable to_____
_____which unpaid balance at closing will be $ _____.
The total current monthly payment including principal, interest and any reserve deposits is $ _____. Buyer's initial payment will be the first payment due after closing.

❑ (2) The unpaid principal balance of a second lien promissory note payable to _____
_____which unpaid balance at closing will be $ _____.
The total current monthly payment including principal, interest and any reserve deposits is $ _____. Buyer's initial payment will be the first payment due after closing.

If the unpaid principal balance of any assumed loan as of the Closing Date varies from the loan balance stated above, the ❑ cash payable at closing ❑ Sales Price will be adjusted by the amount of any variance. If the total principal balance of all assumed loans varies in an amount greater than $500 at closing, either party may terminate this contract and the earnest money will be refunded to Buyer unless the other party elects to pay the excess of the variance.

D. LOAN ASSUMPTION TERMS. Buyer may terminate this contract and the earnest money will be refunded to Buyer if the noteholder requires:
(1) payment of an assumption fee in excess of $ _____in C(1) or $ _____in C(2) and Seller declines to pay such excess, or
(2) an increase in the interest rate to more than _____% in C(1) or_____% in C(2), or
(3) any other modification of the loan documents.

E. CONSENT BY NOTEHOLDER. If the noteholder fails to consent to the assumption of the loan, either Seller or Buyer may terminate this contract by notice to the other party and the earnest money will be refunded to the Buyer.

F. SELLER'S LIENS. Unless Seller is released from liability on any assumed note, a vendor's lien and deed of trust to secure assumption will be required. The vendor's lien will automatically be released on delivery of an executed release by noteholder.

_____
(Address of Property)

G. TAX AND INSURANCE ESCROW. If noteholder maintains an escrow account for ad valorem taxes, casualty insurance premiums or mortgage insurance premiums, Seller shall transfer the escrow account to Buyer without any deficiency. Buyer shall reimburse Seller for the amount in the transferred accounts.

NOTICE TO BUYER: If you are concerned about the possibility of future adjustments, monthly payments, interest rates or other terms, do not sign the contract without examining the notes and deeds of trust.

NOTICE TO SELLER: Your liability to pay the notes assumed by Buyer will continue unless you obtain a release of liability from the noteholders. If you are concerned about future liability, you should use the TREC Release of Liability Addendum.

_____   _____
Buyer   Seller

_____   _____
Buyer   Seller

PROMULGATED BY THE TEXAS REAL ESTATE COMMISSION (TREC)   12-05-11

ADDENDUM FOR
"BACK-UP" CONTRACT

TO CONTRACT CONCERNING THE PROPERTY AT

_____
(Address of Property)

A. The contract to which this Addendum is attached (the Back-Up Contract) is binding upon execution by the parties, and the earnest money and any Option Fee must be paid as provided in the Back-Up Contract. The Back-Up Contract is contingent upon the termination of a previous contract (the First Contract) dated _____, 20_____, for the sale of Property. Except as provided by this Addendum, neither party is required to perform under the Back-Up Contract while it is contingent upon the termination of the First Contract.

B. If the First Contract does not terminate on or before _____, 20_____, the Back-Up Contract terminates and the earnest money will be refunded to Buyer. Seller must notify Buyer immediately of the termination of the First Contract. For purposes of performance, the effective date of the Back-Up Contract changes to the date Buyer receives notice of termination of the First Contract (Amended Effective Date).

C. An amendment or modification of the First Contract will not terminate the First Contract.

D. If Buyer has the unrestricted right to terminate the Back-Up Contract, the time for giving notice of termination begins on the effective date of the Back-Up Contract, continues after the Amended Effective Date and ends upon the expiration of Buyer's unrestricted right to terminate the Back-Up Contract.

E. For purposes of this Addendum, time is of the essence. Strict compliance with the times for performance stated herein is required.

_____   _____
Buyer   Seller

_____   _____
Buyer   Seller

TREC No. 11-7

PROMULGATED BY THE TEXAS REAL ESTATE COMMISSION (TREC)

12-05-11

ADDENDUM FOR
COASTAL AREA PROPERTY
(SECTION 33.135, TEXAS NATURAL RESOURCES CODE)

TO CONTRACT CONCERNING THE PROPERTY AT

_____

(Address of Property)

NOTICE REGARDING COASTAL AREA PROPERTY

1. The real property described in and subject to this contract adjoins and shares a common boundary with the tidally influenced submerged lands of the state. The boundary is subject to change and can be determined accurately only by a survey on the ground made by a licensed state land surveyor in accordance with the original grant from the sovereign. The owner of the property described in this contract may gain or lose portions of the tract because of changes in the boundary.

2. The seller, transferor, or grantor has no knowledge of any prior fill as it relates to the property described in and subject to this contract except:_____
_____
_____.

3. State law prohlbits the use, encumbrance, construction, or placing of any structure in, on, or over state-owned submerged lands below the applicable tide line, without proper permission.

4. The purchaser or grantee is hereby advised to seek the advice of an attorney or other qualified person as to the legal nature and effect of the facts set forth in this notice on the property described in and subject to this contract. Information regarding the location of the applicable tide line as to the property described in and subject to this contract may be obtained from the surveying division of the General Land Office in Austin.

_____   _____
Buyer   Seller

_____   _____
Buyer   Seller

PROMULGATED BY THE TEXAS REAL ESTATE COMMISSION (TREC)   12-05-11

ADDENDUM FOR
PROPERTY LOCATED SEAWARD OF THE
GULF INTRACOASTAL WATERWAY
(SECTION 61.025, TEXAS NATURAL RESOURCES CODE)

TO CONTRACT CONCERNING THE PROPERTY AT

_____

(Address of Property)

DISCLOSURE NOTICE CONCERNING LEGAL AND ECONOMIC RISKS OF PURCHASING COASTAL REAL PROPERTY NEAR A BEACH

WARNING: THE FOLLOWING NOTICE OF POTENTIAL RISKS OF ECONOMIC LOSS TO YOU AS THE PURCHASER OF COASTAL REAL PROPERTY IS REQUIRED BY STATE LAW.

- READ THIS NOTICE CAREFULLY. DO NOT SIGN THIS CONTRACT UNTIL YOU FULLY UNDERSTAND THE RISKS YOU ARE ASSUMING.
- BY PURCHASING THIS PROPERTY, YOU MAY BE ASSUMING ECONOMIC RISKS OVER AND ABOVE THE RISKS INVOLVED IN PURCHASING INLAND REAL PROPERTY.
- IF YOU OWN A STRUCTURE LOCATED ON COASTAL REAL PROPERTY NEAR A GULF COAST BEACH, IT MAY COME TO BE LOCATED ON THE PUBLIC BEACH BECAUSE OF COASTAL EROSION AND STORM EVENTS.
- AS THE OWNER OF A STRUCTURE LOCATED ON THE PUBLIC BEACH, YOU COULD BE SUED BY THE STATE OF TEXAS AND ORDERED TO REMOVE THE STRUCTURE.
- THE COSTS OF REMOVING A STRUCTURE FROM THE PUBLIC BEACH AND ANY OTHER ECONOMIC LOSS INCURRED BECAUSE OF A REMOVAL ORDER WOULD BE SOLELY YOUR RESPONSIBILITY.

The real property described in this contract is located seaward of the Gulf Intracoastal Waterway to its southernmost point and then seaward of the longitudinal line also known as 97 degrees, 12', 19" which runs southerly to the international boundary from the intersection of the centerline of the Gulf Intracoastal Waterway and the Brownsville Ship Channel. If the property is in close proximity to a beach fronting the Gulf of Mexico, the purchaser is hereby advised that the public has acquired a right of use or easement to or over the area of any public beach by prescription, dedication, or presumption, or has retained a right by virtue of continuous right in the public since time immemorial, as recognized in law and custom.

The extreme seaward boundary of natural vegetation that spreads continuously inland customarily marks the landward boundary of the public easement. If there is no clearly marked natural vegetation line, the landward boundary of the easement is as provided by Sections 61.016 and 61.017, Natural Resources Code.

Much of the Gulf of Mexico coastline is eroding at rates of more than five feet per year. Erosion rates for all Texas Gulf property subject to the open beaches act are available from the Texas General Land Office.

State law prohibits any obstruction, barrier, restraint, or interference with the use of the public easement, including the placement of structures seaward of the landward boundary of the easement. OWNERS OF STRUCTURES ERECTED SEAWARD OF THE VEGETATION LINE (OR OTHER APPLICABLE EASEMENT BOUNDARY) OR THAT BECOME SEAWARD OF THE VEGETATION LINE AS A RESULT OF PROCESSES SUCH AS SHORELINE EROSION ARE SUBJECT TO A LAWSUIT BY THE STATE OF TEXAS TO REMOVE THE STRUCTURES.

The purchaser is hereby notified that the purchaser should: (1) determine the rate of shoreline erosion in the vicinity of the real property; and (2) seek the advice of an attorney or other qualified person before executing this contract or instrument of conveyance as to the relevance of these statutes and facts to the value of the property the purchaser is hereby purchasing or contracting to purchase.

_____   _____
Buyer   Seller

_____   _____
Buyer   Seller

TREC No. 34-4

PROMULGATED BY THE TEXAS REAL ESTATE COMMISSION (TREC)   12-05-11

**EQUAL HOUSING
OPPORTUNITY**

ADDENDUM FOR
RELEASE OF LIABILITY ON ASSUMED LOAN
AND/OR RESTORATION OF SELLER'S VA ENTITLEMENT

TO CONTRACT CONCERNING THE PROPERTY AT

_____
(Address of Property)

❑ **A. RELEASE OF SELLER'S LIABILITY ON LOAN TO BE ASSUMED:**

Within _____ days after the effective date of this contract Seller and Buyer shall apply for release of Seller's liability from (a) any conventional lender, (b) VA and any lender whose loan has been guaranteed by VA, or (c) FHA and any lender whose loan has been insured by FHA. Seller and Buyer shall furnish all required information and documents. If any release of liability has not been approved by the Closing Date: (check one box only)

❑ (1) This contract will terminate and the earnest money will be refunded to Buyer.

❑ (2) Failure to obtain release approval will not delay closing.

❑ **B. RESTORATION OF SELLER'S ENTITLEMENT FOR VA LOAN:**

Within _____ days after the effective date of this contract Seller and Buyer shall apply for restoration of Seller's VA entitlement and shall furnish all information and documents required by VA. If restoration has not been approved by the Closing Date: (check one box only)

❑ (1) This contract will terminate and the earnest money will be refunded to Buyer.

❑ (2) Failure to obtain restoration approval will not delay closing.

NOTICE: VA will not restore Seller's VA entitlement unless Buyer: (a) is a veteran, (b) has sufficient unused VA entitlement and (c) is otherwise qualified. If Seller desires restoration of VA entitlement, paragraphs A and B should be used.

Seller shall pay the cost of securing the release and restoration.

Seller's deed will contain any loan assumption clause required by FHA, VA or any lender.

_____   _____
Buyer   Seller

_____   _____
Buyer   Seller

TREC No. 12-3

PROMULGATED BY THE TEXAS REAL ESTATE COMMISSION (TREC)   4-28-2014
NOTICE: Not For Use Where Seller Owns Fee Simple Title To Land Beneath Unit
RESIDENTIAL CONDOMINIUM CONTRACT (RESALE)

1. PARTIES: The parties to this contract are <u>Paul M Kramer and wife, Sarah S Kramer</u>(Seller) and
<u>Brian C Sweeney and wife, Ellie T Sweeney</u> (Buyer). Seller agrees to sell and convey to Buyer and Buyer agrees to buy from Seller the Property defined below.

2. PROPERTY AND CONDOMINIUM DOCUMENTS:

A. The Condominium Unit, improvements and accessories described below are collectively referred to as the "Property".

   (1) CONDOMINIUM UNIT: Unit <u>623</u>, in Building <u>B</u>, of <u>Freedom Flats, Phase II</u>, a condominium project, located at
<u>1215 Market St. Apartment 623</u>

   (address/zip code), City of <u>Corpus Christi</u>, County of <u>Nueces County</u>
Texas, described in the Condominium Declaration and Plat and any amendments thereto of record in said County; together with such Unit's undivided interest in the Common Elements designated by the Declaration, including those areas reserved as Limited Common Elements appurtenant to the Unit and such other rights to use the Common Elements which have been specifically assigned to the Unit in any other manner. Parking areas assigned to the Unit are: <u>1654 and 1658</u>.

   (2) IMPROVEMENTS: All fixtures and improvements attached to the above described real property including without limitation, the following **permanently installed and built-in items**, if any: all equipment and appliances, valances, screens, shutters, awnings, wall-to-wall carpeting, mirrors, ceiling fans, attic fans, mail boxes, television antennas, mounts and brackets for televisions and speakers, heating and air conditioning units, security and fire detection equipment, wiring, plumbing and lighting fixtures, chandeliers, shrubbery, landscaping, outdoor cooking equipment, and all other property owned by Seller and attached to the above described Condominium Unit.

   (3) ACCESSORIES: The following described related accessories, if any: window air conditioning units, stove, fireplace screens, curtains and rods, blinds, window shades, draperies and rods, door keys, mailbox keys, above ground pool, swimming pool equipment and maintenance accessories, artificial fireplace logs, and controls for: (i) garage doors, (ii) entry gates, and (iii) other improvements and accessories.

   (4) EXCLUSIONS: The following improvements and accessories will be retained by Seller and must be removed prior to delivery of possession: <u>N/A</u>.

B. The Declaration, Bylaws and any Rules of the Association are called "Documents". (Check one box only):

☒ (1) <u>Buyer has received a copy of the Documents. Buyer is advised to read the Documents before signing the contract.</u>

☐ (2) Buyer has not received a copy of the Documents. Seller shall deliver the Documents to Buyer within <u>N/A</u> days after the effective date of the contract. Buyer may cancel the contract before the sixth day after Buyer receives the Documents by hand-delivering or mailing written notice of cancellation to Seller by certified United States mail, return receipt requested. If Buyer cancels the contract pursuant to this paragraph, the contract will terminate and the earnest money will be refunded to Buyer.

C. The Resale Certificate from the condominium owners association (the Association) is called the "Certificate". The Certificate must be in a form promulgated by TREC or required by the parties. The Certificate must have been prepared no more than 3 months before the date it is delivered to Buyer and must contain at a minimum the information required by Section 82.157, Texas Property Code.

   (Check one box only):

☒ (1) Buyer has received the Certificate.

☐ (2) Buyer has not received the Certificate. Seller shall deliver the Certificate to Buyer within <u>N/A</u> days after the effective date of the contract. Buyer may cancel the contract before the sixth day after the date Buyer receives the Certificate by hand-delivering or mailing written notice of cancellation to Seller by certified United States mail, return receipt requested. If Buyer cancels the contract pursuant to this paragraph, the contract will terminate and the earnest money will be refunded to Buyer.

☐ (3) Buyer has received Seller's affidavit that Seller requested information from the Association concerning its financial condition as required by the Texas Property Code, and that the Association did not provide a Certificate or information required in the Certificate. Buyer and Seller agree to waive the requirement to furnish the Certificate.

Initialed for identification by Buyer_____ _____ and Seller _____ _____   TREC NO. 30-11

Contract Concerning 1215 Market St. Apartment 623 Corpus Christi_____ Page 2 of 8 4-28-2014
(Address of Property)

3. SALES PRICE:
A. Cash portion of Sales Price payable by Buyer at closing ....$ 103,192.00

B. Sum of all financing described below (excluding any loan funding
fee or mortgage insurance premium)..$ 265,008.00
C. Sales Price (Sum of A and B) ....$ 368,200.00

4. FINANCING (Not for use with reverse mortgage financing): The portion of Sales Price not payable in cash will be paid as follows: (Check applicable boxes below)
☐A. THIRD PARTY FINANCING: One or more third party mortgage loans in the total amount of
$ N/A (excluding any loan funding fee or mortgage insurance premium).
(1) Property Approval: If the Property does not satisfy the lenders' underwriting requirements for the loan(s), (including, but not limited to appraisal, insurability and lender required repairs), Buyer may terminate this contract by giving notice to Seller prior to closing and the earnest money will be refunded to Buyer.
(2) Credit Approval: (Check one box only)
☐ (a) This contract is subject to Buyer being approved for the financing described in the attached Third Party Financing Addendum for Credit Approval.
☐ (b) This contract is not subject to Buyer being approved for financing and does not involve FHA or VA financing.
☒B. ASSUMPTION: The assumption of the unpaid principal balance of one or more promissory notes described in the attached TREC Loan Assumption Addendum.
☐C. SELLER FINANCING: A promissory note from Buyer to Seller of $ N/A , secured by vendor's and deed of trust liens, and containing the terms and conditions described in the attached TREC Seller Financing Addendum. If an owner policy of title insurance is furnished, Buyer shall furnish Seller with a mortgagee policy of title insurance.

5. EARNEST MONEY: Upon execution of this contract by all parties, Buyer shall deposit $ 2,000.00 as earnest money with Buyer's Choice Title Co , as escrow agent, at 104 3rd Ave, Corpus Christi, TX (address). Buyer shall deposit additional earnest money of $ N/A with escrow agent within N/A days after the effective date of this contract. If Buyer fails to deposit the earnest money as required by this contract, Buyer will be in default.

6. TITLE POLICY:
A. TITLE POLICY: Seller shall furnish to Buyer at ☐Seller's ☒Buyer's expense an owner policy of title insurance (Title Policy) issued by Buyer's Choice Title Co (Title Company) in the amount of the Sales Price, dated at or after closing, insuring Buyer against loss under the provisions of the Title Policy, subject to the promulgated exclusions (including existing building and zoning ordinances) and the following exceptions:
(1) Restrictive covenants common to the platted subdivision in which the Property is located.
(2) The standard printed exception for standby fees, taxes and assessments.
(3) Liens created as part of the financing described in Paragraph 4.
(4) Terms and provisions of the Documents including the assessments and platted easements.
(5) Reservations or exceptions otherwise permitted by this contract or as may be approved by Buyer in writing.
(6) The standard printed exception as to marital rights.
(7) The standard printed exception as to waters, tidelands, beaches, streams, and related matters.
(8) The standard printed exception as to discrepancies, conflicts, shortages in area or boundary lines, encroachments or protrusions, or overlapping improvements.
B. COMMITMENT: Within 20 days after the Title Company receives a copy of this contract, Seller shall furnish to Buyer a commitment for title insurance (Commitment) and, at Buyer's expense, legible copies of restrictive covenants and documents evidencing exceptions in the Commitment (Exception Documents) other than the standard printed exceptions. Seller authorizes the Title Company to deliver the Commitment and Exception Documents to Buyer at Buyer's address shown in Paragraph 21. If the Commitment and Exception Documents are not delivered to Buyer within the specified time, the time for delivery will be automatically extended up to 15 days or 3 days before the Closing Date, whichever is earlier. If, due to factors beyond Seller's control, the Commitment and Exception Documents are not delivered within the time required, Buyer may terminate this contract and the earnest money will be refunded to Buyer.
C. OBJECTIONS: Buyer may object in writing to defects, exceptions, or encumbrances to title: disclosed in the Commitment other than items 6A(1) through (8) above; or which prohibit the following use or activity: N/A _____.
Buyer must object the earlier of (i) the Closing Date or (ii) 3 days after Buyer receives the Commitment and Exception Documents. Buyer's failure to object within the time allowed will constitute a waiver of Buyer's right to object; except that the requirements in

Schedule C of the Commitment are not waived by Buyer. Provided Seller is not obligated to

Initialed for identification by Buyer_____ _____ and Seller _____ _____   TREC NO. 30-11

Contract Concerning 1215 Market St. Apartment 623 Corpus Christi_____ Page 3 of 8 4-28-2014
                        (Address of Property)

incur any expense, Seller shall cure the timely objections of Buyer or any third party lender within 15 days after Seller receives the objections and the Closing Date will be extended as necessary. If objections are not cured within such 15 day period, this contract will terminate and the earnest money will be refunded to Buyer unless Buyer waives the objections.

D. TITLE NOTICES:
(1) ABSTRACT OR TITLE POLICY: Broker advises Buyer to have an abstract of title covering the Property examined by an attorney of Buyer's selection, or Buyer should be furnished with or obtain a Title Policy. If a Title Policy is furnished, the Commitment should be promptly reviewed by an attorney of Buyer's choice due to the time limitations on Buyer's right to object.
(2) STATUTORY TAX DISTRICTS: If the Property is situated in a utility or other statutorily created district providing water, sewer, drainage, or flood control facilities and services, Chapter 49, Texas Water Code, requires Seller to deliver and Buyer to sign the statutory notice relating to the tax rate, bonded indebtedness, or standby fee of the district prior to final execution of this contract.
(3) TIDE WATERS: If the Property abuts the tidally influenced waters of the state, §33.135, Texas Natural Resources Code, requires a notice regarding coastal area property to be included in the contract. An addendum containing the notice promulgated by TREC or required by the parties must be used.
(4) ANNEXATION: If the Property is located outside the limits of a municipality, Seller notifies Buyer under §5.011, Texas Property Code, that the Property may now or later be included in the extraterritorial jurisdiction of a municipality and may now or later be subject to annexation by the municipality. Each municipality maintains a map that depicts its boundaries and extraterritorial jurisdiction. To determine if the Property is located within a municipality's extraterritorial jurisdiction or is likely to be located within a municipality's extraterritorial jurisdiction, contact all municipalities located in the general proximity of the Property for further information.
(5) PROPERTY LOCATED IN A CERTIFICATED SERVICE AREA OF A UTILITY SERVICE PROVIDER: Notice required by §13.257, Water Code: The real property, described in Paragraph 2, that you are about to purchase may be located in a certificated water or sewer service area, which is authorized by law to provide water or sewer service to the properties in the certificated area. If your property is located in a certificated area there may be special costs or charges that you will be required to pay before you can receive water or sewer service. There may be a period required to construct lines or other facilities necessary to provide water or sewer service to your property. You are advised to determine if the property is in a certificated area and contact the utility service provider to determine the cost that you will be required to pay and the period, if any, that is required to provide water or sewer service to your property. The undersigned Buyer hereby acknowledges receipt of the foregoing notice at or before the execution of a binding contract for the purchase of the real property described in Paragraph 2 or at closing of purchase of the real property.
(6) TRANSFER FEES: If the Property is subject to a private transfer fee obligation, §5.205, Property Code, requires Seller to notify Buyer as follows: The private transfer fee obligation may be governed by Chapter 5, Subchapter G of the Texas Property Code.
(7) PROPANE GAS SYSTEM SERVICE AREA: If the Property is located in a propane gas system service area owned by a distribution system retailer, Seller must give Buyer written notice as required by §141.010, Texas Utilities Code. An addendum containing the notice approved by TREC or required by the parties should be used.

7. PROPERTY CONDITION:
A. ACCESS, INSPECTIONS AND UTILITIES: Seller shall permit Buyer and Buyer's agents access to the Property at reasonable times. Buyer may have the Property inspected by inspectors selected by Buyer and licensed by TREC or otherwise permitted by law to make inspections. Seller at Seller's expense shall immediately cause existing utilities to be turned on and shall keep the utilities on during the time this contract is in effect .
B. SELLER'S DISCLOSURE NOTICE PURSUANT TO §5.008, TEXAS PROPERTY CODE (Notice): (Check one box only)
☒ (1) Buyer has received the Notice.
☐ (2) Buyer has not received the Notice. Within N/A days after the effective date of this contract, Seller shall deliver the Notice to Buyer. If Buyer does not receive the Notice, Buyer may terminate this contract at any time prior to the closing and the earnest money will be refunded to Buyer. If Seller delivers the Notice, Buyer may terminate this contract for any reason within 7 days after Buyer receives the Notice or prior to the closing, whichever first occurs, and the earnest money will be refunded to Buyer.
☐ (3) The Texas Property Code does not require this Seller to furnish the Notice.
C. SELLER'S DISCLOSURE OF LEAD-BASED PAINT AND LEAD-BASED PAINT HAZARDS is required by Federal law for a residential dwelling constructed prior to 1978.
D. ACCEPTANCE OF PROPERTY CONDITION: "As Is" means the present condition of the Property with any and all defects and without warranty except for the warranties of title and the warranties in this contract. Buyer's agreement to accept the Property As Is under Paragraph 7D(1) or (2) does not preclude Buyer from inspecting the Property under Paragraph 7A, from negotiating repairs or treatments in a subsequent amendment, or from terminating this contract during the Option Period, if any.

Initialed for identification by Buyer_____ _____ and Seller _____ _____   TREC NO. 30-11

Contract Concerning___1215 Market St. Apartment 623 Corpus Christi_____Page 4 of 8   4-28-2014
(Address of Property)

(Check one box only)

☐ (1) Buyer accepts the Property As Is.

☒ (2) Buyer accepts the Property As Is provided Seller, at Seller's expense, shall complete the following specific repairs and treatments: <u>replace garbage disposal and bath faucet</u> (Do not insert general phrases, such as "subject to inspections," that do not identify specific repairs and treatments.)

E. LENDER REQUIRED REPAIRS AND TREATMENTS: Unless otherwise agreed in writing, neither party is obligated to pay for lender required repairs, which includes treatment for wood destroying insects. If the parties do not agree to pay for the lender required repairs or treatments, this contract will terminate and the earnest money will be refunded to Buyer. If the cost of lender required repairs and treatments exceeds 5% of the Sales Price, Buyer may terminate this contract and the earnest money will be refunded to Buyer.

F. COMPLETION OF REPAIRS AND TREATMENTS: Unless otherwise agreed in writing: (i) Seller shall complete all agreed repairs and treatments prior to the Closing Date; and (ii) all required permits must be obtained, and repairs and treatments must be performed by persons who are licensed to provide such repairs or treatments or, if no license is required by law, are commercially engaged in the trade of providing such repairs or treatments. At Buyer's election, any transferable warranties received by Seller with respect to the repairs and treatments will be transferred to Buyer at Buyer's expense. If Seller fails to complete any agreed repairs and treatments prior to the Closing Date, Buyer may exercise remedies under Paragraph 15 or extend the Closing Date up to 5 days if necessary for Seller to complete repairs and treatments.

G. ENVIRONMENTAL MATTERS: Buyer is advised that the presence of wetlands, toxic substances, including asbestos and wastes or other environmental hazards or the presence of a threatened or endangered species or its habitat may affect Buyer's intended use of the Property. If Buyer is concerned about these matters, an addendum promulgated by TREC or required by the parties should be used.

H. RESIDENTIAL SERVICE CONTRACTS: Buyer may purchase a residential service contract from a residential service company licensed by TREC. If Buyer purchases a residential service contract, Seller shall reimburse Buyer at closing for the cost of the residential service contract in an amount not exceeding $<u> N/A   </u>. Buyer should review any residential service contract for the scope of coverage, exclusions and limitations. **The purchase of a residential service contract is optional. Similar coverage may be purchased from various companies authorized to do business in Texas.**

8. BROKERS' FEES: All obligations of the parties for payment of brokers' fees are contained in separate written agreements.

9. CLOSING:

A. The closing of the sale will be on or before <u> June 16   </u>, 20<u>xx </u>, or within 7 days after objections to matters disclosed in the Commitment have been cured, whichever date is later (Closing Date). If either party fails to close the sale by the Closing Date, the non-defaulting party may exercise the remedies contained in Paragraph 15.

B. At closing:

(1) Seller shall execute and deliver a general warranty deed conveying title to the Property to Buyer and showing no additional exceptions to those permitted in Paragraph 6 and furnish tax statements or certificates showing no delinquent taxes on the Property.

(2) Buyer shall pay the Sales Price in good funds acceptable to the escrow agent.

(3) Seller and Buyer shall execute and deliver any notices, statements, certificates, affidavits, releases, loan documents and other documents reasonably required for the closing of the sale and the issuance of the Title Policy.

(4) There will be no liens, assessments, or security interests against the Property which will not be satisfied out of the sales proceeds unless securing the payment of any loans assumed by Buyer and assumed loans will not be in default.

(5) If the Property is subject to a residential lease, Seller shall transfer security deposits (as defined under §92.102, Property Code), if any, to Buyer. In such an event, Buyer shall deliver to the tenant a signed statement acknowledging that the Buyer has received the security deposit and is responsible for the return of the security deposit, and specifying the exact dollar amount of the security deposit.

10. POSSESSION:

A. Buyers Possession: Seller shall deliver to Buyer possession of the Property in its present or required condition, ordinary wear and tear excepted: ☒ upon closing and funding ☐ according to a temporary residential lease form promulgated by TREC or other written lease required by the parties. Any possession by Buyer prior to closing or by Seller after closing which is not authorized by a written lease will establish a tenancy at sufferance relationship between the parties. **Consult your insurance agent prior to change of ownership and possession because insurance coverage may be limited or terminated. The absence of a written lease or appropriate insurance coverage may expose the parties to economic loss.**

B. Leases:

(1) After the Effective Date, Seller may not execute any lease (including but not limited to mineral leases) or convey any interest in the Property without Buyer's written consent.

Initialed for identification by Buyer_____ _____ and Seller _____ _____   TREC NO. 30-11

Contract Concerning___1215 Market St. Apartment 623 Corpus Christi_____Page 5 of 8   4-28-2014
(Address of Property)

(2) If the Property is subject to any lease to which Seller is a party, Seller shall deliver to Buyer copies of the lease(s) and any move-in condition form signed by the tenant within 7 days after the Effective Date of the contract.

11. SPECIAL PROVISIONS: (Insert only factual statements and business details applicable to the sale. TREC rules prohibit licensees from adding factual statements or business details for which a contract addendum, lease or other form has been promulgated by TREC for mandatory use.)

Buyer request Seller furnish them all closing documents at least 48 hours prior to closing.

Seller will deliver a copy of the note and deed of trust to buyer within 3 days of the effective date

12. SETTLEMENT AND OTHER EXPENSES:
  A. The following expenses must be paid at or prior to closing:
    (1) Expenses payable by Seller (Seller's Expenses):
        (a) Releases of existing liens, including prepayment penalties and recording fees; lender, FHA, or VA completion requirements; tax statements or certificates; preparation of deed; one-half of escrow fee; and other expenses payable by Seller under this contract.
        (b) Seller shall also pay an amount not to exceed $ _N/A_____ to be applied in the following order: Buyer's Expenses which Buyer is prohibited from paying by FHA, VA, Texas Veterans Land Board or other governmental loan programs, and then to other Buyer's Expenses as allowed by the lender.
    (2) Expenses payable by Buyer (Buyer's Expenses): Appraisal fees; loan application fees; adjusted origination charges; credit reports; preparation of loan documents; interest on the notes from date of disbursement to one month prior to dates of first monthly payments; recording fees; copies of easements and restrictions; loan title policy with endorsements required by lender; loan-related inspection fees; photos; amortization schedules; one-half of escrow fee; all prepaid items, including required premiums for flood and hazard insurance, reserve deposits for insurance, ad valorem taxes and special governmental assessments; final compliance inspection; courier fee; repair inspection; underwriting fee; wire transfer fee; expenses incident to any loan; Private Mortgage Insurance Premium (PMI), VA Loan Funding Fee, or FHA Mortgage Insurance Premium (MIP) as required by the lender; and other expenses payable by Buyer under this contract.
    (3) Except as provided by 12(A)(4) below, Buyer shall pay any and all Association fees or other charges resulting from the transfer of the Property not to exceed $N/Aand   Seller shall pay any excess.
    (4) Buyer shall pay any deposits for reserves required at closing by the Association.
  B. If any expense exceeds an amount expressly stated in this contract for such expense to be paid by a party, that party may terminate this contract unless the other party agrees to pay such excess. Buyer may not pay charges and fees expressly prohibited by FHA, VA, Texas Veterans Land Board or other governmental loan program regulations.

13. PRORATIONS: Taxes for the current year, interest, maintenance fees, regular condominium assessments, dues and rents will be prorated through the Closing Date. The tax proration may be calculated taking into consideration any change in exemptions that will affect the current year's taxes. If taxes for the current year vary from the amount prorated at closing, the parties shall adjust the prorations when tax statements for the current year are available. If taxes are not paid at or prior to closing, Buyer shall pay taxes for the current year. Cash reserves from regular condominium assessments for deferred maintenance or capital improvements established by the Association will not be credited to Seller. Any special condominium assessment due and unpaid at closing will be the obligation of Seller.

14. CASUALTY LOSS: If any part of the Unit which Seller is solely obligated to maintain and repair under the terms of the Declaration is damaged or destroyed by fire or other casualty, Seller shall restore the same to its previous condition as soon as reasonably possible, but in any event by the Closing Date. If Seller fails to do so due to factors beyond Seller's control, Buyer may (a) terminate this contract and the earnest money will be refunded to Buyer, (b) extend the time for performance up to 15 days and the Closing Date will be extended as necessary or (c) accept the Property in its damaged condition with an assignment of insurance proceeds and receive credit from Seller at closing in the amount of the deductible under the insurance policy. If any part of the Common Elements or Limited Common Elements appurtenant to the Unit is damaged or destroyed by fire or other casualty loss, Buyer will have 7 days from receipt of notice of such casualty loss within which to notify Seller in writing that the contract will be terminated unless Buyer receives written confirmation from the Association that the damaged condition will be restored to its previous condition within a reasonable time at no cost to Buyer. Unless Buyer gives such notice within such time, Buyer will be deemed to have accepted the Property without confirmation of such restoration. Seller will have 7 days from the date of receipt of Buyer's notice within which to cause to be delivered to Buyer such confirmation. If written confirmation is not delivered to Buyer as required above, Buyer may terminate this contract and the earnest money will be refunded to Buyer. Seller's obligations under this paragraph are independent of any other obligations of Seller under this contract.

Contract Concerning __1215 Market St. Apartment 623 Corpus Christi__ Page 6 of 8 4-28-2014
(Address of Property)

15. **DEFAULT:** If Buyer fails to comply with this contract, Buyer will be in default, and Seller may (a) enforce specific performance, seek such other relief as may be provided by law, or both, or (b) terminate this contract and receive the earnest money as liquidated damages, thereby releasing both parties from this contract. If Seller fails to comply with this contract for any other reason, Seller will be in default and Buyer may (a) enforce specific performance, seek such other relief as may be provided by law, or both, or (b) terminate this contract and receive the earnest money, thereby releasing both parties from this contract.

16. **MEDIATION:** It is the policy of the State of Texas to encourage resolution of disputes through alternative dispute resolution procedures such as mediation. Any dispute between Seller and Buyer related to this contract which is not resolved through informal discussion will be submitted to a mutually acceptable mediation service or provider. The parties to the mediation shall bear the mediation costs equally. This paragraph does not preclude a party from seeking equitable relief from a court of competent jurisdiction.

17. **ATTORNEY'S FEES:** A Buyer, Seller, Listing Broker, Other Broker, or escrow agent who prevails in any legal proceeding related to this contract is entitled to recover reasonable attorney's fees and all costs of such proceeding.

18. **ESCROW:**
    A. ESCROW: The escrow agent is not (i) a party to this contract and does not have liability for the performance or nonperformance of any party to this contract, (ii) liable for interest on the earnest money and (iii) liable for the loss of any earnest money caused by the failure of any financial institution in which the earnest money has been deposited unless the financial institution is acting as escrow agent.
    B. EXPENSES: At closing, the earnest money must be applied first to any cash down payment, then to Buyer's Expenses and any excess refunded to Buyer. If no closing occurs, escrow agent may: (i) require a written release of liability of the escrow agent from all parties, (ii) require payment of unpaid expenses incurred on behalf of a party, and (iii) only deduct from the earnest money the amount of unpaid expenses incurred on behalf of the party receiving the earnest money.
    C. DEMAND: Upon termination of this contract, either party or the escrow agent may send a release of earnest money to each party and the parties shall execute counterparts of the release and deliver same to the escrow agent. If either party fails to execute the release, either party may make a written demand to the escrow agent for the earnest money. If only one party makes written demand for the earnest money, escrow agent shall promptly provide a copy of the demand to the other party. If escrow agent does not receive written objection to the demand from the other party within 15 days, escrow agent may disburse the earnest money to the party making demand reduced by the amount of unpaid expenses incurred on behalf of the party receiving the earnest money and escrow agent may pay the same to the creditors. If escrow agent complies with the provisions of this paragraph, each party hereby releases escrow agent from all adverse claims related to the disbursal of the earnest money.
    D. DAMAGES: Any party who wrongfully fails or refuses to sign a release acceptable to the escrow agent within 7 days of receipt of the request will be liable to the other party for liquidated damages in an amount equal to the sum of: (i) three times the amount of the earnest money; (ii) the earnest money; (iii) reasonable attorney's fees; and (iv) all costs of suit.
    E. NOTICES: Escrow agent's notices will be effective when sent in compliance with Paragraph 21. Notice of objection to the demand will be deemed effective upon receipt by escrow agent.

19. **REPRESENTATIONS:** All covenants, representations and warranties in this contract survive closing. If any representation of Seller in this contract is untrue on the Closing Date, Seller will be in default. Unless expressly prohibited by written agreement, Seller may continue to show the Property and receive, negotiate and accept back up offers.

20. **FEDERAL TAX REQUIREMENTS:** If Seller is a "foreign person," as defined by applicable law, or if Seller fails to deliver an affidavit to Buyer that Seller is not a "foreign person," then Buyer shall withhold from the sales proceeds an amount sufficient to comply with applicable tax law and deliver the same to the Internal Revenue Service together with appropriate tax forms. Internal Revenue Service regulations require filing written reports if currency in excess of specified amounts is received in the transaction.

21. **NOTICES:** All notices from one party to the other must be in writing and are effective when mailed to, hand-delivered at, or transmitted by facsimile or electronic transmission as follows:

To Buyer at:	**To Seller at:**
1410 Texas Ave	1215 Market St
Galveston, Tx	Corpus Christi, TX
Telephone: (734) 812-9015	Telephone: (813) 915-4765
Facsimile: ( )	Facsimile: (813) 915-4766
E-mail: brian@sweeneycorp.com	E-mail: N/A

Initialed for identification by Buyer_____ _____ and Seller _____ _____   TREC NO. 30-11

Contract Concerning ___1215 Market St. Apartment 623 Corpus Christi___ Page 7 of 8   4-28-2014
(Address of Property)

22. **AGREEMENT OF PARTIES:** This contract contains the entire agreement of the parties and cannot be changed except by their written agreement. Addenda which are a part of this contract are (check all applicable boxes):

☐ Third Party Financing Addendum for Credit Approval

☒ Loan Assumption Addendum

☐ Buyer's Temporary Residential Lease

☐ Seller's Temporary Residential Lease

☐ Addendum for Sale of Other Property by Buyer

☒ Addendum for "Back-Up" Contract

☐ Seller Financing Addendum

☒ Addendum for Coastal Area Property

☐ Short Sale Addendum

☐ Addendum for Seller's Disclosure of Information on Lead-based Paint and Lead-based Paint Hazards as Required by Federal Law

☐ Environmental Assessment, Threatened or Endangered Species and Wetlands Addendum

☒ Addendum for Property Located Seaward of the Gulf Intracoastal Waterway

☒ Addendum for Release of Liability on Assumption of FHA, VA, or Conventional Loan Restoration of Seller's Entitlement for VA Guaranteed Loan

☐ Addendum for Property in a Propane Gas System Service Area

☐ Other (list): _____

_____

_____

23. **TERMINATION OPTION:** For nominal consideration, the receipt of which is hereby acknowledged by Seller, and Buyer's agreement to pay Seller $ _250.00_ (Option Fee) within 3 days after the effective date of this contract, Seller grants Buyer the unrestricted right to terminate this contract by giving notice of termination to Seller within __7__ days after the effective date of this contract (Option Period). If no dollar amount is stated as the Option Fee or if Buyer fails to pay the Option Fee to Seller within the time prescribed, this paragraph will not be a part of this contract and Buyer shall not have the unrestricted right to terminate this contract. If Buyer gives notice of termination within the time prescribed, the Option Fee will not be refunded; however, any earnest money will be refunded to Buyer. The Option Fee ☒will ☐will not be credited to the Sales Price at closing. **Time is of the essence for this paragraph and strict compliance with the time for performance is required.**

24. **CONSULT AN ATTORNEY BEFORE SIGNING:** TREC rules prohibit real estate licensees from giving legal advice. READ THIS CONTRACT CAREFULLY.

Buyer's
Attorney is: _____

_____

Telephone: ( )_____

Facsimile: ( )_____

E-mail: _____

Seller's
Attorney is: _Michael Holmes_____

1009 Baker Street, Corpus Christi

Telephone: ( )   N/A_____

Facsimile: ( )   N/A_____

E-mail: _Michael.holmes@attorney.com_

EXECUTED the _____ day of ___May 15_____, 20_XX_ (EFFECTIVE DATE).
(BROKER: FILL IN THE DATE OF FINAL ACCEPTANCE.)

Buyer _Brian C Sweeney and Wife_

Buyer _Ellie T Sweeney_

Seller _Paul M Kramer and Wife_

Seller _Sarah S Kramer_

Initialed for identification by Buyer_____ _____ and Seller _____ _____   TREC NO. 30-11

Contract Concerning   1215 Market St. Apartment 623 Corpus Christi   Page 8 of 8 4-28-2014
                              (Address of Property)

BROKER INFORMATION
(Print name(s) only. Do not sign)

Downhome Realty	00000000	Skyline Realty	00000000
Other Broker Firm	License	Listing Broker Firm	License
No.		No.	

represents ☐ Buyer only as Buyer's agent   represents ☐ Seller and Buyer as an intermediary

☒ Seller as Listing Broker's subagent   ☒ Seller only as Seller's agent

Candy Criss, Broker _____   Your Broker _____
Name of Associate's Licensed Supervisor   Telephone   Name of Associate's Licensed Supervisor   Telephone

Candy Criss _____ 815-914-2691   Your Name _____
Associate's Name   Telephone   Listing Associate's Name   Telephone

1921 Krohns Ave _____   Your Office Address _____
Other Broker's Address   Facsimile   Listing Broker's Office Address   Facsimile

Corpus Christi   TX   78411   _____
City   State   Zip   City   State

cc@downhomerealty.biz   Zip   Your Email _____
Associate's Email Address   Listing Associate's Email Address

                                               N/A _____
                                               Selling Associate's Name   Telephone

                                               N/A _____
                                               Name of Selling Associate's Licensed Supervisor   Telephone

                                               N/A _____
                                               Selling Associate's Office Address   Facsimile

                                               N/A _____
                                               City   State   Zip

                                               N/A _____
                                               Selling Associate's Email Address

Listing Broker has agreed to pay Other Broker __3.25%__ of the total sales price when the Listing Broker's fee is received. Escrow agent is authorized and directed to pay other Broker from Listing Broker's fee at closing.

OPTION FEE RECEIPT

Receipt of $__250.00__ (Option Fee) in the form of __personal check__ is acknowledged.

_____   within 3 days of original eff date _____
Seller or Listing Broker Paul M Kramer   Date

CONTRACT AND EARNEST MONEY RECEIPT

Receipt of ☒Contract and ☒$__2,000.00__ Earnest Money in the form of __cashiers check__
is acknowledged.
Escrow Agent: __Buyer's Choice Title Co__   Date: within 2 bus. days of eff date

By: __Weldon Cresson__   __Weldon@buyerschoice.com__
                                               Email Address

__103 3rd Ave__   Telephone (_815_) _915-5284_
Address

Corpus Christi   TX   78411   Facsimile: (_815_) _915-5285_
City   State   Zip

PROMULGATED BY THE TEXAS REAL ESTATE COMMISSION (TREC)   12-05-11

LOAN ASSUMPTION ADDENDUM
TO CONTRACT CONCERNING THE PROPERTY AT

1215 Market St. Apartment 623, Corpus Christi
(Address of Property)

A. CREDIT DOCUMENTATION. To establish Buyer's creditworthiness, Buyer shall deliver to Seller within N/A____days after the effective date of this contract ❑ credit report ❑ verification of employment, including salary ❑ verification of funds on deposit in financial institutions ❑ current financial statement and ❑ N/A_____.

Buyer hereby authorizes any credit reporting agency to furnish copies of Buyer's credit reports to Seller at Buyer's sole expense.

B. CREDIT APPROVAL. If the credit documentation described in Paragraph A is not delivered within the specified time, Seller may terminate this contract by notice to Buyer within 7 days after expiration of the time for delivery, and the earnest money will be paid to Seller. If the credit documentation is timely delivered, and Seller determines in Seller's sole discretion that Buyer's credit is unacceptable, Seller may terminate this contract by notice to Buyer within 7 days after expiration of the time for delivery and the earnest money will be refunded to Buyer. If Seller does not terminate this contract within the time specified, Seller will be deemed to have approved Buyer's creditworthiness.

C. ASSUMPTION. Buyer's assumption of an existing note includes all obligations imposed by the deed of trust securing the note.
☒ (1) The unpaid principal balance of a first lien promissory note payable to Deep Pocket _____ Mortgage Co. Inc._____which unpaid balance at closing will be $ 265,008.00_____. The total current monthly payment including principal, interest and any reserve deposits is $ 2,885.00_____. Buyer's initial payment will be the first payment due after closing.

❑ (2) The unpaid principal balance of a second lien promissory note payable to _____ _____which unpaid balance at closing will be $ _____. The total current monthly payment including principal, interest and any reserve deposits is $ _____. Buyer's initial payment will be the first payment due after closing.

If the unpaid principal balance of any assumed loan as of the Closing Date varies from the loan balance stated above, the ☒ cash payable at closing ❑ Sales Price will be adjusted by the amount of any variance. If the total principal balance of all assumed loans varies in an amount greater than $500 at closing, either party may terminate this contract and the earnest money will be refunded to Buyer unless the other party elects to pay the excess of the variance.

D. LOAN ASSUMPTION TERMS. Buyer may terminate this contract and the earnest money will be refunded to Buyer if the noteholder requires:
(1) payment of an assumption fee in excess of $ 1%_____in C(1) or $ N/A_____in C(2) and Seller declines to pay such excess, or
(2) an increase in the interest rate to more than 5.000 % in C(1) or N/A__ % in C(2), or
(3) any other modification of the loan documents.

E. CONSENT BY NOTEHOLDER. If the noteholder fails to consent to the assumption of the loan, either Seller or Buyer may terminate this contract by notice to the other party and the earnest money will be refunded to the Buyer.

F. SELLER'S LIENS. Unless Seller is released from liability on any assumed note, a vendor's lien and deed of trust to secure assumption will be required. The vendor's lien will automatically be released on delivery of an executed release by noteholder.

Initialed for identification by Buyer_____ and Seller_____   TREC NO. 41-2

Loan Assumption Addendum Concerning

1215 Market St. Apartment 623, Corpus Christi
(Address of Property)

G. TAX AND INSURANCE ESCROW. If noteholder maintains an escrow account for ad valorem taxes, casualty insurance premiums or mortgage insurance premiums, Seller shall transfer the escrow account to Buyer without any deficiency. Buyer shall reimburse Seller for the amount in the transferred accounts.

NOTICE TO BUYER: If you are concerned about the possibility of future adjustments, monthly payments, interest rates or other terms, do not sign the contract without examining the notes and deeds of trust.

NOTICE TO SELLER: Your liability to pay the notes assumed by Buyer will continue unless you obtain a release of liability from the noteholders. If you are concerned about future liability, you should use the TREC Release of Liability Addendum.

Buyer
Brian C Sweeney and Wife

Seller
Paul M Kramer and wife

Buyer
Ellie T Sweeney

Seller
Sarah S Kramer

PROMULGATED BY THE TEXAS REAL ESTATE COMMISSION (TREC)   12-05-11

ADDENDUM FOR
"BACK-UP" CONTRACT

TO CONTRACT CONCERNING THE PROPERTY AT

_____1215 Market St. Apartment 623, Corpus Christi_____
(Address of Property)

A. The contract to which this Addendum is attached (the Back-Up Contract) is binding upon execution by the parties, and the earnest money and any Option Fee must be paid as provided in the Back-Up Contract. The Back-Up Contract is contingent upon the termination of a previous contract (the First Contract) dated __May 5th_____, 20_xx____, for the sale of Property. Except as provided by this Addendum, neither party is required to perform under the Back-Up Contract while it is contingent upon the termination of the First Contract.

B. If the First Contract does not terminate on or before __May 20th_____, 20_xx___, the Back-Up Contract terminates and the earnest money will be refunded to Buyer. Seller must notify Buyer immediately of the termination of the First Contract. For purposes of performance, the effective date of the Back-Up Contract changes to the date Buyer receives notice of termination of the First Contract (Amended Effective Date).

C. An amendment or modification of the First Contract will not terminate the First Contract.

D. If Buyer has the unrestricted right to terminate the Back-Up Contract, the time for giving notice of termination begins on the effective date of the Back-Up Contract, continues after the Amended Effective Date and ends upon the expiration of Buyer's unrestricted right to terminate the Back-Up Contract.

E. For purposes of this Addendum, time is of the essence. Strict compliance with the times for performance stated herein is required.

_____   _____
Buyer   Seller
Brian C Sweeney and wife   Paul M Kramer and wife

_____   _____
Buyer   Seller
Ellie T Sweeney   Sarah S Kramer

TREC No. 11-7

PROMULGATED BY THE TEXAS REAL ESTATE COMMISSION (TREC)   12-05-11

ADDENDUM FOR
COASTAL AREA PROPERTY
(SECTION 33.135, TEXAS NATURAL RESOURCES CODE)

TO CONTRACT CONCERNING THE PROPERTY AT

1215 Market St. Apartment 623, Corpus Christi
(Address of Property)

NOTICE REGARDING COASTAL AREA PROPERTY

1. The real property described in and subject to this contract adjoins and shares a common boundary with the tidally influenced submerged lands of the state. The boundary is subject to change and can be determined accurately only by a survey on the ground made by a licensed state land surveyor in accordance with the original grant from the sovereign. The owner of the property described in this contract may gain or lose portions of the tract because of changes in the boundary.

2. The seller, transferor, or grantor has no knowledge of any prior fill as it relates to the property described in and subject to this contract except: N/A
_____
_____.

3. State law prohibits the use, encumbrance, construction, or placing of any structure in, on, or over state-owned submerged lands below the applicable tide line, without proper permission.

4. The purchaser or grantee is hereby advised to seek the advice of an attorney or other qualified person as to the legal nature and effect of the facts set forth in this notice on the property described in and subject to this contract. Information regarding the location of the applicable tide line as to the property described in and subject to this contract may be obtained from the surveying division of the General Land Office in Austin.

Buyer
Brian C Sweeney and wife

Seller Paul M Kramer and wife

Buyer Ellie T Sweeney

Seller Sarah S Kramer

TREC No. 33-2

PROMULGATED BY THE TEXAS REAL ESTATE COMMISSION (TREC)   12-05-11

ADDENDUM FOR
PROPERTY LOCATED SEAWARD OF THE
GULF INTRACOASTAL WATERWAY
(SECTION 61.025, TEXAS NATURAL RESOURCES CODE)

TO CONTRACT CONCERNING THE PROPERTY AT

1215 Market St. Apartment 623, Corpus Christi
(Address of Property)

DISCLOSURE NOTICE CONCERNING LEGAL AND ECONOMIC RISKS OF PURCHASING COASTAL REAL PROPERTY NEAR A BEACH

WARNING: THE FOLLOWING NOTICE OF POTENTIAL RISKS OF ECONOMIC LOSS TO YOU AS THE PURCHASER OF COASTAL REAL PROPERTY IS REQUIRED BY STATE LAW.

- READ THIS NOTICE CAREFULLY. DO NOT SIGN THIS CONTRACT UNTIL YOU FULLY UNDERSTAND THE RISKS YOU ARE ASSUMING.

- BY PURCHASING THIS PROPERTY, YOU MAY BE ASSUMING ECONOMIC RISKS OVER AND ABOVE THE RISKS INVOLVED IN PURCHASING INLAND REAL PROPERTY.

- IF YOU OWN A STRUCTURE LOCATED ON COASTAL REAL PROPERTY NEAR A GULF COAST BEACH, IT MAY COME TO BE LOCATED ON THE PUBLIC BEACH BECAUSE OF COASTAL EROSION AND STORM EVENTS.

- AS THE OWNER OF A STRUCTURE LOCATED ON THE PUBLIC BEACH, YOU COULD BE SUED BY THE STATE OF TEXAS AND ORDERED TO REMOVE THE STRUCTURE.

- THE COSTS OF REMOVING A STRUCTURE FROM THE PUBLIC BEACH AND ANY OTHER ECONOMIC LOSS INCURRED BECAUSE OF A REMOVAL ORDER WOULD BE SOLELY YOUR RESPONSIBILITY.

The real property described in this contract is located seaward of the Gulf Intracoastal Waterway to its southernmost point and then seaward of the longitudinal line also known as 97 degrees, 12', 19" which runs southerly to the international boundary from the intersection of the centerline of the Gulf Intracoastal Waterway and the Brownsville Ship Channel. If the property is in close proximity to a beach fronting the Gulf of Mexico, the purchaser is hereby advised that the public has acquired a right of use or easement to or over the area of any public beach by prescription, dedication, or presumption, or has retained a right by virtue of continuous right in the public since time immemorial, as recognized in law and custom.

The extreme seaward boundary of natural vegetation that spreads continuously inland customarily marks the landward boundary of the public easement. If there is no clearly marked natural vegetation line, the landward boundary of the easement is as provided by Sections 61.016 and 61.017, Natural Resources Code.

Much of the Gulf of Mexico coastline is eroding at rates of more than five feet per year. Erosion rates for all Texas Gulf property subject to the open beaches act are available from the Texas General Land Office.

State law prohibits any obstruction, barrier, restraint, or interference with the use of the public easement, including the placement of structures seaward of the landward boundary of the easement. OWNERS OF STRUCTURES ERECTED SEAWARD OF THE VEGETATION LINE (OR OTHER APPLICABLE EASEMENT BOUNDARY) OR THAT BECOME SEAWARD OF THE VEGETATION LINE AS A RESULT OF PROCESSES SUCH AS SHORELINE EROSION ARE SUBJECT TO A LAWSUIT BY THE STATE OF TEXAS TO REMOVE THE STRUCTURES.

The purchaser is hereby notified that the purchaser should: (1) determine the rate of shoreline erosion in the vicinity of the real property; and (2) seek the advice of an attorney or other qualified person before executing this contract or instrument of conveyance as to the relevance of these statutes and facts to the value of the property the purchaser is hereby purchasing or contracting to purchase.

Buyer Brian C Sweeney and wife   Seller Paul M Kramer and wife

Buyer Ellie T Sweeney   Seller Sarah S Kramer

TREC No. 34-4

PROMULGATED BY THE TEXAS REAL ESTATE COMMISSION (TREC)   12-05-11

EQUAL HOUSING
OPPORTUNITY

ADDENDUM FOR
RELEASE OF LIABILITY ON ASSUMED LOAN
AND/OR RESTORATION OF SELLER'S VA ENTITLEMENT

TO CONTRACT CONCERNING THE PROPERTY AT

1215 Market St. Apartment 623, Corpus Christi
(Address of Property)

☒ **A. RELEASE OF SELLER'S LIABILITY ON LOAN TO BE ASSUMED:**

Within __3__ days after the effective date of this contract Seller and Buyer shall apply for release of Seller's liability from (a) any conventional lender, (b) VA and any lender whose loan has been guaranteed by VA, or (c) FHA and any lender whose loan has been insured by FHA. Seller and Buyer shall furnish all required information and documents. If any release of liability has not been approved by the Closing Date: (check one box only)

☒ (1) This contract will terminate and the earnest money will be refunded to Buyer.

☐ (2) Failure to obtain release approval will not delay closing.

☐ **B. RESTORATION OF SELLER'S ENTITLEMENT FOR VA LOAN:**

Within __N/A__ days after the effective date of this contract Seller and Buyer shall apply for restoration of Seller's VA entitlement and shall furnish all information and documents required by VA. If restoration has not been approved by the Closing Date: (check one box only)

☐ (1) This contract will terminate and the earnest money will be refunded to Buyer.

☐ (2) Failure to obtain restoration approval will not delay closing.

NOTICE: VA will not restore Seller's VA entitlement unless Buyer: (a) is a veteran, (b) has sufficient unused VA entitlement and (c) is otherwise qualified. If Seller desires restoration of VA entitlement, paragraphs A and B should be used.

Seller shall pay the cost of securing the release and restoration.

Seller's deed will contain any loan assumption clause required by FHA, VA or any lender.

Buyer
Brian C Sweeney and wife

Seller
 Paul M Kramer and wife

Buyer Ellie T Sweeney

Seller Sarah S Kramer

TREC No. 12-3

Notes

Notes

Notes

Notes

Notes